Tornado GR 1 of the TWCU fitted with practice bomb p

Encyclopaedia of the

MODERN ROYAL AIR FORCE

RESCUE
PUSH TRIGGER

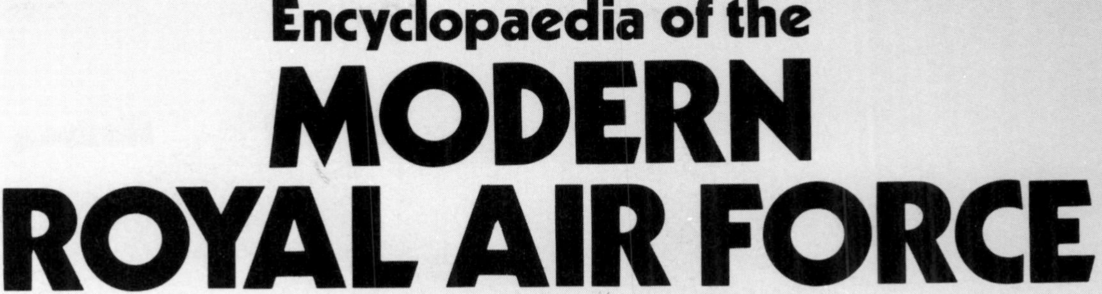

Encyclopaedia of the MODERN ROYAL AIR FORCE

Terry Gander

Technical Consultant — Peter Guiver

2nd edition

Patrick Stephens
Wellingborough, Northamptonshire

Title page *Line-up of No 18 Squadron Chinook HC 1's at RAF Gutersloh.*

First published August 1984
Second edition published August 1987

British Library Cataloguing in Publication Data

Gander, Terry
Encyclopaedia of the modern Royal Air Force
2nd ed. Great Britain. *Royal Air Force* — History
I. Title
358.4'00941 UG635.G7

ISBN 0-85059-859-1

Patrick Stephens Limited is part of the Thorsons Publishing Group

Printed and bound in Great Britain.

10 9 8 7 6 5 4 3 2 1

Contents

Foreword

by Air Marshal Sir John Fitzpatrick KBE CB CBIM RAF(Rtd)

In 1988 the Royal Air Force celebrates its 70th birthday. That lifetime has coincided with a period of extraordinary advances in science and technology, fields in which the Service has always been prominent and to which it has contributed much.

I am fortunate in having served in most of the main operational roles; fighter, bomber, reconnaisance and maritime. Then, as now, the individual's ability to change rapidly from one demanding activity to another owed much to the high quality of the basic training provided by the Service for all airmen, whatever their rank or future duties. Such excellent training, now provided by Support Command, has formed the bedrock on which experience and personal skills have been built and has been the hallmark of the Service from Trenchard to Today.

Posting from one role to another occurs less frequently today, principally because of the expensive retraining required to fit the individual for his or her new duties. At the same time, we have seen fewer aircraft types take on the tasks of more numerous predecessors. Streamlining in the air has been matched by the slimming of staffs on the ground. The formation of Strike Command in 1968 enabled the earlier separate role skills to be harnessed together and directed to a common aim. Since then the bond between Strike Command and the operational Headquarters of the other two Services at home has grown stronger; with the Army over Home Defence and with the Royal Navy over NATO's Eastern Atlantic and Channel Areas.

Coordination of the Nimrods of No 18 Group with the anti-submarine forces of the Fleet is total and continuous. The full integration of the RAF's maritime strike attack and air defence squadrons into the sea battle is now a reality. Such arrangements not only enhance the air defences of the Fleet at sea but serve to improve that of the United Kingdom.

In Germany, the organizational changes have been less marked, perhaps because the RAF's HQ has been co-located, from the outset, alongside that of the British Army of the Rhine. The RAF in Germany is rightly regarded by other NATO countries as one of the best equipped and trained air forces in the Alliance, a view constantly reinforced by the Command's exceptionally high ratings in NATO's Tactical Evaluation exercises.

Today the influence of air power in war planning is all pervasive. No military planner can afford to ignore its likely impact on the outcome of land or maritime battles. The burgeoning of our air-to-air refuelling capability is today enabling the advantages of reach, time on task, and flexibility to be extended to all the operational roles. The major part which would be played by the RAF in any future conflict cannot, therefore, be overemphasised and the present high degree of interservice cooperation persuades me that our military leaders are well seized of that fact.

It is to Terry Gander's great credit that the strong flavour of the modern Royal Air Force comes across in this well produced and detailed volume; he is deserving of our congratulations for such an accurate description of the RAF's range of roles, equipment, skills and activities.

Introduction

'(they) travelled a short way towards the sun and left the vivid air signed with their honour.'

Stephen Spender.

The author of this book is in a rather odd position. Years ago he served in the Royal Air Force, in a rather lowly position from where he could look upwards and see the odd way in which the Service conducted itself at that time. Perhaps the last days of National Service had something to do with it, but one item the Royal Air Force was not short of then was manpower. Consequently, most people's main problem was to find something useful and interesting to pass the time, otherwise someone would force some uncongenial duties upon them. If one thing has emerged during the writing of this book, it is that those days are long since gone. Today, every member of the Service has his part to play, and everyone sets about it with a will. Everywhere I have been during the preparation of this book I have noticed that, although the surroundings do not look too dissimilar, the atmosphere is very different compared with how it used to be. There is now a set meaning in every action, an aura of urgency and, above all, a sense of carrying out a worthwhile task. People move from place to place with a definite sense of purpose instead of the aimless meandering of my time. The surroundings still have the appearance of a bygone era but the additions of barbed wire and bunkers add their own particular sense of imminent action. This is particularly true in RAF Germany where the previous brightly-painted exteriors have given way to a more warlike drab appearance.

These changes have not, of course, been brought about solely by the reduction in manpower, although that has been one obvious factor in the change. The alterations have also come from the fact that

Above right *The front line (1): a Harrier GR 3 lands aboard HMS* Hermes *after an epic flight from Ascension in May 1982.*

Below *Up and away as a Puma HC 1 makes its exit after depositing its load of troops on an 'enemy' airfield.*

we are still living in times where the prospect of some form of future conflict is as immediate as ever. Despite the efforts of NATO and other such organisations over the years, the Royal Air Force still finds itself as much in the front line as it was in the years just after the 1939–1945 war. The recent events in the South Atlantic have provided that 'whiff of gunpowder' which is so often lacking in peacetime exercises, but it has also shown that the Royal Air Force is overstretched. From the manpower surpluses of my time, the Service is now in a state where every body on the ground and in the air is at a premium.

The restriction on manpower has been imposed by ministers but the government has of late been more generous in the provision of new equipment. The period since the first edition of this book has seen the delivery of new aircraft such as the Tornado F 2/F 3, more Tornado GR 1s and Tristar tankers. The RAF Regiment has been provided with new weapons and other kit. More new equipment is in the pipeline, including the Tucano trainer (which will replace the veteran Jet Provosts) and the Nimrod AEW 3 development saga, which seemed destined to 'run and run', has finally been ended by the ordering of the E-3 Sentry AWACS early warning aircraft.

This programme of re-equipment should not cloud the fact that the Royal Air Force is still too small. Even in these days of advanced technology the sheer arithmetic of trained manpower and aircraft in the air still counts for a great deal. All recent experiences of air warfare have emphasised that numbers still matter and the Royal Air Force is thus still too small compared to the size of the task it might have to carry out. Even as part of NATO, the nation could still do with more aircraft and men to support and fly them.

So this book is not just a straightforward account. It is a catalogue of where things could begin. I would not have been able to compile all the facts that this book contains without, first and foremost, the help of the many officers and men who have been kind enough to pass on information and provide facilities. During my visits my questions have all been answered patiently; permission has been granted to see many things and my heartfelt thanks are given to all. Great assistance was also provided by the many information and facility officers at the Ministry of Defence, in Strike and Support Commands and in RAF Germany. They have all been of the greatest assistance to me in my badgering for assistance and my thanks go out to them all. On a personal level, Mr Peter Guiver's guidance and contributions have been invaluable.

Billingshurst
April 1987

The RAF since 1945

When contemplating the years since 1945, it comes as something of a surprise to learn that the Royal Air Force has been in existence for longer since the war than prior to it. In 1945 the Royal Air Force was only 27 years old but, such is the scale of memory and time, that the years subsequently appear to have passed in a mere flash. For all that, in 1983 the Royal Air Force was 38 years older than it was in 1945 and in that time as much, if not more, has happened as in the early years. The period since 1945 has seen the Royal Air Force move from an era when propeller-driven aircraft were the norm to a period when operational aircraft are now almost all jets. It has seen the change from the primitive waveguide and the thermionic valve to the computer and the silicon chip, and it has seen the change from the conventional explosive to the thermonuclear device.

In 1945 the Royal Air Force was a mighty machine encompassing tens of thousands of men and thousands of aircraft. Over Europe the strength of Bomber Command could turn the skies dark with their numbers and in every corner of the Earth the Service was represented in some form or another. The V-Day air parades over London made the spectator dizzy with the numbers of aircraft involved as they flew over in Wing after Wing formation, but within a few short months all this strength and experience was dissipated by the understandable return to civilian life of the vast bulk of the manpower involved. The 'hostilities only' personnel flocked to their homes and on the numerous airfields scattered all over the world aircraft stood idle for want of aircrews or maintenance fitters. Other aircraft were lost as the return to the more sedate Service practices of peacetime took their toll on a Service more used to 'pressing on' at all costs. Peacetime operational procedures, with their emphasis on safety, were hard to adopt by men more used to the less stringent requirements of war operations and the result was a string of needless accidents that cost both machines and lives. New Flight Safety regulations and disciplines eventually took hold but the years after the war were all too often littered with wrecked aircraft and funeral parades.

As the numbers of squadrons contracted the peacetime responsibilities did not. Looking back it is now possible to see that the month of June 1948 was a watershed in the history of the Royal Air Force. Up till that month the Service continued its former duties of showing the flag and policing the colonies. The United Kingdom acted as a home training base which had to be defended using the new Vampire and Meteor jet fighters and the large Service establishments in Germany were kept in being. The old aircraft dating from the war years were adequate for all this. Manpower totals gradually dropped to totals more acceptable to the

Opposite *Things to come? The roll-out of the British Aerospace Experimental Aircraft Programme as part of a programme to produce the air superiority aircraft of the future.*

Below *A link with the war years that lingers on yet, as the Shackleton can trace its ancestry back to the Lancaster bomber of the war years; this MR2 belonged to No 38 Squadron which was for many years resident at RAF Luqa on Malta.*

tax-paying public and all seemed well to the casual observer of world affairs.

Of course, things were not all right. The growing threat presented by the size and belligerence of the Soviet Bloc armed forces gradually increased in dimensions and ubiquity. In June 1948 they forced their way to the forefront. In Germany the Soviet Army closed the road and rail approaches to Berlin, and in Malaya armed insurrection by Communist guerrillas commenced. The reaction to the former was the now-famous Berlin Airlift, carried out by Transport Command in conjunction with the US Air Force. The reaction to the latter was the establishment of 'Operation Firedog', in which the Royal Air Force played a major part for the 12 years up to 1960 when the only successful campaign waged against Communist-inspired guerrillas during the postwar years was officially brought to an end.

These two operations were long hard flogs but they were not the only operations of their type carried out in those years. They formed a watershed by the fact that they demonstrated once and for all that the postwar years were not going to be the peaceful ones in which people everywhere hoped to re-build and rest after the pre-1945 period. Once more a new threat to the Western way of life was looming, this time under the ever-present menace of the atomic bomb. Under such circumstances it was time to look to the nation's defences once again and by the late 1940s the Royal Air Force was in a bit of a state.

There were plenty of aircraft to hand, many of them dating from the war years or adaptations of wartime designs. The main problem was men. The immediate postwar years had seen the standing-down of what was the bulk of the Services experience at all levels, from fitter to aircrew captain. The immediate answer was the attraction of new intakes of men and their subsequent training but that took time. As a short term measure the Royal Auxiliary Air Force was expanded but at one point in 1949 Bomber Command would have been hard put to raise 100 bombers for a single operation. To add to this rundown state of affairs, in 1950 the conflict in Korea underlined the growing aggressiveness of the Communist Bloc.

To some extent the situation had been pre-

Right *After 1945 the RAF Regiment remained in being and this photograph depicts a 3-inch mortar team.*

Below *From the Berlin Airlift onwards the Hastings was one of the Royal Air Force's workhorses; this is a C2 of No 24 Squadron.*

Below right *The Valiant was the first of the V-bombers to enter service. This B 1 was a 90 Squadron aircraft.*

empted. For a start, NATO had been formed in 1949 and new equipment was on the drawing boards ready for use when the newly-trained men emerged from their training establishments. But in 1950 this was still in the future and the Royal Air Force still had commitments world-wide. The situation had been partly eased by the commencement of the long drawn-out handing over of the old British Empire, with the 'jewel in the Crown' that was India being given its independence in 1949. While this unprecendented hand-over of power was no doubt a measure that had to be taken, it was one that had an effect which was not immediately recognised at the time, and has still to sink into the national ego: that is, when the colonies went, so did the nation's prime source of income. No longer would cheap imports be available to fuel the industries based on the servicing of an Empire on which the sun never set and thus those industries could no longer provide the revenue that created the nation's well-being, education, health services and defence. Thus the United Kingdom was in a political cleft stick. It badly needed new defence and other services at a time when the national exchequer was becoming impoverished. This process took years and is with us still but in the early 1950s it was a problem that had yet to reveal its full scope.

Thus the Royal Air Force's new equipment programme and the training of its new technically-accomplished manpower went ahead at full steam. The mid-1950s and the years immediately thereafter were good ones to serve through. New aircraft, radar and all manner of equipment was pouring from the factories or being imported from the United States. Recruits joining then could look forward to serving at locations all over the world for, despite the gradual withdrawal from Empire, the Commonwealth still provided many attractive stations and the oil interests in the Middle East ensured that a fair proportion of serving personnel, both Regular and National Service, got their knees brown. During that period the Service expanded the knowledge of its new equipment by a series of record-breaking attempts that took the Royal Air Force to altitudes and distances at greater speeds than ever before. Once the stop-gap Sabres had

Left *The Canberra was for many years the most numerous of the bomber aircraft in service; typical of the many in use was this Canberra B 6.*

Below *One of the least known of the many Canberra variants was the U 10, a remotely controlled version which could be used for a number of purposes ranging from aerial target to flying through the clouds of nuclear explosions.*

Right *Widely used in the Far East, the Twin Pioneer CC 2 was also used for many years in Africa, but this No 230 Squadron example was at one time based at RAF Odiham.*

Below right *Another workhorse of the 1950s and early 1960s was the Beverley C 1; the main operating base for these giants for many years was RAF Abingdon.*

served their turn they were replaced by shiny new Hunters, Swifts, Javelins and the Vampire/Venom night fighters. Canberras made their first operational flights and the A-bomb joined the Service following tests in Australia. The V-bombers were on the immediate horizon with the Valiant becoming operational in 1955. The same year saw the introduction of the first 'all-jet' flying training courses.

By 1955 it looked as though the Royal Air Force was set for a brilliant future. The numbers were up to establishment, it had good and modern equipment, more was on the way and it was a substantial part of NATO. In fact all was not completely well for the Service was, as ever, only an instrument of a political executive, and in 1956 that executive over-played its hand. Although the Royal Air Force played its part well at Suez, and without any large-scale mishaps, the campaign slammed home the fact that the United Kingdom was no longer a world power but a small nation dependent on imports and financial assistance from outside. The world closed ranks in its condemnation of what can now be seen as an old-style colonial punitive operation that belonged to a former era. The United Kingdom suffered badly in both political and financial terms and it was a time for re-assessment of the nation's whole attitude to its former responsibilities.

One result of this was the acceleration of the process of withdrawal from Empire. Once India had gone there was no real need for the long string of former communication and coaling stations that had been needed to provide the link between India and the United Kingdom; these had been retained for a variety of reasons ranging from strategic necessity to sheer nostalgia. They became a luxury that was no longer affordable. The Canal Zone had already gone and in the long term Aden, Cyprus, Malta and the many other outposts followed. In all this the Royal Air Force played its part, often returning to provide disaster assistance or support tottering regimes for short periods. This process continued until well into the 1960s.

The second post-Suez result was the questioning of the very role that the Royal Air Force was to play in the long term. The Service provided part of the NATO nuclear deterrent force with the V-bomber squadrons but the role of the rest of the Service was not so clear cut. The post-Suez financial shambles also provided ingredients to the brew that produced the now infamous Sandys Defence White Paper of 1957. The results of that document seemed to indicate at the time that the role of the manned aircraft was in seeming decline as the automated guided missile took over many of its roles in both offence and defence. There were other restrictions placed upon spending and equipment acquisition but to balance this was the realisation that the Royal Air Force would in future no longer have a world-wide commitment but would gradually revert to becoming a European-based air force. Unfortunately, the 'end of the manned air-

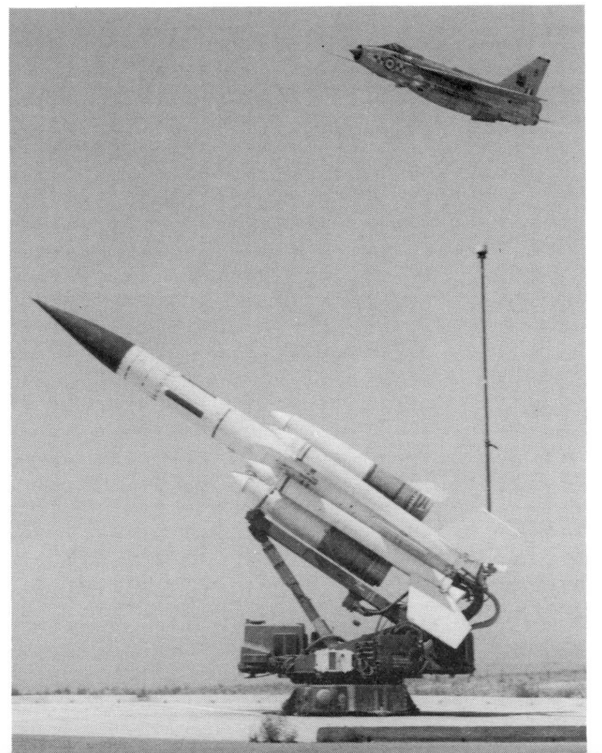

Above *The Hunter started its operational career as an interceptor but later became a potent ground attack aircraft; this example is a F 6 of No 43 Squadron.*

Left *Signs of changes and modernisation as a Lightning F 6 of No 56 Squadron flies over a No 112 Squadron Bloodhound based at Paramali, Cyprus.*

craft' statement in the White Paper received a disproportionate degree of attention and led to an almost immediate drop in recruitment at a time when new aircrew and technicians were becoming desperately needed at all levels. Subsequent statements did their best to overcome this imbalance but it took several years for the damage to be cleared.

By the late 1950s the Royal Air Force was in the ballistic missile game. A number of Thor intermediate range ballistic missiles was obtained from the United States and for some years they added their potential to the deterrent balance. They were meant to be a stop-gap until the British Blue Streak missile was ready for service. But the Blue Streak never did see service and its name now almost epitomises the period when defence spending cuts made in order to allay the United Kingdom's deepening financial crisis laid low many promising equipment projects. Without going into detail over a long period, several projects were financed to the hardware stage only to be chopped in order to save money. The list was a long one, but a few names may conjure up the memories: the Blue Steel stand-off bomb, the HS 681 jet transport, the TSR 2 that left so much acrimony in its wake, and so on. Anticipated imports fared no better as the Skybolt fiasco and the F-111 sagas testified. It was a frustrating time for the Royal Air Force, which felt itself becoming a political football for the British Parliamentary system to kick about. From this unhappy time, however, several useful long-term programmes emerged unscathed or at least still intact. The P 1127 V/STOL prototypes survived to provide the basis for the Harrier strike aircraft. International programmes that included the Jaguar also survived and several rather less glamorous aircraft such as the Andover and the huge Belfast got through the scrutinity net.

By the early 1960s the massive contraction period that started so soon after Suez had at last been brought to the point where so many overseas committments had been dropped that National Service could come to an end. In numerical terms National Service in the Royal Air Force had always lagged well behind that for the Army and the intake was usually of a well motivated and technically-trained kind. All too often these well-endowed and involuntary recruits were wasted in mundane tasks, but many were able to add their civilian expertise and knowledge to a Service that was usually inclined to accept their input. This transfer was aided by the gradual run-down in the unnecessary disciplines and parades that were all too often a feature of postwar Service life. As the numbers contracted, each airman and officer had more to do and time-wasting requirements such as parades and musters could only prevent the increasing efficiency demanded from each person from being realised. Thus, just at the time when National Service ended, this relaxation could be even better utilised. The training and administration of the constant stream of bodies released more men for the essential tasks and they settled to it with a will. With the short-term National Service-

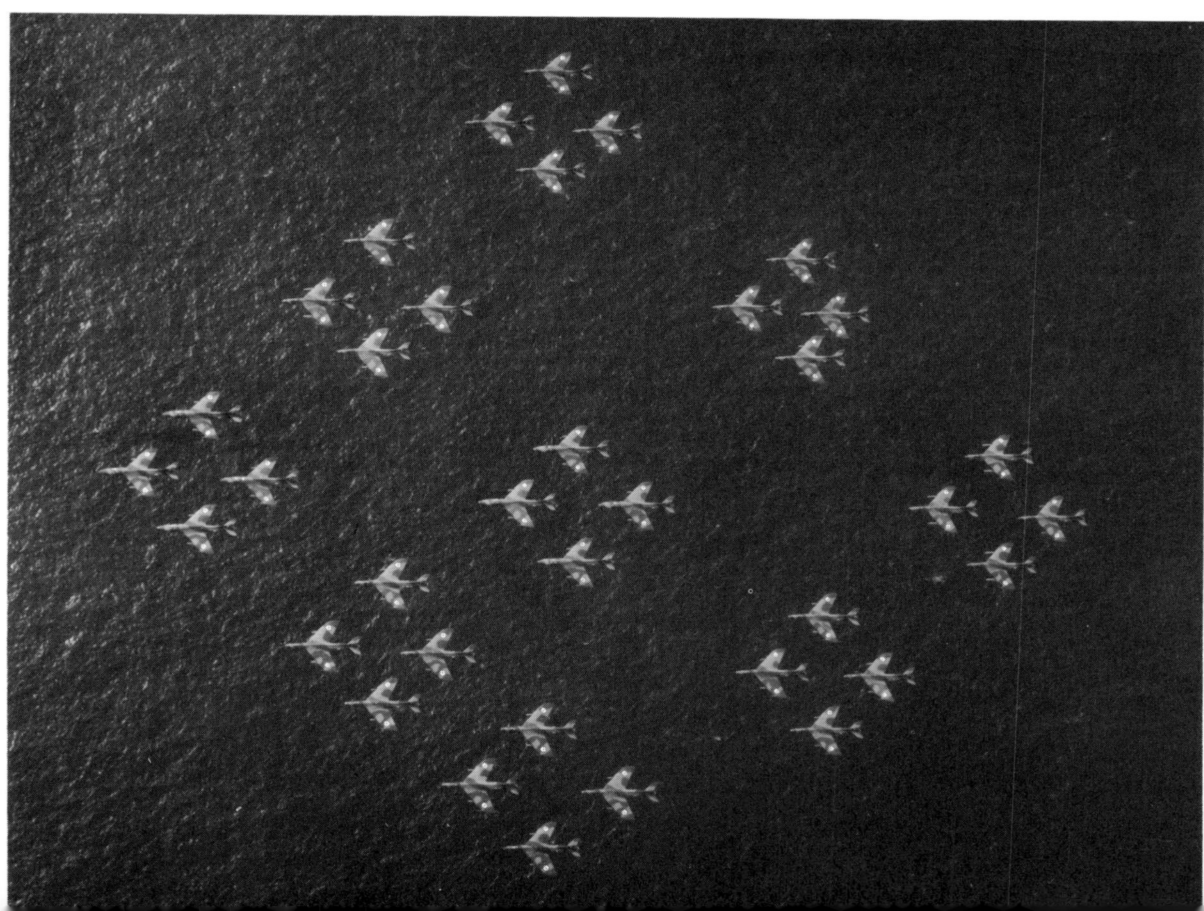

Hunters from No 229 OCU, RAF Chivenor, in 1971.

Lightnings of No 23 Squadron during the late 1960s.

men gone the Royal Air Force could settle down to the long-term job chosen.

Even though he has long gone, the National Serviceman has left his mark. That constant stream of uniformed civilians has ensured that the Royal Air Force has not returned to the tight little band of career airmen that was so often the case before 1939. Now the Royal Air Force is a part of the national make-up. It occupies large expanses of what is very often coveted real estate and it absorbs a very large slice of the national exchequer so it has to constantly justify its position in the establishment. This it does by adopting civilian methods in all manner of things from working methods to public relations. Service families play their part in communities all over the country and abroad in a way the pre-1939 Service would have found unthinkable. This is a residue of the days when the Service was part of the social progress of British youth, but this public-mindedness is not the only reason for this outward approach.

By the early 1960s what the Royal Air Force required was not just recruits but the right type of recruits. The Service was constantly assuming more and more technical responsibilities, typical of which was the operational debut of the Fylingdales long-range early warning radar establishment during 1964. To service this complex facility required not only technical expertise of a high order but the administrative skills to maintain the complex equipments and keep them operational for extended periods. To do this requires people with a broad base of knowledge and skills. The Royal Air Force had to find such people, train them, use them as efficiently as possible and to add to all this, keep them. Keeping them was not, and is still not, easy for every year sees a stream of highly qualified technicians and aircrew leaving the Service to enjoy the attractions of civilian life.

To get the right type of people and keep them the Royal Air Force had to adopt civilian approaches and outlooks at all levels from everyday working methods to the large scale systems approaches adopted by large business corporations. Most of the current working methods date from the mid-1960s or are extensions of programmes initiated at that time. These have produced some drastic innovations. Some Maintenance Units now operate along factory lines and include large numbers of civilians among their staffs. Computers are used at virtually all levels to check accounts, maintain stores stock levels, organise transport, and so on. Modern teaching and training methods are employed at all stages of imparting skills and knowledge. On the social side the married man is now the norm in the Service and he is usually provided with every required facility, even at remote outposts. Pay is always a point of contention

Operation Corporate, 1982, and a Victor K 2 touches down at Wideawake, deploying its tail 'chute.

but present levels rarely fall behind civilian equivalents to any large extent.

This, then, is the outward-looking Royal Air Force of today. Internally it has realised that the old days of world travel are just about over and has organised itself into the current command structure that has eliminated the historic Fighter, Bomber, Transport, Training and other commands. Lacking as they do the inherent time-honoured traditions that sometimes tend to restrict similar actions in the Army or Royal Navy, today Strike Command and RAF Germany are powerful forces that demand respect from any potential aggressor, and they have been given funds to keep their power. These funds will be directed along the lines outlined in the pages of this book. High on the list of priorities is the Tornado strike aircraft, capable of deep interdiction into enemy rear areas where it will be able to wreak havoc. The Harrier is ensured of a long life with the ordering of the AV-8B. New weapons such as the Sea Eagle will do much to maintain the Service's maritime traditions. The ever-present need to save defence funds can be seen in the improvisations that have converted the VC-10 to a tanker aircraft and the civilian Tristar to the same role.

While the 1970s was a period of quiet contraction in numbers it was not a period of inaction. Airmen and aircraft of the Royal Air Force turned up all over the globe to carry out medical or rescue missions and to deliver disaster relief supplies, but the move to Europe grew more and more marked. Only a relative few could look forward to sunshine postings such as Hong Kong or Cyprus, although training tours and odd missions could supply some variety. Throughout this period the actual atmosphere of the Service changed. Manpower reserves dropped to the stage where every man had his own particular task to carry out, and being career Servicemen they did their best to ensure that task was carried out to the full. Royal Air Force stations gradually adopted a new and more purposeful air. More men could be seen at work and fewer wandering around looking for something to do. The stations themselves altered by the addition of more purposeful local security and defence measures. Hangars sprouted sandbag sangars and barbed wire snaked across what had once been carefully-cut areas of grass. NBC measures began to mean something instead of abstract lessons, and so on.

It was all just as well for in 1982 came the Falkland Islands campaign. Out of the blue a remote corner of the South Atlantic became the focal point of a great deal of thought and effort. While the main campaign was a Royal Navy and Army effort, the Royal Air Force is now the Islands' life-line as every day Hercules transports and their associated in-flight tanker aircraft carry out their long and tedious missions across the Atlantic. On the Islands, Harriers, Phantoms and Sea Kings stand guard. The RAF Regiment man their Rapier fire posts and RAF Stanley is now a well-established name on the airfield list. Maintaining and manning the Falklands Islands establishment is a considerable strain on the Royal Air Force's resources but to date it is managing. Just as much a strain on resources is the manning and operation of the Service's facilities on Ascension Island. Some extra monetary resources have been forthcoming to offset the costs but, as always, it is manpower that is the main stricture. Transport aircrew who not so long ago were restricted to only a few hours' flying time every month due to fuel-saving measures now have to fly for protracted periods without relief.

Meanwhile, the Tornados roll off the production lines and new crews and maintenance staffs train for the future. The mighty Nimrod AEW 3 is in the offing and the Tornado F 2 is well advanced

The end of the Falklands campaign as a Hercules flies towards Stanley airfield over a graveyard of Pucaras and UH-1Ds.

along its development path. More Phantoms have been ordered, and so have new airfield attack weapons, anti-radiation missiles, more Chinooks, new airfield radars, new ground defence weapons, and so on. But there are still many items in Royal Air Force service that have more than a whiff of the frantic improvisation or geriatric oddity about them. However arming of Hawk trainers with Sidewinders for the local defence of the United Kingdom has proved to be a successful utilisation of resources. On a less involved scale the Lightning and Canberra are still with us, to say nothing of the elderly Pembrokes and Devons that seem at long last to have a replacement in sight. Much has been done to correct some of the worst shortcomings in equipment but the modern Royal Air Force still requires one important item and that is (it has to be said again) the trained and experienced technician. In these days of technological warfare, the technician, at all levels from barely-trained mechanic to highly-qualified engineering officer, is as important to the defence of NATO and the United Kingdom as the man in the cockpit. The Royal Air Force still needs technicians and it needs to hang on to those it already has.

In the meantime the servicemen who have been around in recent years have certainly had plenty of opportunities to take in a bit of really active service. The Falkland Islands still require RAF manpower although aircraft are no longer needed on the scale that once prevailed. Famine in Africa has led to some spectacular and much-needed relief operations.

Few sectors of the Royal Air Force have had much time to draw breath as new equipment continues to reach the front-line and other units and old equipment has been replaced. The Vulcans had their final fling over Port Stanley in 1982 and have now all gone. The venerable Hunters are now barely hanging on and the life of at least some of the Jet Provost veterans is in sight as the Tucano prepares for what promises to be a long and busy training career. Tornado F 2 and F 3s are now reaching the squadrons to provide a much more viable defence of the United Kingdom home base and in the offing is the airborne early warning aircraft to go with them. The decision to cancel Nimrod AEW 3 and buy the Boeing AWACS system was taken in late 1986. In-flight refuelling Tristars are now to hand.

To cap all this the Royal Air Force has made its bid for the next move in its history and that is into Space. Squadron Leader Nigel Wood was selected as a crewman for the American Space Shuttle programme before the ill-fated *Challenger* exploded to become the most widely-observed aviation mishap of all time (to date). The resultant delays will no doubt mean that it will be some time yet before the Royal Air Force makes its first tentative move into Space, but whenever it happens, that move will herald another aspect of the Royal Air Force's history.

The Royal Air Force of today is a very different organisation to that of 1945. Although 1945 slipped by just a few short years ago it already seems as remote as 1918 when the Royal Air Force was first formed. To the younger generation 1945 must seem as remote as 1066 and in terms of power, lethality and sheer weapon potential that comparison is not too impossible to comprehend. Today's Royal Air Force has a task to maintain peace and it is one of modern life's most illogical tenets that peace can only be maintained under a nuclear umbrella, an umbrella that contains weapons so powerful that the bomb loads of 1945 now seem to have the same striking power as the longbows of 1066. What will the next 38 years bring?

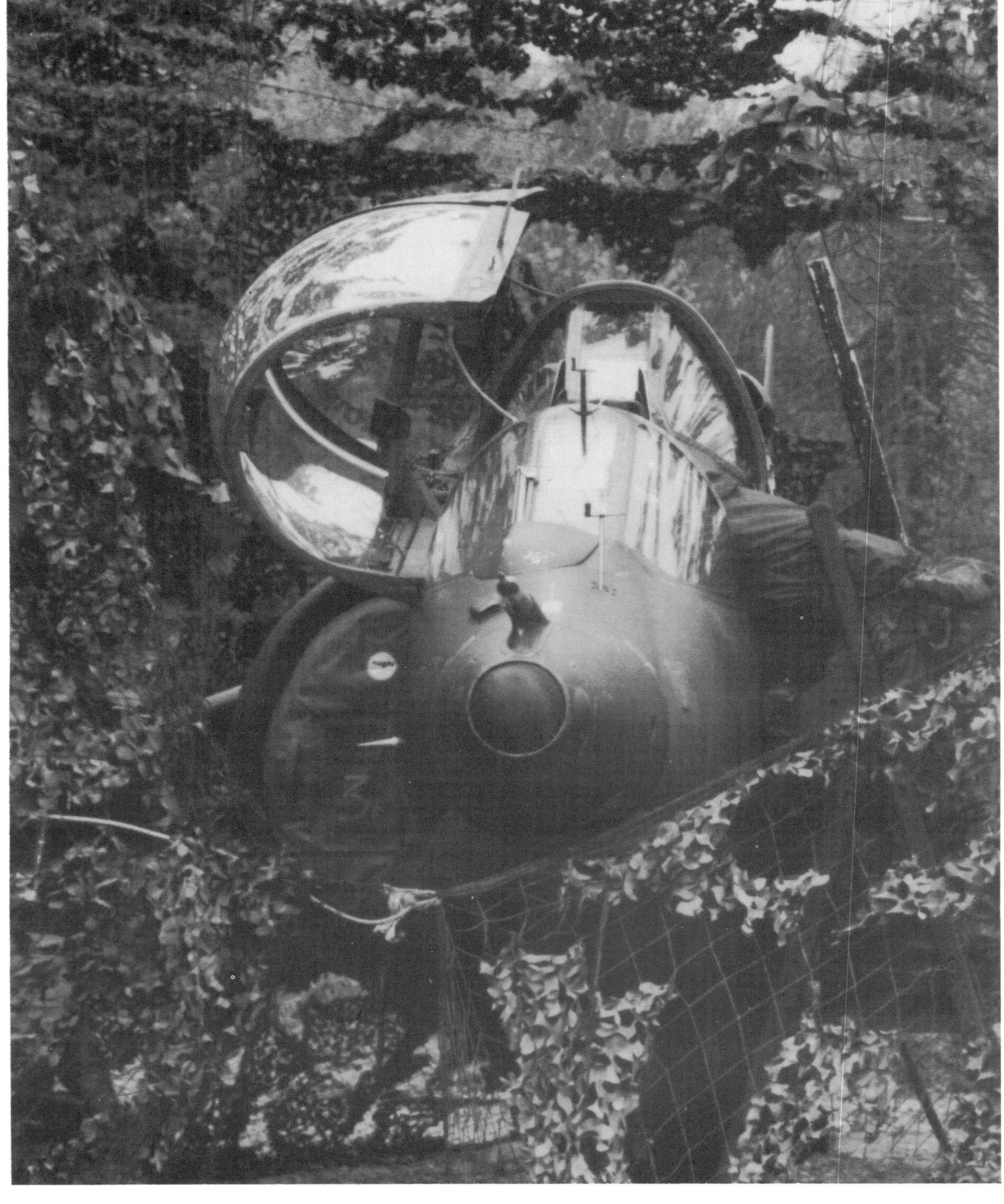

Strike Command

Strike Command is, in historical terms, one of the newer formations of the RAF as it first came into being on April 30 1968 with the merging of the two most famous names in RAF history, namely Fighter Command and Bomber Command. The merger was made for a number of reasons, not the least of which was the then gradual reduction in numbers of aircraft involved as the RAF shed its overseas commitments and assumed a European role. At the same time Coastal Command and Signals Command became part of Strike Command but, by 1972, Signals Command (by then No 90 Group), moved to become part of Support Command. Coastal Command Group became No 18 (Maritime) Group and is still under the Strike Command umbrella. The final reshuffling (to date) took place in September 1972 when the old Air Support Command amalgamated with Strike Command to form a single operational command.

To put things in simple terms, RAF Strike Command is the 'teeth' of the RAF. Strike Command has operational responsibility for RAF units in all parts of the world, apart from RAF Germany, and has four main functions. These are: to defend the United Kingdom Air Region against all air attack; to provide combat-ready air forces for employment by, or in support of, other forces in accordance with SACEUR's approved plans or as directed by SACEUR; to participate, on receipt of orders, in SACEUR's nuclear programmes; to act in support of SACEUR's General Defence Plan.

To carry these tasks out Strike Command cannot operate in isolation, and ever since 1975 it has been an integral segment of NATO to the extent that the AOC Strike Command is a major subordinate commander under SACEUR with the NATO title of Commander-in-Chief United Kingdom Air Forces, or CINCUKAIR, and many Strike Command officers have NATO functions in addition to their own command responsibilities. These units are distributed in four Groups, three of which Groups are in the United Kingdom; Nos 1, 11 and 18. The fourth Group is AHQ Cyprus. Group functions are as follows: No 1 Group—strike/attack and air support for the Army in the field; No 11 Group—air defence of the United Kingdom and its approaches; No 18 Group—maritime reconnaissance and maritime operations.

Opposite *The RAF Wittering Harriers frequently have to deploy to various field hides during training exercises all over Europe: here a T 4 sits behind its camouflage netting.*

No 1 Group

The role of No 1 Group is a complicated one for its activities cover all aspects of air operations from the control and training of all United Kingdom-based strike-attack aircraft plus their tanker force and the complex task of providing offensive air support for the Army in the field.

The headquarters of No 1 Group is at RAF Upavon where things are still settling down after the merger of No 1 Group and the old No 38 Group. From RAF Upavon the Group commands the United Kingdom-based Tornado squadrons that form the main striking power of No 1 Group and the Harrier and Jaguar squadrons that provide air support and tactical reconnaissance for the Army. The Group also commands the supporting Tristar and VC 10 tankers and the remaining Victor tankers. For Army support there are the Chinook and Puma squadrons and for the heavier and longer-distance lifts there are the four Hercules squadrons of the 'Lyneham Wing'. For really long range or special jobs there is the single VC 10 squadron, No 10, at RAF Brize Norton. The Hercules and VC 10s are the heart of the Air Transport Fleet (ATF). For movements within the United Kingdom and nearby countries No 32 Squadron operates a number of VIP transports from RAF Northolt.

The role of Army support involves a great deal of 'out of country' activity so that No 1 Group aircraft can be found operating from bases as far apart as Belize and Norway. To cope with this far-flung role No 1 Group has taken over the Mobile Air Movement Squadron (MAMS), a unit based at RAF Lyneham that travels to wherever it is needed to carry out or supervise the loading or unloading of aircraft and associated tasks.

Other units that come under No 1 Group's control include the United Kingdom-based squadrons of the RAF Regiment, including their depot at RAF Catterick, the various Wing headquarters, station defence and the home-based Rapier squadrons. No 1 Group also administers No 1 Parachute Training School that trains Army and RAF parachutists at RAF Abingdon, and also under No 1 Group's administrative wing is the Queen's Flight at RAF Benson.

Above *Part of the Ballistic Missile Early Warning System (BMEWS) at RAF Fylingdales in Yorkshire.*

Below *One of the New Tristar K 1 in-flight refuelling tankers that will enable No 1 Group to have a far more substantial tanker capability.*

Above right *One of the RAF Coltishall Jaguar GR 1s.*

No 11 Group

One of the prime tasks for Strike Command is the air defence of the United Kingdom and its approaches. It is a massive task for the area that the Command has to defend covers no less than 1,000 nautical miles from north to south. For obvious reasons the main defended area is to the north-east and the area of the North Sea between the United Kingdom and Europe, but the Command's defended region is but one portion of the area under the command of NATO's SACEUR.

The aircraft types involved are the Tornados, Phantoms and the remaining Lightnings of No 11 Group. As these words are written Tornado F 3s are still being delivered and it will be some time before all 165 that have been ordered are finally handed over and are up to full combat proficiency. A squadron of Phantom F–4J(UK)s (No 74 Squadron) have been delivered direct from the United States to partially cover the shortfall that will exist when the last of the Lightnings are phased out and before the Tornado F 3 squadrons come up to full strength. Also as a stop-gap measure there are the 72 Hawk T 1As, Hawks modified to carry Sidewinder missiles and a single 30 mm Aden cannon to perform last-ditch interception duties. They are flown by instructors from the two Hawk-equipped Tactical Weapon Units (TWUs).

Not to be forgotten is No 23 Squadron with its Phantom FGR 2s, away down south in the Falkland Islands. They provide local defence for the islands and the seas inside the maritime exclusion zone but still come under the auspices of No 11 Group.

Missiles in the form of Bloodhound squadrons add to the overland defence and for airfield and local defences there are the Rapier missiles manned by the RAF Regiment.

With such a large area to defend, the region is divided into 12 or 13 segments. These regions are controlled by three sector operation centres (SOC) which are fed from above with information dealing with possible attack threats. This information comes from the general NATO Air Defence Ground Environment, or NADGE, which is formed from the overall lattice of the various NATO members' individual air defence networks. In this way the United Kingdom is usually provided with advanced information well before the threat actually appears within range of the No 11 Group network, but recent advances in Soviet attack aircraft capabilities have meant that there is now a large area to the west where threats might appear without long-range warning. To supplement the NADGE system the RAF makes use of other long-range detection methods in the form of the Ballistic Missile Early Warning System (BMEWS) station at Fylingdales in Yorkshire which is, in turn, connected with the rest of the BMEWS chain at Thule in Greenland and Clear in Alaska. This is primarily a missile attack warning system but it can be used to detect aircraft. To back up these systems the RAF provides its own airborne early warning aircraft which at present are the elderly Shackleton AEW 2s. These relics of a former era were scheduled to have been replaced by the Nimrod AEW 3 but technical problems with the system electronics delayed the introduction into service of the aircraft and the point was finally reached where the Nimrod AEW 3 was cancelled and the American E-3 Sentry AWACS was ordered in its place. It will be 1991 before the first of these aircraft arrives so until then the poor old Shackletons will have to flog away at their airborne early warning task.

All these various sources supply threat information to the three SOCs which are at RAF Neatishead in Norfolk, RAF Boulmer in Northumberland and RAF Buchan in the North of

Royal Air Force Stations

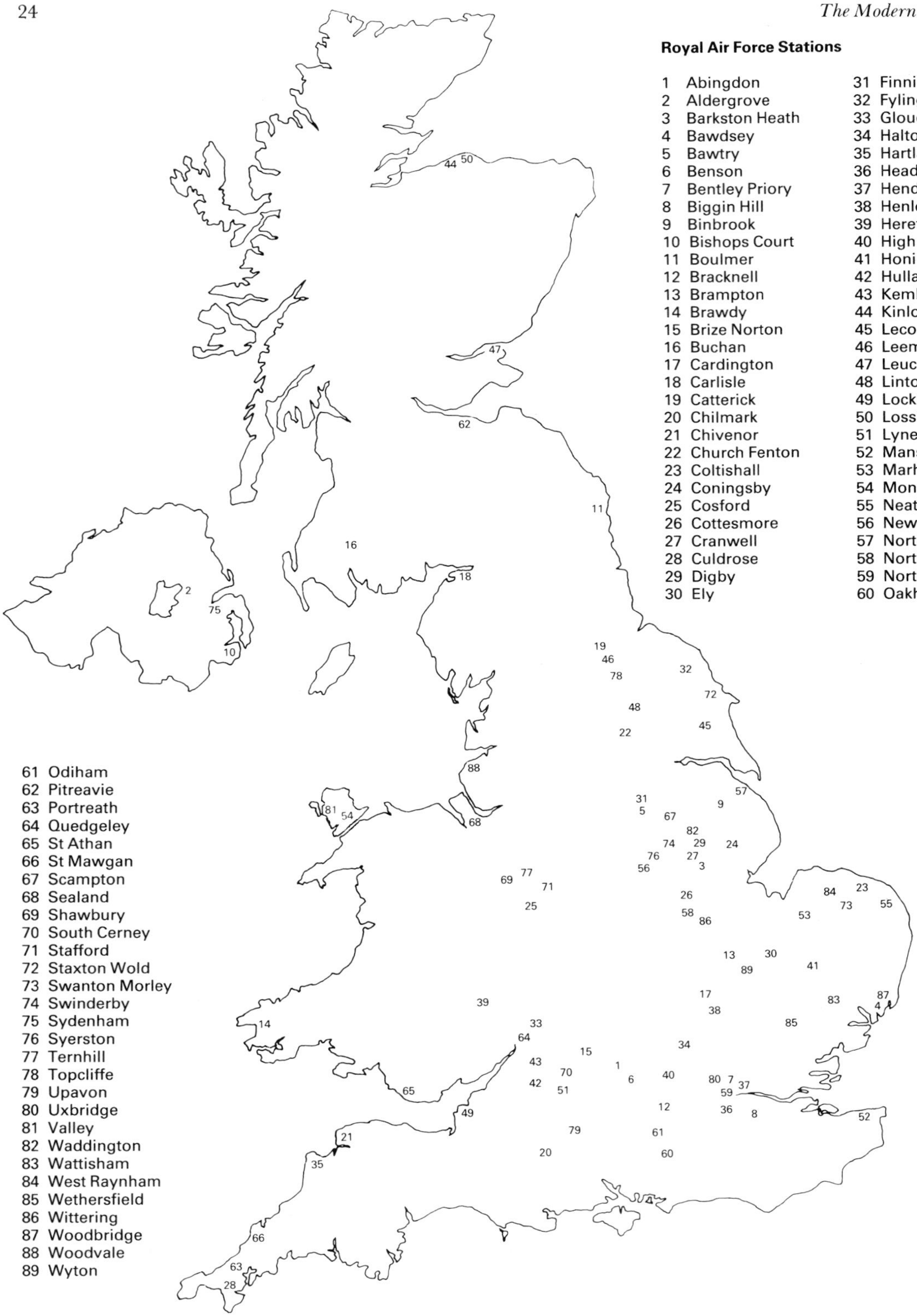

1 Abingdon
2 Aldergrove
3 Barkston Heath
4 Bawdsey
5 Bawtry
6 Benson
7 Bentley Priory
8 Biggin Hill
9 Binbrook
10 Bishops Court
11 Boulmer
12 Bracknell
13 Brampton
14 Brawdy
15 Brize Norton
16 Buchan
17 Cardington
18 Carlisle
19 Catterick
20 Chilmark
21 Chivenor
22 Church Fenton
23 Coltishall
24 Coningsby
25 Cosford
26 Cottesmore
27 Cranwell
28 Culdrose
29 Digby
30 Ely
31 Finningley
32 Fylingdales
33 Gloucester
34 Halton
35 Hartland Point
36 Headley Court
37 Hendon
38 Henlow
39 Hereford
40 High Wycombe
41 Honington
42 Hullavington
43 Kemble
44 Kinloss
45 Leconfield
46 Leeming
47 Leuchars
48 Linton-on-Ouse
49 Locking
50 Lossiemouth
51 Lyneham
52 Manston
53 Marham
54 Mona
55 Neatishead
56 Newton
57 North Coates
58 North Luffenham
59 Northolt
60 Oakhanger
61 Odiham
62 Pitreavie
63 Portreath
64 Quedgeley
65 St Athan
66 St Mawgan
67 Scampton
68 Sealand
69 Shawbury
70 South Cerney
71 Stafford
72 Staxton Wold
73 Swanton Morley
74 Swinderby
75 Sydenham
76 Syerston
77 Ternhill
78 Topcliffe
79 Upavon
80 Uxbridge
81 Valley
82 Waddington
83 Wattisham
84 West Raynham
85 Wethersfield
86 Wittering
87 Woodbridge
88 Woodvale
89 Wyton

Scotland. Each SOC has its own radar data supplied by outlying stations. In the south, RAF Neatishead is supplied from RAF Hartland Point in Devon and RAF Portreath in Cornwall. The SOC at RAF Boulmer is fed from RAF Bishop's Court in County Down, Northern Ireland, and from RAF Staxton Wold in Yorkshire. The SOC at RAF Buchan is supplied with radar data from two of the most far-flung of all the United Kingdom RAF stations, namely by a radar unit on Benbecula in the Hebrides and another on Saxa Vord in the Shetlands.

Of course, not all the aircraft movements spotted by all these radars and defence systems are likely to be military aircraft alone. To eliminate the various civil aircraft movements from the plots the data from the SOCs has to be passed through a communications chain to the United Kingdom Region Air Operations Centre (UKRAOC) at High Wycombe (of which more below). The data is also passed to HQ No 11 Group at RAF Bentley Priory before it is passed back to the SOCs for action. The data is also passed to Supreme Headquarters Allied Powers Europe (SHAPE) at Mons in Belgium.

The three SOCs (they are but three of a chain of 37 sectors that extends from Norway to Turkey) can each assess the threat potential in their own sector and take the defence actions they each think fit. In practice these actions have been rendered down into the form of a series of drills or procedures which are kept well up-to-date and operationally effective by a long string of Soviet reconnaissance missions that fly towards the United Kingdom. To counter these incursions No 11 Group always has aircraft from at least one squadron ready to perform possible interceptions from a QRA pad. The response time for these alerts was at one time as short as two minutes in the southern sector to as long as ten minutes in the north. These times enable interceptions to be made as much as 500 nautical miles from the coast.

These procedures apply in times of peace. In time of war the entire air space of the United Kingdom and its approaches will come under the direct command of UKRAOC at High Wycombe and this will include the civil air control centres and personnel. All aircraft movements and control will then be under No 11 Group control. UKRAOC is housed at RAF High Wycombe in a fully protected underground location.

Strike Command Harriers deployed on Wideawake during the Falklands aftermath; note the in-flight refuelling probe on the right-hand aircraft.

A No 33 Squadron Puma on exercises in Norway.

It is difficult to outline a precise description of how the actual interception procedures and tactics will be used, for obvious reasons. It is expected that the bulk of the attack threats will originate across the North Sea with only a limited long-range threat coming from the west. To provide more warning of attacks from this direction No 11 Group is now equipped with a number of mobile Marconi Martello phased-array mobile radars with a range of 300 nautical miles—the fixed site Marconi S-631 radars used in conjunction with the S-669 height-finder radar have a range of 389 nautical miles. These radars would be able to provide advanced warning to allow the long-range Phantom interceptors to patrol over the North Sea some hundreds of miles from the coast. Providing them with extra radar information and long-range airborne radar data for the SOCs will be the Shackleton AEW 2s patrolling up and down the North Sea. In-flight refuelling could be provided for the Phantoms by Victor K 2s if a longer sortie time was necessary. Closer to the coastline the Lightnings would be used for the shorter-range interceptions and if attack aircraft ever penetrate the defences to fly over land they would be subject to further defending sorties from the short-range Hawks and the attentions of the Bloodhound missile squadrons. Further defence support might be provided from Royal Navy vessels and from the Fleet Air Arm, especially in the western approaches where No 11 Group frequently carries out defence exercises in conjunction with the Royal Navy.

No 11 Group is also responsible for the Royal Observer Corps in a roundabout way, but this is perhaps better described in the chapter dealing with the Royal Observer Corps. The ROC also brings home the point that No 11 Group, via the

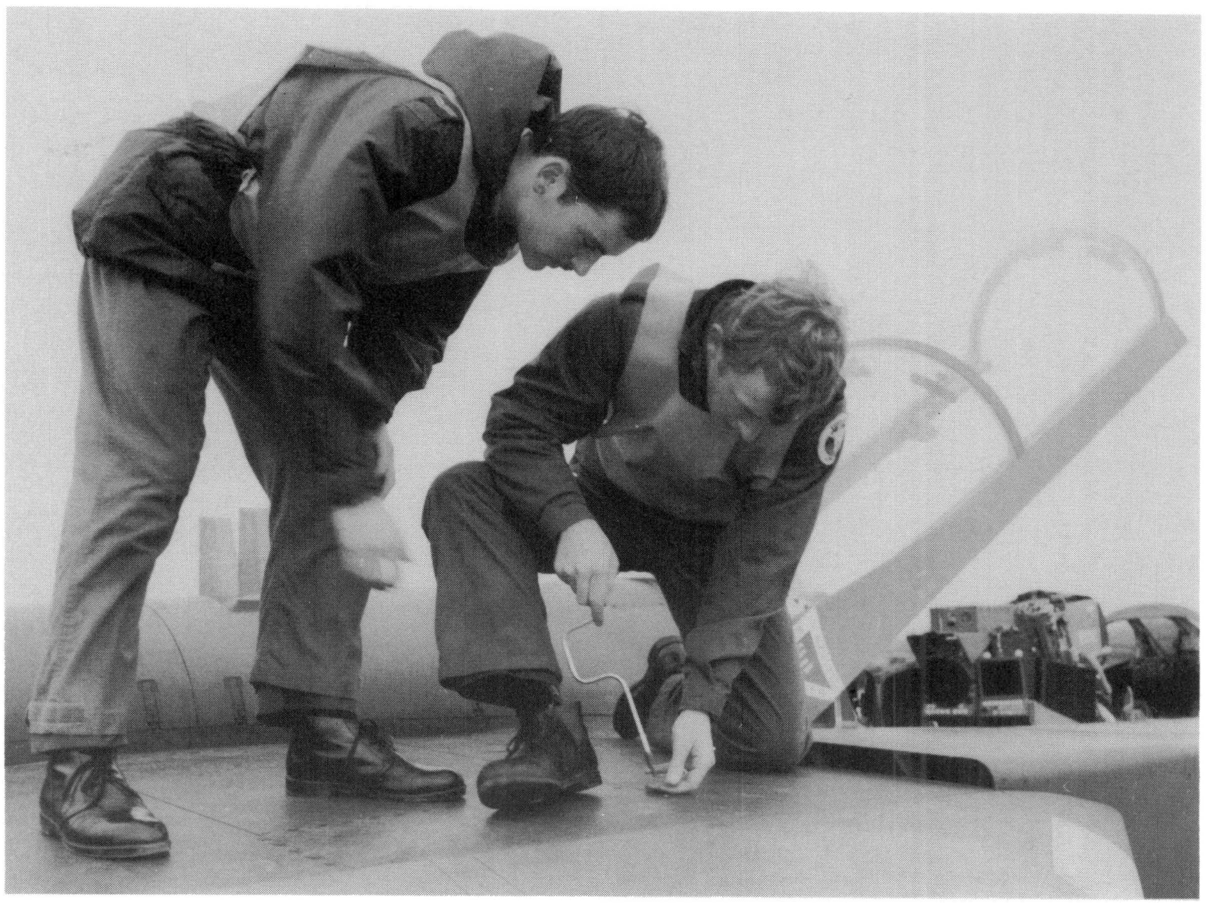

Technicians at work on the wing of a Tornado GR 1.

BMEWS chain, is responsible for providing warning for the United Kingdom of the approach of intermediate range ballistic missiles launched against the country or against Western Europe. It is also a link in the chain that provides the United States with warnings of the approach of inter-continental ballistic missiles against them.

No 18 Group

For want of a better description, No 18 Group may be regarded as the maritime arm of Strike Command. It covers the whole spectrum of maritime operations from the anti-submarine and patrol actions of the Nimrod squadrons, through the anti-shipping strike functions of the Buccaneer squadrons, to the important Search and Rescue (SAR) function carried out by the Group's Wessexes and Sea Kings.

The main tasks of No 18 Group in peacetime are maritime surveillance, anti-submarine training, SAR, patrolling the North Sea oil and gas rigs and fishery patrol. The North Sea activities are co-ordinated by the Maritime Region at Pitreavie in Fife. In time of war No 18 Group would become a fully maritime force operating under the command of the Supreme Allied Commander Atlantic (SACLANT) with the AOC No 18 Group taking over the NATO posts of Commander Maritime Air Eastern Atlantic (COMMAIREASTLANT) and Commander Maritime Air Channel Command (COMMAIRCHAN). To these two commands would be allotted the Nimrod squadrons based at RAF Kinloss in Scotland and RAF St Mawgan in Cornwall as well as the Buccaneer squadrons at RAF Lossiemouth in Scotland.

Under No 18 Group's wing also come the control of the two maritime air regions. There are two of these, both with a co-located rescue co-ordination centre. As mentioned above the Northern Maritime Air Region is at RAF Pitreavie in Scotland.

No 18 Group now includes the last strategic reconnaissance unit in the Royal Air Force, 1 Photographic Reconnaissance Unit (1 PRU). This unit is based at RAF Wyton and, equipped with Canberra PR 9s, carries out long range strategic reconnaissance as opposed to the battlefield tactical reconnaissance carried out by Jaguars and Tornados. It usually spends a great deal of its time in various parts of the world taking high altitude photographs for cartographic purposes.

AHQ Cyprus

The home of AHQ Cyprus is RAF Akrotiri. It is the smallest of the Strike Command Groups in aircraft strength as it has but a single Wessex helicopter squadron with its responsibilities split between two tasks. Four of the Cyprus Wessexes are allotted to the United Nations Forces In Cyprus (UNFICYP) and the rest of the squadron carries out local SAR duties. In the main, AHQ Cyprus is kept in being as resident unit to accommodate visiting units, air-craft and aircrew who use the clear skies of Cyprus for clear-weather training on training tours (Sunspots) or long-range navigation exercises.

Other Strike Command locations

Strike Command has a world-wide task and so it comes as no surprise to find its units in many overseas locations. One of these is RAF Gibraltar where

The search and rescue (SAR) Sea Kings of No 202 Squadron are part of Strike Command.

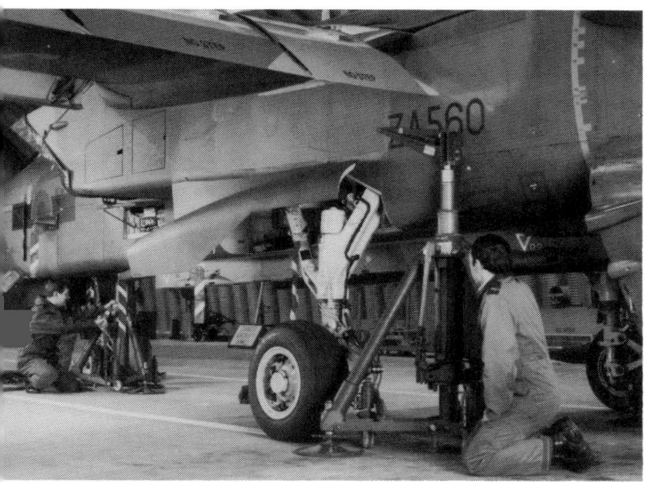

the single-runway airfield is operated by RAF personnel. There is no resident RAF aircraft unit (other than two Hunters operated by a Royal Navy Fleet Requirements Unit) but the facilities are often used by visiting RAF operational and training units.

In Hong Kong Strike Command operates a single Wessex squadron and also has responsibilities for administration and engineering units. These units provide the local operating facilities for visiting VC-10s as well as any other transit aircraft.

North America is another Strike Command location for it has two permanent units resident, one

Left *Technicians at work on a Tornado GR 1 of No 617 Squadron at RAF Marham.*

Below *The new power of Strike Command, the Tornado GR 1 seen here with its full array of ordnance.*

at Offutt Air Force Base in Nebraska and the other at Goose Bay in Labrador. Both units provide local support facilities for the many training missions that share local facilities with the US Air Force and the Canadian Armed Forces.

Military Air Traffic Operations

Often overlooked in the Strike Command hierachy is the Military Air Traffic Operations (MATO), a unit with Group Status within Strike Command and based at Hillingdon House at Uxbridge, Middlesex. It is a joint civil-military operation as it is co-located with Civil Air Traffic Operations (CATO) under a Joint Field Commander (JFC) who is responsible for the implementation of National Air Traffic Services (NATS) policy for the control of civil and military aircraft in the United Kingdom. The AOC MATO is operationally responsible to the Controller NATS for all the military air traffic control services in United Kingdom airspace other than that provided at the various airfields.

Central Trials and Tactics Organisation

Directly administered by HQ Strike Command and located on the same site at High Wycombe is one of the least known of all the various Strike Command functions. This is the Central Trials and Tactics Organisation (CTTO), a research unit that is charged with the formulation of tactical doctrine and conducting operational trials. The CTTO is only administered by HQ Strike Command but is responsible jointly to the Vice-Chief of Air Staff and to the Commander-in-Chief for the conduct of trials and the development of tactics for all RAF operational aircraft. As such it is one of the most sought-after stepping stones in any officer's career structure for the tasks involved include close contacts and co-operation not only with the various RAF commands but also with the Royal Navy, the Army, some Allied armed forces, various aspects of industry, and very often some of the numerous Ministry of Defence research establishments. Working as they do in concepts and equipments that will not be in service for some years to come, the officers concerned find that a spell with the CTTO is a most worthwhile experience and can often lead to useful contacts and promotion for the future.

* * *

It would be futile to regard the above as a complete listing of all the many roles and functions of Strike Command. No mention can be made in a work of this nature of the various electronic warfare functions of the Command and no mention has been made of some of the smaller Strike Command units such as those based on the training ranges in Sardinia and Alberta.

RAF Germany

'Keepers of the Peace'

Royal Air Force Germany, usually referred to as RAF Germany or even RAFG, operates as part of the NATO air forces over mainland Europe. The exact reason why the Royal Air Force still operates from West Germany can perhaps be best explained using the official text in its full NATO-ese, but this explanation is basically a statement of a commitment left over as a legacy from the Second World War:

'In peacetime, under responsibilities retained by the United Kingdom pending the conclusion of a German peace treaty and in close integration with NATO, the defence of the integrity of the airspace of the northern half of the Federal Republic of Germany and, with the Unites States Air Force and the French Air Force, the maintenance of access to Berlin in the three air corridors.'

Hence the presence of a fair proportion of the Royal Air Force's strength within the German borders.

One of the main points to understand regarding RAF Germany is that it remains a national force in times of peace only. In time of war it would become part of a major NATO air force that extends from northern Norway to southern Turkey. To see exactly where RAF Germany is placed in this structure, reference must be made to the highest NATO command level. This is Supreme Allied Powers Europe (SHAPE) based at Mons in Belgium. Under SHAPE is the Headquarters Allied Forces Central Europe (AFCENT) at Brunssum which commands (among other formations) Headquarters Allied Air Forces Central Europe (AAFCE) at Ramstein. AAFCE has two formations to control in the NATO Central Region, namely the Fourth Allied Tactical Air Force (FOURATAF or 4 ATAF) in the south and Second Tactical Air Force (TWOATAF or 2 ATAF) in the north. Royal Air Force Germany is part of 2 ATAF, and the other units involved in 2 ATAF can be seen in the accompanying table.

This rather tortuous chain of command has been outlined in order to emphasise the point that RAF Germany is very much part of NATO's defensive stance. 2 ATAF is made up of units from the Royal Air Force, the United States Air Force, and the air forces of Belgium, the Netherlands and West Germany. Its operational area extends from the borders of the Federal Republic of Germany in the east to the Danish border in the north, out over the North Sea, south along the Franco-Belgian border to the northern point of Luxembourg and then north of a line running north-east to Kassel and Gottingen. The commander of 2 ATAF is always a Royal Air Force officer and his headquarters in time of peace is at Rheindahlen, near the Dutch border. Rheindahlen is also the headquarters of RAF Germany and the Commander of RAF Germany also has the NATO post of Commander 2 ATAF, so in time of war the Commander RAF Germany would immediately become Commander 2 ATAF and move to his wartime headquarters just over the border in Holland.

In time of peace, Headquarters RAF Germany is responsible for the operational training of its units and oversees the general administration and logistic support. Once the NATO alert system is in operation at a prescribed instant RAF Germany becomes part of 2 ATAF and RAF Germany is then primarily concerned with the support role for all units under its peacetime control. This transition of control is an important stage as in peacetime the only sectors of RAF Germany under NATO control are the two Phantom squadrons (Nos 19 and 92) based at RAF Wildenrath. Along with all other 2 ATAF fighter and surface-to-air missile units, these two squadrons are used for the general policing of their allotted air space and for the interception of unknown aircraft in the Air Defence Identification Zone, which is a buffer region in the sky along the length of the border with East Germany. Any suspect aircraft in this zone are intercepted by 2 ATAF fighters under the control of an Allied Task and Operations Centre

2 ATAF UNITS

Nationality/Headquarters	Squadron/Wing	Base	Aircraft types
Belgian Tactical Air Force Command/Evere	349/1	Beauvechain	F-16
	350/1	Beauvechain	F-16
	1/3	Bierset	Mirage 5BA
	8/3	Bierset	Mirage 5BA
	2/2	Florennes	Mirage 5BA
	42/2	Florennes	Mirage 5BR
	23/10	Kleine Brogel	F-16
	31/10	Kleine Brogel	F-16
German Air Force Tactical Command (GAFTAC)/Köln	JBG 31 'Boelke'	Norvenich	Tornado
	JBG 33	Buchel	F-104G
	JBG 36	Hopsten	F-4F
	JBG 38	Jever	Tornado
	JBG 41	Husum	Alpha Jet
	JBG 43	Oldenburg	Alpha Jet
	AKG 52	Leck	RF-5E
	JG 71 'Richthofen'	Wittmundhafen	F-4F
Netherlands Tactical Air Force/Zeist	306	Volkel	F-16
	311	Volkel	F-16
	312	Volkel	F-16
	313	Twenthe	NF-5A
	314	Eindhoven	NF-5A
	315	Twenthe	NF-5A
	316	Gilze Rijen	NF-5A
	322	Leeuwarden	F-16
	323	Leeuwarden	F-16
Royal Air Force Germany (RAFG)/Rheindahlen	2	Laarbruch	Jaguar GR 1
	3	Gutersloh	Harrier GR 3
	4	Gutersloh	Harrier GR 3
	9	Bruggen	Tornado GR 1
	14	Bruggen	Tornado GR 1
	XV	Laarbruch	Tornado GR 1
	16	Laarbruch	Tornado GR 1
	17	Bruggen	Tornado GR 1
	19	Wildenrath	Phantom FGR 2
	20	Laarbruch	Tornado GR 1
	31	Bruggen	Tornado GR 1
	92	Wildenrath	Phantom FGR 2
United States Air Force Europe (USAFE)/Ramstein	55 TFS/20 TFW	Upper Heyford	F-111E
	77 TFS/20 TFW	Upper Heyford	F-111E
	79 TFS/20 TFW	Upper Heyford	F-111E
	91 TFS/81 TFW	Bentwaters	A-10 Thunderbolt II
	92 TFS/81 TFW	Bentwaters	A-10 Thunderbolt II
	78 TFS/81 TFW	Woodbridge	A-10 Thunderbolt II
	32 TFS	Soesterberg	F-15 Eagle

Location of the main RAF Germany bases.

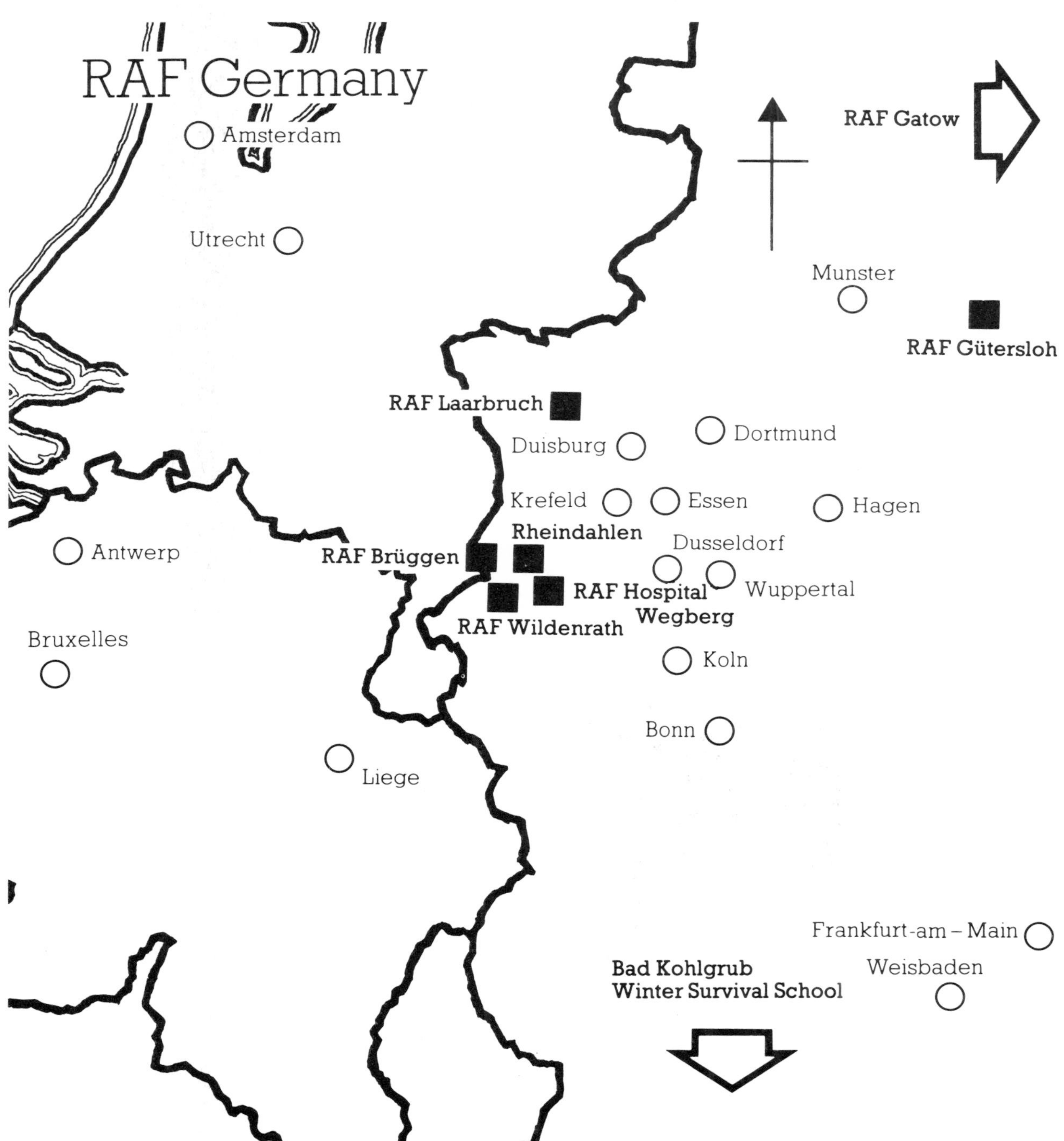

(ATOC). In turn the fighters are controlled by one of two Sector Operations Centres (SOC).

RAF Germany has four main airfields which will be described below. These four airfields, known as the 'Clutch' airfields, now contain the main striking force not only of RAF Germany but of the Royal Air Force as a whole for they are the bases for the bulk of the service's Tornado GR 1 squadrons. Over the last few years the old mix of Buccaneers and Jaguars have been withdrawn and Tornados have taken their place. The change-over was still not quite complete at the time of writing for No 2 Squadron still retained its Jaguar GR 1s for the tactical reconnaissance role. It too is scheduled for replacement by Tornados that will be used in the same purpose. The Harrier GR 3s of Nos 3 and 4 Squadrons at RAF Gutersloh are also scheduled for replacement by the more advanced Harrier GR 5.

'Real estate' in RAF Germany is based on four airfields, three of them grouped in what are known as the 'Clutch' airfields of RAF Bruggen, Laarbruch

Above *A Unimog tractor using a tow bar to position a Harrier in its camouflaged field hide.*

Below *Tornado GR 1s armed with 1,000-lb bombs—these aircraft are from No 9 Squadron, formerly based at RAF Honington but now at RAF Bruggen.*

Above *Inside a Tornado HAS.*

Right *A corner of one of the Clutch airfields showing not only masses of barbed wire but also a pill-box to emphasise the degree of importance given to perimeter security.*

and Wildenrath, all west of the Rhine. The only airfield east of the Rhine is RAF Gutersloh which is placed adjacent to its main 'customers' in 1 (BR) Corps. In the Berlin enclave is RAF Gatow, but this airfield is not used by combat aircraft, solely by transport types.

Also under RAF Germany control is a bombing range at Nordhorn with another range far to the south at Decimomannu on Sardinia. A Royal Air Force Hospital at Wegberg, close to the 'Clutch' airfields, makes up the facilities. Rheindahlen itself must not be forgotten for not only is it the headquarters of RAF Germany and the peacetime headquarters of 2 ATAF but it is also the headquarters of the Northern Army Group (NORTHAG) and the British Army of the Rhine (BAOR). To support these headquarters Rheindahlen itself has grown into a small military township with all the attendant services and facilities. Almost hidden among the many buildings on the site is the bandroom of the Band of the Royal Air Force Germany. These musicians not only make music for all to enjoy or march to but they also have a wartime role as medical attendants at the Wegberg hospital.

The best way of explaining the equipments involved is to describe their bases at the four airfields.

RAF Bruggen

RAF Bruggen is so placed that its perimeter brushes the Dutch border on one side—many personnel living off base live in Holland. It is the home of four Tornado squadrons, Nos 9, 14, 17, and 31, all equipped with the Tornado GR 1 but with a few Tornado GR 1(T)s among them for check-outs and in-squadron training. At the time of writing No 9 Squadron was still back in the United Kingdom at RAF Honington but has since moved to RAF Bruggen. Like the other three airfields in Germany, RAF Bruggen is equipped with hardened dispersals for the aircraft and personnel and has its own integral air defence provided by a Royal Air Force Regiment squadron, in this case No 37 Squadron, RAF Regiment, equipped with the Rapier SAM. Also based at RAF Bruggen is 431 Maintenance Unit which can best be described as Support Command in miniature, for under its auspices are carried out all the maintenance support functions that in the United Kingdom are carried out by several units. No 431 MU is involved in aircraft and propulsion engineering, battle damage repair and training, aerial erection and training, ground radio maintenance support, a crane test facility, vehicle maintenance and supply (it has the only vehicle park in the Royal Air Force and normally has about 600 vehicles stored ready for use), furniture storage and repair, and all-round transport requirements. No 431 MU is the only unit of its kind in RAF Germany and, indeed, in the Royal Air Force, for its limitations seem to be few and its capabilities many. It even concerns itself with ammunition supply from the main aircraft ammunition depot at Bracht. The unit is entirely self-contained and has its own supply, administrative and engineering personnel. It even has its own movements personnel, so wide-ranging are its transport and other activities.

RAF Laarbruch

RAF Laarbruch will eventually have three Tornado squadrons based within its perimeter and it was actually the first RAF Germany base to house Tornados. No XV Squadron received its first

Above *An RAF Police Dog Handler on patrol at Rheindahlen; the police dogs are normally trained at RAF Newton.*

Right *A Puma carrying out exercises with students at the RAF Winter Survival School at Bad Kohlgrub.*

work-up aircraft during 1983 and for a while the station operated with Tornados and Buccaneer S2s operating alongside each other. Now No 16 Squadron and No 20 Squadron (formerly at RAF Bruggen) also have Tornado GR 1s and eventually No 2 Squadron will also exchange its Jaguar GR 1s for Tornados. No 2 Squadron is devoted to the tactical reconnaissance role but by late 1987 the squadron will be using Tornado GR 1s for the same task—it will be the last RAF Germany squadron to convert to the Tornado.

RAF Laarbruch has a considerable RAF Regiment presence for not only does it have its own Rapier squadron in the form of No 26 Squadron, RAF Regiment, but it is also the base of No 1 Squadron, RAF Regiment, which is equipped with Scorpions and Spartans for the defence of the RAF Gutersloh Harriers once they leave for their field sites.

RAF Wildenrath

The third of the 'Clutch' bases, RAF Wildenrath is the home of two Phantom FGR 2 squadrons, Nos 19 and 92. These two squadrons operate under NATO control at all times and maintain aircraft on a permanent scramble alert basis. The other aircraft squadron at RAF Wildenrath is No 60 operating the Pembroke C 1 to provide a general internal Command 'airline'. Some of the aircraft are maintained with an interna! VIP configuration but others have more prosaic interiors and are used for a regular stores run to the United Kingdom. The Pembrokes may also be used at short notice at air ambulances to take Service personnel or their dependents to hospitals in Germany or the United Kingdom.

The RAF Wildenrath Rapier squadron is No 16 Squadron RAF Regiment.

Perhaps RAF Wildenrath is best known to all serving personnel in BAOR as their main trooping terminal. The number of Servicemen and dependents travelling through the airield has led to the provision of a fully-equipped airline terminal to be used by all the various types of transport aircraft involved, both military and civil. The current civil charter aircraft involved in the RAF Germany and BAOR trooping role are Brittania Airways Boeing 737s. RAF Wildenrath is also the main Freight Distribution Centre for RAF Germany.

RAF Gutersloh

RAF Gutersloh differs from the 'Clutch' airfields in several ways for not only is it the only RAF Germany airfield east of the River Rhine but it is the only one of the four that was once a pre-1939 Luftwaffe airfield. Thus it has its own unique atmosphere imparted by the architecture, much of which dates from the World War II era. Another point to mention regarding RAF Gutersloh is that it is the home of two Harrier squadrons, Nos 3 and 4. Apart from the Harriers, RAF Gutersloh is the base of two helicopter squadrons, No 230 operating Puma HC 1s and No 18 operating Chinook HC 1s. All four of these squadrons are intended for the support of 1 (BR) Corps as the Army is RAF Gutersloh's main customer. It is located not far from Bielefeld, the headquarters of 1 (BR) Corps, and is situated only about 129 kilometres from the border with East Germany. For this reason the units based on the airield will disperse to field sites in an emergency and operate from them. This rapid dispersal is constantly practised and full dispersal exercises are carried out at least three times every year. These involve all the personnel on the station along with their transport, living support and their defensive measures.

The RAF Regiment Rapier unit at RAF Gutersloh is No 63 Squadron, but in time of war airfield defence will be augmented by the arrival of the RAF Regiment Queen's Colour Squadron which will form a mobile rifle squadron using Land Rovers after arrival.

RAF Gutersloh has its own air trooping terminal which is much used by 1 (BR) Corps personnel and their dependents.

RAF Gatow

As mentioned above, RAF Gatow does not handle any combat aircraft and its use is confined to transport aircraft. Part of the airfield perimeter actually skirts the infamous Berlin Wall. Together with Tegel in the French Sector and Tempelhof in the American Sector, Gatow acts as the air head for the Allied military units still based in Berlin under the 1945 Treaty arrangements and all traffic to and from the city is controlled by the Berlin Air Safety Centre which is manned by American, British, French and Soviet air controllers who guide all aircraft along three air corridors. The most northerly of these corridors is from Hamburg to Berlin, the Centre Corridor is from Hanover to Berlin and the South Corridor is from Frankfurt to Berlin.

RAF Germany has RAF Gatow under its command but the only aircraft maintained on the airfield are the two Chipmunk T 10s operated by the Berlin Station Flight. These two training aircraft fly regularly from RAF Gatow purely to maintain their right to do so under the Treaty arrangements.

Left *Aircrew students undergoing the joys of a Winter Survival Course at Bad Kohlgrub.*

Below *The RAF Police and the West German LandesPolizei operate from a Joint Police Station at Rheindahlen.*

Apart from RAF Gatow, the RAF Germany airfields all present a difficult target to any would-be attacker. This has been brought about by a long programme of hardening and toning down the airfield structures and surroundings. All the airfields now have fully equipped Hardened Aircraft Shelters (HAS) and protected operations centres, crew shelters, stores and other installations. All communications systems are underground and all airfield equipment is kept under cover whenever possible. To add further protection all visible surfaces have been toned down in colour to the extent that hardstandings, runways and taxi-ways have been coloured green or grey to match their surroundings. All vehicles and other equipment have also been given the tone-down treatment and the aircraft themselves have long been provided with subdued colour schemes. To the observer on the ground these measures may not appear to do very much but to an attacking pilot they appear very different. The airfield blends almost exactly with the surrounding terrain and even locally-based aircrew often have difficulty in finding their home

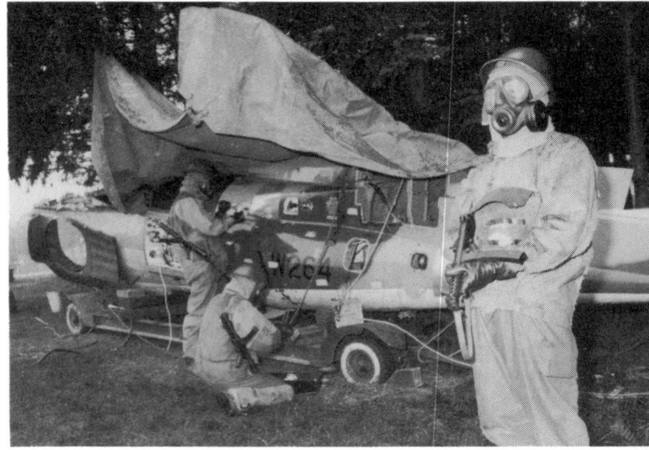

Above *Airmen from No 431 MU at RAF Bruggen undergoing training in repairing simulated battle damage on a Harrier fuselage under NBC conditions.*

Below *An RAF Regiment Spartan APC in unmistakeable German surroundings.*

Phantom FGR 2 of No 92 Squadron, RAF Wildenrath.

base after a sortie. If the tone-down programme can have that effect on locally-based personnel it can be appreciated what effect it could have on enemy aircrew who might be tensed-up and frightened, operating in haze or smoke and expecting defensive measures to be thrown at them at any instant. But the toning-down process, which encourages local vegetation to grow over structures, does not extend to letting the airfield grass grow too long. That has to be kept cut short to prevent birds moving in to build their nests and thereby creating a hazard to aircraft.

The HAS distribution is calculated to house about 70 per cent of the operational aircraft on any one airfield. In some cases this can be extended to 100 per cent as in the instance of the Jaguar and Harrier squadrons where two aircraft can be accommodated in a single HAS. Tornados will be housed at the rate of one aircraft to a HAS. Inside the HAS, aircraft can be refuelled, rearmed and serviced and the engines can be started and preflight checks carried out before the large armoured doors are opened. Each HAS is so positioned that a single pass from an attacking aircraft could not knock out more than one HAS, even supposing the strike could penetrate the hardened structure.

Apart from the concealment angle, airfield defence looms large in RAF Germany. Every member of ground crew, aircrew and the administrative staff has his part to play in this, but in Germany the problem is greater than in the United Kingdom. Every aircraft hardstanding is surrounded with liberal amounts of barbed wire built up into formidable barricades and at intervals brick built bunkers are situated to command lengths of wire. Maintaining the wire barricades is a formidable ongoing task for all station personnel, and the station manpower manifest has been adjusted to reflect this. It is also a task that has to be carried out in all weathers. To assist in the local defence of the bases, the RAF Regiment would move in to add their strength, usually with their mobile armoured field squadrons. Once in Germany these extra squadrons would come under the control of Headquarters 33 Wing, RAF Regiment, located at RAF Gutersloh. In time of peace this Wing has direct command of only one unit, No 1 Squadron, RAF Regiment, based at RAF Laarbruch but intended for use with the Harrier squadrons at their field locations. In an emergency this squadron would be reinforced by four RAF Regiment squadrons moved over from the United Kingdom plus a further squadron from Cyprus (34 Squadron, RAF Regiment). These squadrons are mobile armoured units equipped with Scorpions and Spartans and would be distributed among the 'Clutch' airfields for local airfield defence. As mentioned above, the Queen's Colour Squadron would also be moved to Germany to provide local defence at RAF Gutersloh using Land Rovers. The RAF Regiment armoured squadrons are based in the United Kingdom but regularly train at their RAF Germany bases every year, bringing their vehicles with them in freight containers and on normal commercial freightliner shipping. In this way they are able to train without causing any local upsets with the possible sight of what the public think of as 'tanks' being seen unloading in European ports.

Of course, the RAF Germany airfields would be prime targets in any future conflict and using the operational experience gleaned from several recent conflicts measures have already been taken to offset the worst that might happen. Any aircraft attack is bound to create damage to runways and taxiways and consequently each airfield has ready to hand large dumps of gravel and other materials from which instant repairs can be made. After any attack the first move would be a rapid local reconnaissance carried out by at least one of the two Gazelle HT 3s located at each airfield. These Gazelles are flown over from RAF Shawbury in any possible TTW (Time of Tension to War) precisely for this task. Once any damage has been assessed priorities can be arranged and the repair teams get to work. Each of the four main airfields has its own Royal Engineers Airfield Damage Repair Squadron, each with all their heavy equipment already pre-placed 'under wraps' somewhere on the airfield location. Normally these Royal Engineer units are based in the United Kingdom and would be flown out in an emergency. The units involved are 48, 50, 52 and 53 Field Squadrons (Construction). The Royal Engineers are also involved with the Harrier force in the preparation of field sites and their approaches and one of these units, 10 Field Squadron, is based in BAOR. Two further units, 11 and 32 Field Squadrons, would move from the United Kingdom in an emergency. Also heavily involved with the Harrier force are several Royal Signal units.

At present the RAF Regiment Rapier squadrons are gaining a great deal of 'operational' experience in the Falkland Islands. Based at several exposed sites around the Islands, the Rapier crews are detached on three-month tours which in practice extend to slightly more than that. All four RAF Germany Rapier squadrons are involved in the roulement process.

Station security in time of war would, of course, be considerably assisted by the RAF Police based on each airfield. In RAF Germany the Provost Branch is divided into two main sections. One is the Provost and Security Service (P & SS) who act in much the same manner as the civil police back in the United Kingdom. They have police authority over all serving personnel and their dependents and at all times function in close co-operation with the local West German police forces. The other branch is the Station Police who guard the RAF Germany airfields and other installations. They are responsible for all domestic policing and also administer the physical security of the installations. This includes the RAF dogs, who number not only the guard dogs who are released to roam around such places as ammunition dumps but also the highly-trained sniffer dogs who can detect explosives and drugs. The RAF Police presence in RAF Germany is quite large. At RAF Laarbruch and Bruggen are Police Squadrons each some 600 to 800 strong, operating on a 24-hour basis in shifts. Smaller Flights are maintained at such locations as RAF Wildenrath and in Berlin. The equipment

Opposite *Laser nose of a Harrier GR 3 of No 3 Squadron deployed in a field hide.*

Right *Although some Unimog tractors are used in the UK at RAF Wittering, most are used by the Harrier squadrons in RAF Germany.*

Below *One corner of the vehicle park of No 431 MU at RAF Bruggen showing (left) a Van, ¼ ton, 4 × 2, Morris Mini and right, one of the relatively new Cars, Utility, 4 × 2, Vauxhall Chevette E.*

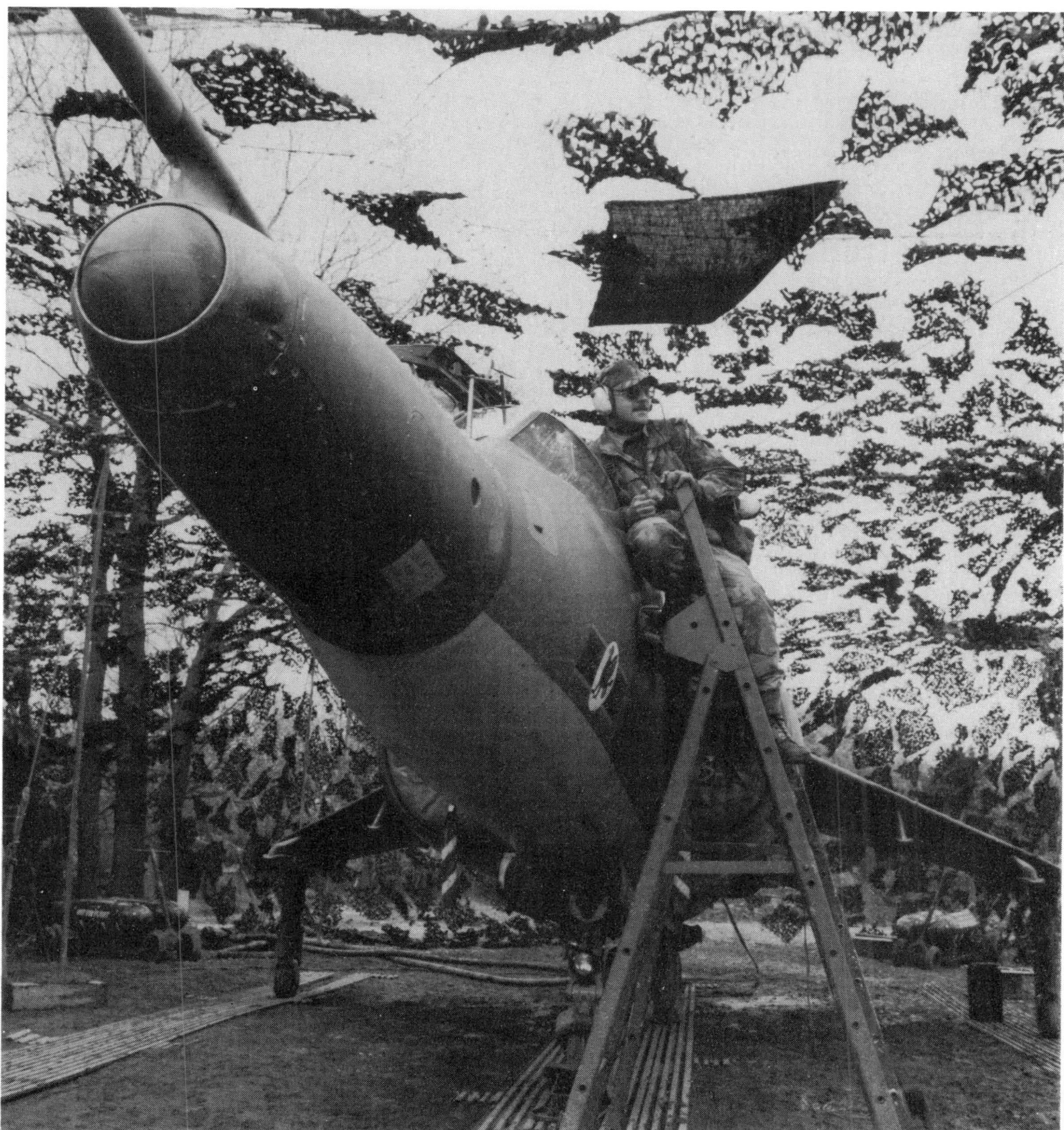

used by the RAF Police includes specially-equipped Range Rovers although the Land Rover is the more normal vehicle involved. In some locations such as Rheindahlen the RAF Police work in close cooperation with the Army's Royal Military Police. In time of war the RAF Police branch is one that would not expect to receive large reinforcements from the United Kingdom for no more than 60 P & SS personnel are expected to arrive, so the existing personnel would have to cope by means of extended shifts. In war the Police would carry out their normal duties plus anti-sabotage and anti-

Tornado GR 1s from the TWCU, RAF Honington, during one of their first-ever visits to RAF Germany. The first Tornados were issued to XV Squadron in October 1983.

looting patrols and other such duties. In the last resort they are all combat-trained and so would assist in the local defence of their bases.

Service life in RAF Germany differs in many respects from that in the United Kingdom. For the Serviceman there is the stricture that very little formal training can be carried out other than locally generated on-the-job training. The only formal 'school' operated by RAF Germany is the Winter Survival School located at Bad Kohlgrub near Oberammergau in Bavaria. This school runs survival courses for aircrew and others and is managed by RAF Germany. Trade training is, of course, continued for all RAF personnel in Germany but they have to return to the United Kingdom to carry it out.

Locally, language training is extended to all serving personnel and their dependents. German is the obvious main language taught by numerous local and centralised teaching establishments at all stations and headquarters, but Dutch is also important, especially as many families from the 'Clutch' stations have their quarters just over the border in Holland. Language training is available at all levels from everyday 'shopping' usage to full interpreter standards—there is even a NATO standard for all these levels.

Formal education for serving personnel and their dependents is made more difficult by the absence of any handy educational facilities such as there would usually be in the United Kingdom. Thus the Station Education Centres have a more important role to play than their equivalents back home. Education up to Open University Foundation Level is readily available on many stations. For elementary and secondary schools there is one unusual administrative quirk in RAF Germany as all schools on the stations and other installations come directly under the command of the local Station Commander. Apart from this, the Education Officer strength on all RAF Germany bases is at least four, one of whom is always able to impart language training.

Mention should be made of one other group of civilians who have an important role to play in RAF Germany. These are the Meteorological Officers who supply important weather information on all the RAF Germany airfields. Each airfield has at least one weather observer and one forecaster on duty at any given time; in an emergency they would operate from a small underground chamber outside the main control tower. This chamber is equipped with a clear vision dome for direct observation and if it came to the worst the team would have to be prepared to wear NBC clothing and are thus trained for the role. In time of peace the met men obtain their weather information from as many sources as possible, including observations from the east and from the main German observation collecting point at Traben-Trarbach, but in war these sources would, of course, be lost.

To return to the full operational side of RAF Germany, the present updating programme and gradual hardening of all facilities is to continue unabated. By 1987 the full complement of eight Tornado squadrons will be well established, the two Harrier squadrons will still be operational and looking forward to their full complement of Harrier GR 5s, the Phantom squadrons will still fulfil their interceptor role and the Chinook squadron will be up to full strength. The No 230 Squadron Pumas will still be around and no doubt the RAF Gatow Chipmunks will still be chugging around the Berlin airscape, but one venerable aircraft will have disappeared. The No 60 Squadron Pembroke C 1s are now due to be replaced by a mix of HS 125s and Andovers, but the exact date and composition of this new transport fleet introduction was not certain at the time of writing. When the re-equipment programme is complete RAF Germany will be in the position where it will have about one third of the front-line strength of the Royal Air Force but only one ninth of the manpower.

Harriers in the field.

Royal Air Force squadron check list (as at September 1986)

Squadron	Group/Command	Aircraft type(s)	Base	Notes
1	1/Strike	Harrier GR 3, T 4A	RAF Wittering	
2	RAF Germany	Jaguar GR 1, T 2	RAF Laarbruch	Scheduled to convert to Tornado GR 1
3	RAF Germany	Harrier GR 3, T 4A	RAF Gutersloh	Scheduled to convert to Harrier GR 5
4	RAF Germany	Harrier GR 3, T 4A	RAF Gutersloh	Scheduled to convert to Harrier GR 5
5	11/Strike	Lightning F 3, T 5, F 6	RAF Binbrook	
6	1/Strike	Jaguar GR 1, T 2	RAF Coltishall	
7	1/Strike	Chinook HC 1	RAF Odiham	
8	11/Strike	Shackleton AEW 2	RAF Lossiemouth	
9	RAF Germany	Tornado GR 1, GR 1T	RAF Bruggen	
10	1/Strike	VC 10 C1	RAF Brize Norton	
11	11/Strike	Lightning F 3, T 5, F 6	RAF Binbrook	
12	18/Strike	Buccaneer S 2B	RAF Lossiemouth	
14	RAF Germany	Tornado GR 1, GR 1T	RAF Bruggen	
XV	RAF Germany	Tornado GR 1, GR 1T	RAF Laarbruch	
16	RAF Germany	Tornado GR 1, GR 1T	RAF Laarbruch	
17	RAF Germany	Tornado GR 1, GR 1T	RAF Bruggen	
18	RAF Germany	Chinook HC 1	RAF Gutersloh	
19	RAF Germany	Phantom FGR 2	RAF Wildenrath	
20	RAF Germany	Tornado GR 1, GR 1T	RAF Laarbruch	
22	18/Strike	Wessex HC 2, HAR 2	'A' Flight RAF Chivenor 'B' Flight RAF Leuchars 'C' Flight RAF Valley 'D' Flight RAF Leconfield 'E' Flight RAF Manston 'F' Flight RAF Coltishall	
23	11/Strike	Phantom FGR 2	RAF Mount Pleasant	
24	1/Strike	Hercules C 1, C 3	RAF Lyneham	
25	11/Strike	Bloodhound	RAF Wyton 'A' Flight RAF Barkston Heath 'B' Flight RAF Wyton 'C' Flight RAF Wattisham	

Squadron	Group/Command	Aircraft type(s)	Base	Notes
27	1/Strike	Tornado GR 1, GR 1T	RAF Marham	
28		Wessex HC 2	RAF Sek Kong	
29	11/Strike	Phantom FGR 2	RAF Coningsby	
30	1/Strike	Hercules C 1, C 3	RAF Lyneham	
31	RAF Germany	Tornado GR 1, GR 1T	RAF Bruggen	
32	1/Strike	HS 125 CC 3, Andover C 1, CC 2, Gazelle HCC 4	RAF Northolt	
33	1/Strike	Puma HC 1	RAF Odiham	
38	18/Strike	Nimrod MR 2	RAF St Mawgan	Shadow squadron for 236 OCU
41	1/Strike	Jaguar GR 1, T 2	RAF Coltishall	
42	18/Strike	Nimrod MR 2	RAF St Mawgan	
43	11/Strike	Phantom FG 1	RAF Leuchars	
45	1/Strike	Tornado GR 1, GR 1T	RAF Honington	Shadow squadron for TWCU
47	1/Strike	Hercules C 1, C 3	RAF Lyneham	
51	18/Strike	Nimrod R 1, Canberra B 6, Andover C 1	RAF Wyton	
54	1/Strike	Jaguar GR 1, T 2	RAF Coltishall	
55	1/Strike	Victor K 2	RAF Marham	
56	11/Strike	Phantom FGR 2	RAF Wattisham	
60	RAF Germany	Pembroke C 1	RAF Wildenrath	
63	1/Strike	Hawk T 1A	RAF Chivenor	Shadow squadron in 2 TWU
64	11/Strike	Phantom FGR 2	RAF Coningsby	Shadow squadron in 228 OCU
70	1/Strike	Hercules C 1, C 3	RAF Lyneham	
72	1/Strike	Wessex HC 2	RAF Aldergrove	
74	11/Strike	F-4J(UK) Phantom	RAF Wattisham	
78	1/Strike	Chinook HC 1, Sea King HAR 3	RAF Mount Pleasant	
79	1/Strike	Hawk T 1A	RAF Brawdy	Shadow squadron in 1TWU
84	1/Strike	Wessex HC 2	RAF Akrotiri	'A' Flight Akrotiri, 'B' Flight Nicosia
85	11/Strike	Bloodhound	RAF West Raynham 'A' Flight RAF West Raynham 'B' Flight RAF Bawdsey 'C' Flight RAF North Coates	
92	RAF Germany	Phantom FGR 2	RAF Wildenrath	
100	18/Strike	Canberra B 2, T 4, PR 7, E 15, TT 18	RAF Wyton	
101	1/Strike	VC 10, K 2, K 3	RAF Brize Norton	
111	11/Strike	Phantom FG 1	RAF Leuchars	
115	1/Strike	Andover C 1, E 3, E 3A	RAF Benson	
120	18/Strike	Nimrod MR 2	RAF Kinloss	
151	1/Strike	Hawk T 1A	RAF Chivenor	Shadow squadron in 2 TWU
201	18/Strike	Nimrod MR 2	RAF Kinloss	
202	18/Strike	Sea King HAR 3	'A' Flight RAF Boulmer 'B' Flight RAF Brawdy 'D' Flight RAF Lossiemouth	'C' Flight now part of 78 Squadron
206	18/Strike	Nimrod MR 2	RAF Kinloss	
208	18/Strike	Buccaneer S 2, Hunter T 7	RAF Lossiemouth	
216	1/Strike	Tristar K 1, KC 1, K 2	RAF Brize Norton	
230	RAF Germany	Puma HC 1	RAF Gutersloh	
234	1/Strike	Hawk T 1A	RAF Brawdy	Shadow squadron in 1 TWU
360	18/Strike	Canberra T 17	RAF Wyton	Joint RAF/RN unit
617	1/Strike	Tornado GR 1, GR 1T	RAF Marham	
1417 Flight	1/Strike	Harrier GR 3	Belize	
1563 Flight	1/Strike	Puma HC 1	Belize	

Royal Air Force check list of flying units other than squadrons

Unit	Aircraft type(s)	Base	Notes
TTTE	Tornado GR 1, GR 1T	RAF Cottesmore	Tornado OCU, A, B, C and Standardization Squadrons: includes Italians and West Germans
TWCU	Tornado GR 1, GR 1T	RAF Honington	

Squadron	Group/Command	Aircraft type(s)	Base	Notes
1 TWU		Hawk T 1, T 1A, Jet Provost T 4	RAF Brawdy	
2 TWU		Hawk T 1, T 1A	RAF Chivenor	
1 PRU		Canberra PR 9	RAF Wyton	
226 OCU		Jaguar GR 1, T 2	RAF Lossiemouth	
228 OCU		Phantom FGR 2	RAF Coningsby	
229 OCU		Tornado F 2, F 3	RAF Coningsby	
231 OCU		Canberra B 2, T 4	RAF Wyton	
233 OCU		Harrier GR 3, T 4A	RAF Wittering	
236 OCU		Nimrod MR 2	RAF St Mawgan	
237 OCU		Buccaneer S 2A, S 2B, Hunter T 7B, T 8B, T 8C	RAF Lossiemouth	
240 OCU		Puma HC 1, Chinook HC 1	RAF Odiham	
241 OCU		VC 10 C 1	RAF Brize Norton	Uses 10 Squadron aircraft
242 OCU		Hercules C 1, C 3	RAF Lyneham	
ATF		Andover C 1, E 3	RAF Benson	
RAFSKTU		Sea King HAR 3	RNAS Culdrose	RAF Sea King Training Unit
SARTU		Wessex HC 2	RAF Valley	Search and Rescue Training Unit, pooled with 'C' Flight 22 Squadron
CFS		Jet Provost T 3A, T 5A	RAF Scampton	
		Hawk T 1A	RAF Scampton	Red Arrows
		Hawk T 1, T 1A	RAF Valley	With 4 FTS
		Bulldog T 1	RAF Scampton	
		Gazelle HT 3	RAF Shawbury	Pooled with 2 FTS
RAF College		Jet Provost T 5A	RAF Cranwell	
FSS		Chipmunk T 10	RAF Swinderby	Flying Selection Centre
1 FTS		Jet Provost T 3A, T 5A	RAF Linton-on-Ouse	Contains Refresher Flying School (RFS)
		Bulldog T 1	RAF Topcliffe	Contains Royal Navy Elementary Flying Training Squadron (RNEFTS)
2 FTS		Gazelle HT 2, HT 3, Wessex HC 2, HAR 2	RAF Shawbury	
4 FTS		Hawk T 1, T 1A	RAF Valley	
6 FTS		Jet Provost T 5B, Dominie T 1, Jetstream T 1	RAF Finningley	
7 FTS		Jet Provost T 3A, T 5B	RAF Church Fenton	
CATCS		Jet Provost T 4	RAF Shawbury	Central Air Traffic Control School
Queen's Flight		HS 146 CC 2, Wessex HCC 4	RAF Benson	
Historical Aircraft Flight		Hurricane II, Spitfire IIA, VB, PR 19, Lancaster 1, Chipmunk T 10	RAF Coningsby	'Battle of Britain' Flight
CINCAFNE		Andover C 1	Oslo	Commander-in-Chief Air Forces Northern Europe
Berlin Station Flight		Chipmunk T 10	RAF Gatow	
EWAU		Andover C 1(mod)	RAF Wyton	Electronic Warfare Avionics Unit
TOEU		Tornado GR 1	RAE Boscombe Down	Tornado Operational Evaluation Unit

Support Command

'Ut Aquilae Volent – That Eagles May Fly'

RAF Support Command is a mighty edifice. Headquartered at RAF Brampton near Huntingdon in Cambridgeshire, it has been in existence since June 1977 when it was formed by the merging of the old Training and Support Commands. The merger brought together all the various elements that in the past had formed the old Flying Training, Technical Training, Maintenance and Signals Commands to provide a simple and logical three-Command structure for the RAF. Today, RAF Support Command provides the support that its title implies to the other two 'teeth' Commands, namely RAF Strike Command and RAF Germany.

Support Command is responsible for flying training, the training of officers and airmen in the ground branches and trades, the performance of the electrical and mechanical engineering functions which are beyond the capabilities of the individual stations, communications, storage and supply facilities, the medical services and the numerous administrative services throughout the Service. To carry out these varied tasks the Command has two functional groups embodied in the Command Headquarters, one for training and the other for maintenance. To add to these the Command can also use the facilities of the RAF College at Cranwell and the RAF Staff College at Bracknell. The Command also has under its wing the HQ Air Cadets at RAF Newton. Not yet mentioned is the responsibility of the Command for the Supply and Movements function, and there are a number of RAF and other units which Support Command has the task of administering but for which it does not have a control responsibility.

To carry out these numerous tasks RAF Support Command has an annual budget well in excess of £500 million. The Command embraces a total of 53 major units with a gaggle of 136 smaller units, making a total of 189. The manpower for all these units is in the region of 49,000 of which about 14,000 are civilians. At any one time about 8,000 of the total are trainees passing through the Command, although at the time of writing this figure was of the order of 6,700. Another indication of the size of the Command is that at any one time there are about 500 aircraft on the Command inventory, either undergoing repair or maintenance or in store.

Training

One of the main functions of RAF Support Command is training. The Command has the responsibility of nearly all the flying and ground training required by the Service, including the important basic training (for which the Command alone is responsible), trade, staff and refresher training of both officers and airmen. To add to the RAF personnel training the Command also has to provide training for the personnel of Commonwealth and foreign air forces and for some Government departments. It also carries out some training of the civilian personnel working in the Command.

High on the training list of priorities is that of RAF officers, both for flying and ground duties. Of these two functions, the flying training aspect is considered to be of such importance that it warrants its own chapter and will thus be dealt with there. This section will deal with the training of the ground duties branches alone.

All officer candidates for the RAF, whatever their ultimate career path, have to undergo their Initial Officer Training at the RAF College Cranwell, near Sleaford in Lincolnshire. If they pass the exacting and searching course successfully they then continue to attend their specialist training courses, complete with their newly awarded commissions. These courses are carried out at several locations. RAF Shawbury is the location for the Air Traffic Control training establishment. RAF Hereford is where officer training for the Catering and Secretarial branches is carried out. Education officers, most of whom will have university degrees to qualify them for their posts, will be given their specialist Service training at the RAF School of Education at RAF Newton. RAF Newton is also the location of the RAF Police School to which Provost Branch officers are sent for their training. Engineer and Supply officers are provided with their training at RAF Cranwell. Courses are also provided at RAF Cranwell for those officers who will join the Service with their professional qualifications completed. Officers in this category include chaplains and medical officers. They are usually given a short four-week course to orientate them into their Service background and responsibilities.

Once the initial training is complete the officer can then proceed to his first posting. Once there his training is far from complete. Not only is the officer provided with on-the-spot training to guide him in his current duties but as time progresses he will be provided with more formal training to enable him to assume the duties and responsibilities of higher rank. After he has been in the Service for some years each officer will attend an Officers Command Course at the RAF Officers Command School at RAF Henlow in Bedfordshire. This is a non-specialist course and is followed by the

Above *Part of the Skynet Satellite Communications complex at RAF Oakhanger.*

Below *Changing a Harrier engine at RAF Wittering.*

Above *A small idea of the complexities of modern aircraft engines can be seen from this picture of a Buccaneer Spey engine.*

Below *The RAF School of Firefighting is at RAF Manston and here a foam tender is being used to extinguish a fire on an old Vulcan hulk.*

Individual Staff Studies course which is a correspondence course lasting 18 months. These two courses take place while the officer is still a Flight Lieutenant and with both courses successfully completed he can then qualify for the one month Basic Staff Course which is carried out at RAF Bracknell, Berkshire. When the officer becomes a Squadron Leader he may then be selected for the ten-month Advanced Staff Course, again held at RAF Bracknell, but many officers are not selected until they are Wing Commanders. The Advanced Staff Course provides the officer trainees concerned with a broad and firm grounding for them to proceed to the higher levels of the Service, where they will become key leaders.

The training of Airmen and Airwomen will always commence with six weeks' basic training (the well-known 'squarebashing') at the Recruit Training School. Airmen and airwomen are given their basic training at RAF Swinderby. From the Recruit Training School the newly-minted personnel then proceed for their training in any one of 150 separate trades in 19 basic trade groups. By far the largest of these is the Engineering trade group and the bulk of the training involved is carried out at the four main engineering schools, although in some trades there may be an overlapping of courses with other establishments. The four main schools include RAF Halton, near Aylesbury, which is also the RAF Engineering Apprentice School; RAF Cosford near Wolverhampton; RAF Locking, near Weston-super-Mare

and the home of No 1 Radio School; and the massive sprawl of RAF St Athan in South Wales, the location of No 4 School of Technical Training.

There are a further four main centres of ground training for non-commissioned personnel. It will be noted that, at some schools, facilities are provided for both officer and airman training but as a general rule officer training is provided at separate locations wherever possible.

RAF Hereford: Secretarial, Supply, Catering and Airmen's Command School; RAF Shawbury: Air Traffic Control; RAF Cosford: Air Electronics, Communications, Photography, Physical Education, Aircraft Weapons; RAF Newton: Guided Weapons, School of Education, RAF Police, Management; RAF Swinderby: Administration; RAF Halton: Engineering, Dental, Medical; RAF St Athan: Engineering, Motor Transport; RAF Locking: Radio Engineering, Ground Electrical; RAF West Drayton: School of Fighter Control; RAF Wyton: Joint School of Photographic Interpretation.

At these, and a few other locations, Support Command provides about 680 different courses ranging in length from one week for providing skilled typists with their Service requirements to three years for RAF Apprenticeships. New courses are continually being added to meet new Service requirements and existing courses are continually monitored and amended to meet current changes. Every year between 15,000 to 20,000 Service personnel pass through training carried out by Support Command. The Command's responsibility does not stop there for it also provides training for about 750 civilians every year. These civilians are provided with training that ranges from basic to advanced and includes a number of four-year craft and technical apprenticeships. The training is normally carried out at RAF Henlow, RAF St Athan and RAF Sealand, but every year some 500 junior and middle grades of civilian management are provided with administrative and management training at the RAF School of Management at RAF Newton, near Nottingham.

Just as career advancement training is provided for officers by the Command so is similar training provided for airmen and airwomen. This is provided in two stages. The first step is a recent innovation and is provided for Senior aircraftmen and women (SAC/SACW) in the form of a General Service Training 1 (GST 1) course held at RAF Henlow. This course must be successfully completed before promotion to Corporal is given. The second stage is General Service Training 2 (GST 2), also carried out at RAF Henlow, and must be successfully completed before a Corporal can be promoted to Sergeant. Both courses provide their candidates with the necessary grounding and training that their new ranks will require.

Maintenance

RAF Support Command maintenance functions can be divided into Aerosystems Engineering (which can be defined as those engineering functions connected with aircraft and their weapons), Signals, and Supply and Movements. The Signals function includes Ground Electronics and communications generally.

In size alone the largest of these functions is Aerosystems Engineering. RAF Support Command provides aircraft engineering support not only for the RAF but also for the fixed-wing aircraft of the Royal Navy and the Army Air Corps. This support includes scheduled major servicing, rectifications, reconditioning and the modification of a wide variety of aircraft. It must be stressed that this support is very rarely carried out on an *ad hoc* basis. Wherever possible it is provided on a carefully planned and scheduled basis to obtain the maximum cost efficiency from the facilities and manpower involved. To this end continuous attention and effort is devoted to the improvement of servicing and other facilities with the introduction of new tools and working methods to increase efficiency and reduce costs. But all this striving for efficiency does not mean that the Command cannot accept tasks at short notice. There are times when operational requirements will impose their own short-term workloads and the system is geared for such emergencies. In these days, the cost of front-line aircraft is so high that only relatively limited numbers can be obtained by the Service and to gain the maximum benefit and cost-effectiveness from them they have to be kept in a state of maximum availability and readiness in the front line for the maximum portion of their Service life.

The two major Aircraft Engineering Units are at RAF St Athan and RAF Abingdon. RAF St Athan has an Aircraft Servicing Wing and a General Engineering Wing. The Aircraft Servicing Wing has for many years been responsible for the major servicing of up to 25 aircraft at any one time, the types involved being the Phantom, Tornado, Buccaneer and Victor. The General Engineering Wing carries out the major servicing of the Adour engines for the Jaguar and Hawk and has a similar facility for the RB 199 engines of the Tornado. The General Engineering Wing also has a versatile role to play in the production of aircraft parts and modification kits under some circumstances. An example might be the production of a part for a Phantom when the part concerned would normally have to be obtained from the parent company in the USA. At St Athan the General Engineering Wing has a fully-equipped machine shop and drawing office with the capability of producing just about any aircraft part or component the Service might require. Both the St Athan units have a joint Service-civilian work force.

RAF Abingdon has an Aircraft Servicing Wing for the major servicing of the Hawk and the Jaguar. Aircraft storage of up to 80 aircraft at any one time used to be carried out at RAF Kemble but with the closure of that station at the end of March 1983 the storage task switched to RAF Shawbury. The storing of aircraft is no simple task for not only do the aircraft concerned have to be prepared for long-term storage, they also have to be kept in a serviceable state while they remain in 'mothballs'.

Away from the aircraft aspect, the Command maintains a large Maintenance Unit (No 30) at RAF Sealand, near Chester. This facility is used for the large-scale repair and maintenance of airborne electronics and instruments, including instrument engineering generally. The Unit is a joint civil-military personnel undertaking that provides a service not only for the RAF but also for the Royal Navy, the Army and for some Ministry of Defence research stations, not only in the United Kingdom but also overseas. The Unit is run very much like a factory with production lines, large workshops and numerous test facilities. Every year the Unit services more than 100,000 items which are then distributed to the user units on a direct exchange one-for-one basis. The Unit even runs its own road service to units in the United Kingdom and Germany. Other Maintenance Groups are located at RAF Carlisle, RAF Stafford and RAF Abingdon.

RAF Abingdon is also the home of the Field Repair Squadron, a versatile unit with several functions. It is firstly responsible for the salvaging

Above *Engine change on a Puma at RAF Odiham.*

Left *Major servicing of Hawk T 1s at RAF Valley.*

of crashed RAF, Army and Royal Navy fixed-wing aircraft in most parts of the world. As a direct result of its salvaging duties the Squadron also has the task of devising various methods of repairing battle damage to return damaged aircraft to service. To add to this the Squadron also has the task of sending teams of tradesmen to various stations and locations to carry out maintenance programmes that do not require the aircraft to be sent to a second or third-line unit but which are nevertheless beyond the capabilities of the units concerned. As if these tasks were not enough, the Squadron also undertakes the preparation, transport and erection of aircraft for the recruiting and other displays held by the RAF throughout the United Kingdom.

RAF Support Command also has the considerable responsibility of repairing just about any item of RAF equipment when it is economical and expedient to do so. The range of equipment covers every item held in Supply Depots or returned in an unserviceable condition. Each of the Equipment Supply Depots has its own workshop where all manner of equipment from furniture to parachutes is repaired, modified or serviced. The Command also has maintenance facilities for medical and dental equipment in support of the RAF Hospitals, and repairs and calibrates over 35,000 items every year.

The maintenance facilities of Support Command have the overall responsibility of returning the equipment that passes through their hands in as short a time as possible. To accomplish this requires planning, advanced management techniques and a well-trained work force. RAF Support Command has all three of these requirements.

Signals

RAF Support Command responsibilities fall into three main categories, namely telecommunications, signals engineering and ground radio repair, and electronic warfare (EW). The Command is also responsible for operating the RAF element of the Defence Communications Network, or DCN. Operating this strategic communications system, Support Command acts as the sole system and engineering design authority for the DCN world-wide. The Command also acts as a consultant to the Ministry of Defence, to the other RAF Commands, and to Commonwealth and other Allied Air Forces for all aspects of communications.

The operating responsibilities fall into four categories. First, there is the large complex of high frequency transmitter and receiver facilities in the United Kingdom, including some communications centres with computer-controlled automatic message routeing equipment. These centres undertake operations on behalf of NATO, Strike Command, the Military Air Traffic Organisation and the Meteorological Office. As a second responsibility the Command operates a number of message relay centres, some of which are fully automatic and some of which are still manual. Then comes the main operation of the Skynet Satellite Communications System. This system offers overseas formations both telegraph and speech capabilities, all under the control of Support Command.

The final operating category is that the Command provides an aerial erection service on a world-wide basis. The aerials involved are used for communications, radars and for navigation aids, and their erection is a highly specialised and skilled task. Training for this role is carried out by the Command at the Aerial Erector School at RAF Digby in Lincolnshire.

Signals equipment encompassed by Support Command includes the entire field of communications equipment, air traffic control, defence radar systems and ground-based navigational aids. The

Command responsibilities include system design, manufacture, selection and survey of sites, installations and the subsequent commissioning which may include flight checking and calibration. All this is of little effect, however, if it is not accompanied by planning and management of the complete system task. Once any system is installed and working the Command usually retains a responsibility to help the operational units maintain the system in use. This involves regular in-flight checking of the various systems, often using operational aircraft from Strike Command. Major routine servicing and repairs are carried out by the Command Servicing Repair Centre located at RAF North Luffenham in Leicestershire.

The Command Signals Headquarters is also at RAF North Luffenham where it retains a large engineering design staff of draughtsmen, technicians and engineers under its control. If necessary it can produce its own equipment using several facilities, including a precision engineering factory in Woolwich, East London. There is also a general mechanical engineering and calibration capability at the RAF Signals Engineering Establishment at RAF Henlow in Bedfordshire. This establishment not only provides installation teams for most signals systems but also produces the many odd items that are required to make basic industrial items fit into a Service military environment.

Needless to say, little enough can be mentioned regarding the Command's function in the EW sphere other than to say that much of the Command's work in this area is carried out at RAF Benson and RAF Wyton. In anodyne terms the Command states that it maintains the engineering capability and the expertise to enable quick reaction assistance to be provided to the front line. In this field the Command staff work particularly closely with the operational commands.

Supply and movements

RAF Supply Command is fond of relating its supply task to the commercial wholesale and retail functions. The wholesale side provides a complete functional supply service for the RAF at home and abroad, as well as air stores and accommodation stores for the Royal Navy and the Army. The retail function is the provision of supply support for the Command's engineering commitments described elsewhere in these pages.

To provide these twin services the Command operates a number of Supply Units scattered around the United Kingdom and varying in size from massive warehouse complexes to relatively small fuel depots and stores. The Command holds at any one time around one million separate items varying from highly expensive and technical units of electronic equipment to consumable items of domestic utility. The locations involved include equipment supply depots, petroleum supply depots, ammunition depots and gas storage depots. Each location may hold stocks to last only a few months or up to several years' consumption, depending on the economic rate at which the items involved can be replaced. In some cases it is more economic to bulk-purchase well in advance or because replacing the items involved would take a long period. Other items can be easily replaced once used so it then makes economic sense to hold stocks at a level sufficient only to meet short-term needs. This economic stock-level juggling is a complex business but the peculiar nature of Service requirements and contingencies often means that stock levels are maintained at far higher levels and in far greater variety than would be necessary for any commercial concern.

The three largest equipment supply depots are at RAF Stafford, RAF Carlisle and RAF Quedgeley. RAF Stafford has an annual turnover of some one million items every year. RAF Quedgeley in Gloucestershire is a tri-Service establishment which deals with barrack and other accommodation items, among other things. Smaller Command supply establishments are at Woolwich, which deals with the huge number of Air Publications (APs) and all the various types of form used by the Service; RAF Cardington which acts as a gas supply store; and RAF Chilmark which is the main ammunition holding depot, although there are others.

As can be imagined, fuel supply is one of the Command's priorities.To this end a special Supply Wing at RAF Stafford is equipped and charged with the movement of all types of fuel to the locations where they are needed. Their duties involve all manner of fuel handling methods from tankers to pillow tank depots in the field. This unit is part of the RAF Stafford-based Tactical Supply Wing (TSW) which was called upon to perform all manner of feats during the Falkland Islands campaign. Almost as soon as the word was given the TSW was on its way to Ascension Island (where it still is at the time of writing) and, along with its associated Mobility Supply Flights, then proceeded to carry out the RAF's largest supply operation since the 1948–1949 Berlin Airlift. Under normal circumstances the Command supply network operates a Priority Freight Distribution System that is intended to get important supply items to where they are required in as short a time as is possible. In normal times this would operate a twice-a-day road and air service only when required. At the height of

Airmen of the Tactical Supply Wing from RAF Stafford using fuel lines near a Harrier hide.

the Falkland Islands crisis the system was operating twice a day, seven days a week, regularly.

Even under normal circumstances the operation of the Command's supply service is a round-the-clock operation. The vast experience gained through years of stock recording and stock location have led to the point that the rapid handling of any item has become almost routine and the Falkland Islands crisis required only moving the system into top gear. At the best of times, without the Falklands upset, high priority items can be on their way within six hours or less on the receipt of a demand and even the lowest priority demands would be met within seven days. Needless to say, the system required to achieve this performance is now computer-based with the central computer working on a 24 hours a day basis at the Supply Control Centre at RAF Hendon, North London (due to move to RAF Stanbridge near Leighton Buzzard by 1986–87). The computer holds the central records of the location and quantity held of every item of spare equipment throughout the RAF. All the equipment supply depots and about 100 RAF stations at home and overseas are directly connected to the computer system, whose records are updated every day. This enables the computer to locate any required item, either in a depot or at a station. Costs can be saved very often by transferring an item from one RAF station to another rather than sending it direct from a depot. But this is not the only facility that the Hendon computer can provide for it also gives a constant read-out of equipment consumption rates and other such data, enabling stocks to be maintained and updated at cost-effective levels.

Administration

As well as the administration of the units that fall directly under its control, Support Command also has the task of providing administrative support for a further 140 units both in the United Kingdom and abroad. These units normally do not come under the direct control of Support Command; the Command only administers them, and the range of units covered by this arrangement is very wide. As examples that can be quoted are the Officer and Aircrew Selection Centre at RAF Biggin Hill, Kent; the Personnel Management Centre at RAF Gloucester; the RAF personnel working in Ministry of Defence (Procurement Executive) establishments such as that at the Royal Aircraft Establishment (RAE) Farnborough; the 71 RAF Careers Information Offices; the RAF bands; the Air Force Department of the Ministry of Defence; and some units operating in Italy, Norway and Turkey. These multifarious units come under the control of the Air Officer Administration (AOA) in his capacity as Air Officer Commanding Directly Administered Units (AOC DAUs).

One of the main portions of the administrative task is the support of the RAF medical services, including the hospitals. The hospitals involved are at RAF Ely, Cambridgeshire; RAF Halton, Buckinghamshire; and RAF Wroughton, Wiltshire, while the hospital at RAF Nocton Hall, Lincolnshire, was closed during 1983 with the bulk of its work load being transferred to RAF Ely. Another medical establishment administered by Support Command is the RAF Medical Rehabilitation Unit at Headley Court in Surrey which, by late 1983, was planned to be amalgamated with the nearby Joint Service Medical Rehabilitation Unit at Chessington; both units will be located as one unit at RAF Headley Court. This support of the medical services has led to an internal split of responsibilities within Support Command in that, although the administration of the medical units is the responsibility of the AOA, the task is actually carried out by the Principal Medical Officer of HQ RAF Support Command who is a specialist officer with the role of Inspector of Medical Establishments.

To explain this internal control of Support Command a stage further, there are three Air Vice-Marshals at HQ RAF Support Command to control the functions of Training, Maintenance and Administration. The Air Officer Training (AOT) is the Air Officer Commanding Training Units, or AOC TUs. The Air Officer Maintenance is the Air Officer Maintenance (AOMaint) and also the AOC Maintenance Units, or AOC MUs. As mentioned above, the Air Officer Administration, or AOA, is the AOC Directly Administered Units (AOC DAUs).

To add to these officers there are a further five AOCs within Support Command. They are: AOC and Commandant, RAF Staff College, Bracknell, Berkshire; AOC and Commandant, RAF College, Cranwell, near Sleaford, Lincolnshire; AOC and Commandant Officers and Aircrew Selection Centre, RAF Biggin Hill, Kent; AOC and Commandant, Air Cadets, RAF Newton, near Nottingham; and AOC Personnel Management Centre, RAF Gloucester.

* * *

Two aspects of RAF Support Command activities are considered so important that they have been given their own sections. They are Aircrew Training and the activities of the Air Training Corps.

Air Cadets

The term Air Cadets is used for this section advisedly for, although the Air Training Corps is the main component of the Air Cadets, there are also the various air-inclined elements of the Combined Cadet Force based at schools. There is, moreover, a small but growing girl's element in the Air Training Corps. It is very much in the interest of the Royal Air Force to make these Air Cadets as much a part and parcel of the Service as is possible, for they provide a reservoir not only of potential recruits but also of an 'air minded' future populace that will understand and appreciate the role that the Royal Air Force has to play.

To oversee the Air Cadets, the Royal Air Force maintains an Air Officer Commanding (AOC) at RAF Newton charged with the administering and general supervision of the 1,000-plus units of the Air Cadets in the United Kingdom. From Headquarters Air Cadets (HQAC) at RAF Newton operates a team of officers and civilians who do their level best to see that as many youngsters as possible join the Air Cadets, learn the various technical and other skills that are taught, and get a chance to fly as often as possible.

The opportunity to fly is the one item that makes many youngsters join the Air Cadets. To make sure they get that chance as soon and as often as possible the HQAC maintains 13 Air Experience Flights (AEF) and 27 gliding schools operating in all parts of the United Kingdom. HQAC also administers a number of schemes whereby further flying training or air experience can be gained by a number of methods ranging from indulgence flights on transport aircraft to Flying Scholarships run by local flying clubs.

The AEFs are the main chance for most Air Cadets to fly and it is one of the AEF's objectives to provide 25 minutes of flying time to each eligible cadet each year. The various Squadrons, Sections and Wings are all affiliated to one of the AEFs and mainly operate from Air Cadet camps or their home bases. The main locations of the AEFs are as follows (some are based on civil airfields while some are at Service stations):

1 AEF	RAF Manston
2 AEF	Hurn
3 AEF	Bristol (Filton)
4 AEF	Exeter
5 AEF	Cambridge (Teversham)
6 AEF	RAF Abingdon
7 AEF	RAF Newton
8 AEF	RAF Cosford
9 AEF	RAF Finningley
10 AEF	RAF Woodvale
11 AEF	Teeside
12 AEF	RAF Turnhouse
13 AEF	RAF Sydenham

The mainstay of the AEFs is the Chipmunk T 10. About 50 of them have been shouldering the AEF task since the late 1950s and have proved ideal for the role. To add to the Chipmunks, the inevitable anomalies arise for 5 AEF operates the only Beagle Husky in the Royal Air Force (it came to the Service by a very roundabout route and was donated to the Air Training Corps). Another anomaly is at 13 AEF in Northern Ireland where a Bulldog T 1 is operated in place of the Chipmunk T 10 as the Bulldog can then be serviced together with the local Queen's UAS.

Each of the AEF aircraft has a team of four staff pilots plus a fifth supernumerary pilot who is an Air Training Corps Squadron officer. Thus the basic AEF staff is 263 made up from 13 flight commanders, 200 staff pilots and 50 supernumerary pilots. To these must be added the admin and the engineering staff. Extra help is provided from time to time by Royal Air Force officers helping out in their spare time or while awaiting postings. The return the Service obtains from this small band of pilots and aircraft is out of all proportion to the efforts involved, for it provides youngsters with what is very often their first

and only chance to fly.

The various gliding schools are also administered by HQAC. Instructors for the gliding schools are trained at the Central Gliding School at Swanton Morley. This unit operates all types of glider used by the various Volunteer Gliding Schools (VGS) and has a few of its own used by no other establishment. Among these are two Janus sailplanes, and Schleicher ASW 19 (Valiant TX 1) and ASK 21 (Vanguard TX 1) sailplanes are in the process of delivery as these words are written. The main types of glider used by the VGS include the Sedburgh TX 1, five Swallow TX 1s and the powered Venture self-launching glider.

The VGS are located as follows:

611 VGS RAF Swanton Morley
612 VGS RAF Benson

Left *The Venture T 2 self-launching glider.*

Below *The only one – the Beagle Husky used by 5 AEF at Cambridge.*

613 VGS RAF Halton
614 VGS RAF Wethersfield
615 VGS RAF Kenley
616 VGS RAF Henlow
617 VGS RAF Manston
618 VGS West Malling
621 VGS Weston-super-Mare
622 VGS RAF Upavon
624 VGS RAF Chivenor
625 VGS South Cerney
626 VGS RNAS Predannack
631 VGS RAF Sealand
632 VGS RAF Ternhill
633 VGS RAF Cosford
634 VGS RAF St Athan
635 VGS Salmesbury
636 VGS RAF Swansea
637 VGS Little Rissington
642 VGS RAF Linton-on-Ouse
643 VGS RAF Scampton
644 VGS RAF Syerston
645 VGS RAF Catterick
661 VGS RAF Kirknewton
662 VGS Arbroath
663 VGS RAF Kinloss
Cranwell Glider Flight
Halton Glider Flight

At all these VGSs, gliding instruction is usually provided from basic to advanced for suitable students. Safety standards are high, and so is the standard of instruction. The new self-launching Venture T 2 has proved to be a great success in use.

There are four units known as Mobile Glider Service Parties (MGSP) who are tasked with the repair and overhaul of Air Cadet gliders at the various Volunteer Gliding Schools. These MGSPs and their bases are as follows:

No 1 MGSP RAF Halton
No 2 MGSP RAF Locking
No 3 MGSP RAF Cosford
No 4 MGSP RAF Dishforth

Flying is a large factor in Air Cadet training but it is not the only training provided. There is a wide range of subjects on the ground-based side as well, ranging from rifle shooting, both small- and full-bore, to photography, initiative and junior leadership training, basic survival skills, some groundings in mechanics and many more subjects. Visits to local Royal Air Force stations are usually arranged locally but there are also the Annual Camps at flying stations and other visits to places of aeronautical interest.

The Air Cadets are not all Service-orientated or motivated. A great deal of time is devoted to such schemes as the Duke of Edinburgh's Award and many outdoor activities and sports. The basic idea is not only to make the youngsters air-minded and Service-motivated but to encourage character development and community service. Both Regular and Volunteer officers and NCOs devote a great deal of time to this end and they are considerably aided by the large number of civilian instructors who give so freely of their spare time.

Aircrew training

Aircrew training is carried out and administered under the auspices of RAF Support Command. It is a complex and involved task and a chapter of this nature cannot delve into every facet of the subject. It should also be borne in mind that changes have to be made to the various training programmes from time to time in order to keep abreast of current requirements or to save costs, so while this chapter is as accurate as can be determined at the time of writing some changes may well have taken place in detail by the time these words are read.

Aircrew training costs a great deal of money but the RAF investment in any particular trainee individual must be seen in perspective. From the training system will not only emanate tomorrow's pilots and aircrew but also the leaders, the decision makers who will affect the future of the RAF in up to five decades from now, and the combat aircrew who will be in tomorrow's front line. Seen in this light the costs and care involved became more understandable, but it must be emphasised that they are now so high that every effort is made in the training system and programmes to eliminate any possible trainees who might turn out to be under par as soon as possible. At times this means some ruthless decisions have to be made that might affect an individual's life and career, but the decisions just have to be made. Standards for aircrew are very high and the RAF can pick only the best. With the cost of an operational pilot's training up to the point where he joins an operational squadron being in the region of £1.7 million, only the best will serve. To emphasise the point, in the year ending in March 1982 over 6,000 people applied to become aircrew. Only 364 of them were selected to become pilots, and not all of them completed the course.

To the recruit such a selection process must seem daunting but it is necessary. The actual aircrew recruiting is carried out not by the RAF itself but by a branch of the Ministry of Defence known as Ministry of Defence S10c(Air). They offer several methods of joining the RAF for aircrew training, one of which is Direct Entry (DE) from civil life with the minimum educational requirement being at least five GCE 'O' level passes. The lower age limit is 17 years with the highest being 26. There are also forms of Cadetships, Scholarships and Bursaries that assist an individual through university up to degree level when the trainee then joins the RAF proper. There are ways of becoming an officer while at university but these variations are many and various and outside the scope of this book. Suffice to say that anyone wishing to train for RAF aircrew has to pass through the initial selection process that takes place at the Officers and Aircrew Selection Centre at RAF Biggin Hill in Kent.

At the Selection Centre all candidates have to pass through a two-part selection process. Part 1

Right *A Jet Provost against the sun.*

Below *Aircrew student training with his parachute equipment.*

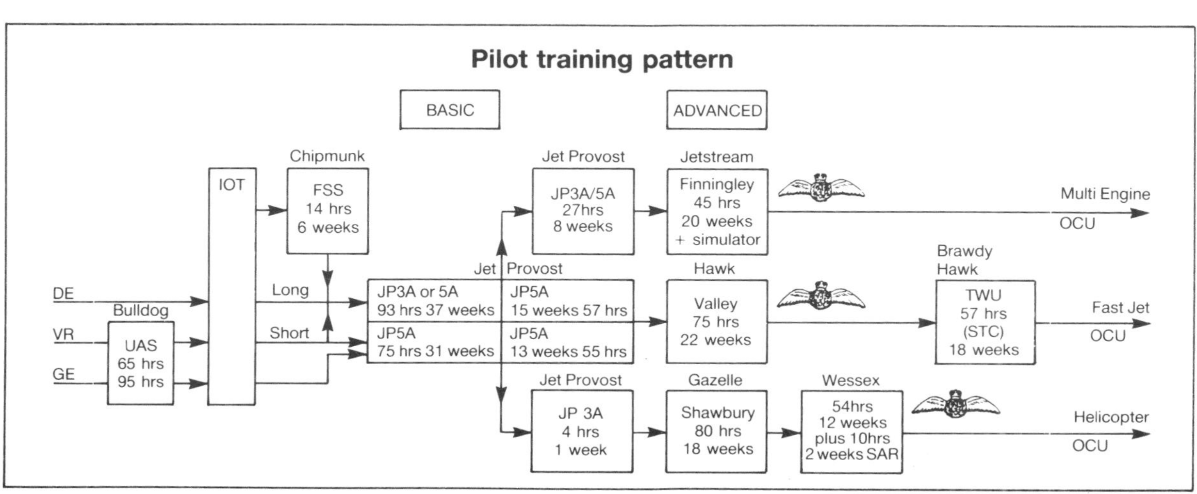
Pilot training pattern
BASIC
ADVANCED
IOT
Chipmunk
FSS
14 hrs
6 weeks
Jet Provost
JP3A/5A
27hrs
8 weeks
Jetstream
Finningley
45 hrs
20 weeks
+ simulator
Multi Engine
OCU
Jet Provost
JP3A or 5A
93 hrs 37 weeks
JP5A
15 weeks 57 hrs
JP5A
75 hrs 31 weeks
JP5A
13 weeks 55 hrs
Long
Short
DE
VR
GE
Bulldog
UAS
65 hrs
95 hrs
Hawk
Valley
75 hrs
22 weeks
Brawdy
Hawk
TWU
57 hrs
(STC)
18 weeks
Fast Jet
OCU
Jet Provost
JP 3A
4 hrs
1 week
Gazelle
Shawbury
80 hrs
18 weeks
Wessex
54hrs
12 weeks
plus 10hrs
2 weeks SAR
Helicopter
OCU

consists of a very thorough medical examination and at least one aptitude interview. Part 2 consists of a series of syndicate exercises that take place under unusual conditions which will demonstrate to the selection personnel any individual's potential character for leadership and personal application. These exercises will then be followed by more interviews. What the selection board will be looking for is a combination of co-ordination, medical fitness, character and that elusive quality of leadership. Candidates can expect to be thoroughly tested in all these aspects and the full selection process takes at least two days.

If a candidate passes the selection process he can then join the RAF proper and commence his training. Those passing through university and studying for a degree may have the chance to sample RAF life even before they join for they have the chance of joining one of the 16 University Air Squadrons (UAS) where some flying training will be given. On the squadron will be those aircrew candidates who are taking RAF schemes through university. Some 33 per cent of pilot intake for the RAF comes through the UAS system and the output also makes up some 30 per cent of pilots in operational squadrons. The UASs train not only pilots but navigators as well and provide some flying experience for potential officers joining other branches of the service.

The University Air Squadrons have their Headquarters at RAF Cranwell (HQ UAS Wing). The aircraft type used by the UAS is the Bulldog T1, and UAS units fly from either RAF stations or civil airfields, depending on the location. Up to 30 hours' flying training a year will be provided, both at weekends and during an annual training period leading to a possible maximum of 95 hours by the time the candidate has left university. Time spent with the UAS is not allowed to be detrimental to any university education process to the extent that any failure to maintain a satisfactory level in university studies could lead to a withdrawal of any RAF assistance.

Whatever the form of entry, either from university, direct entry from civilian life or entry from within the ranks of the RAF itself, all candidates become officer cadets at the RAF College Cranwell where they undergo Initial Officer Training (IOT) on a course that lasts 18 weeks. The IOT consists of a broad-based programme containing everything from basic drill on the square to camping out in rough country and undertaking cross-country leadership tests. The course is arduous but not overly so, and the normal failure rate averages out at about 15 per cent.

From IOT, which every officer serving in the RAF has to undergo, whatever his branch of the Service, the paths divide. From here we will follow what is the most involved of all the training paths, namely that of pilots, but we will return to the other aircrew skills later in this chapter.

The 16 UAS are at the following locations:

UAS	**Headquarters**	**Airfield**
Aberdeen and St Andrews	RAF Leuchars	RAF Leuchars
Birmingham	Birmingham	RAF Cosford
Bristol	Bristol	Filton (civil)
Cambridge	Cambridge	Teversham (civil)
East Lowlands	Edinburgh	RAF Turnhouse
East Midlands	Nottingham	RAF Newton
Glasgow and Strathclyde	Glasgow	Glasgow/Abbotsinch
Liverpool	Liverpool	RAF Woodvale
London	London	RAF Abingdon
Manchester and Salford	Manchester	RAF Woodvale
Northumbrian	Newcastle upon Tyne	RAF Leeming
Oxford	Oxford	RAF Abingdon
Queen's	Belfast	RAF Sydenham
Southampton	Southampton	Hurn (civil)
Wales	RAF St Athan	RAF St Athan
Yorkshire	RAF Finningley	RAF Finningley

Above *The Jet Provost is used at all levels of RAF aircrew training; this is a Mark T 5A from RAF Linton-on-Ouse.*

Top *A Jet Provost T 5 used for low level navigation training at No 6 FTS, RAF Finningley.*

Pilot training

Pilot candidates first travel to the RAF Aeromedical Training Centre at RAF North Luffenham. Here they are issued with their flying clothing and equipment and are taught various survival drills, are subjected to the uncomfortable decompression chamber processes and are taught how to use their parachutes. They are also instructed on how to use their oxygen systems to the extent of experiencing hypoxia (oxygen starvation). The relentless selection process then goes one stage further. All pilot trainees who have not undergone at least 30 hours of recognised flying experience then have to pass through a flying aptitude course. Most ex-UAS trainees will have passed this mark already, but well over half of the potential pilots who have passed through IOT will not have any flying experience or qualification and they proceed to the Flying Selection Squadron (FSS) at RAF Swinderby, near Lincoln.

The FSS stage has been built into the pilot training system to eliminate those candidates who, through no fault of their own, turn out to have no personal flying aptitude or whose level of personal co-ordination is below that required for the task. This is something that can only be determined once a candidate actually gets into an aircraft cockpit and starts to manipulate the controls. The FSS stage was introduced in 1974 when it was found that starting directly on to flying jet-engined trainers was a very expensive way of determining those with a poor aptitude for further pilot training. Thus the aircraft used at the FSS is the venerable Chipmunk, an aircraft which has been used to train past generations of pilots and which has proved to be an excellent selector of the wheat from the chaff in aptitude terms. It is a delight to fly but demands a high standard of handling at all stages, so anyone who lacks all the co-ordination and other inherent skills required to fly an aircraft will soon be highlighted. The full FSS course lasts six weeks and involves 14 or 15 flying hours. During the course some 25 per cent of candidates for later training are eliminated at a relatively low cost, but their elimination does not mean that those failing the FSS course are lost to the Service. Only about nine per cent actually leave the RAF, and on average about 72 per cent opt to train as navigators or transfer to some other branch of the Service.

With the FSS course behind them, the potential pilots then journey to one of two stations for their basic flying training. These are RAF Linton-on-Ouse and RAF Church Fenton. There they stay for a period of 37 weeks where they carry out all their basic training in a mix of Jet Provost T 3s and T 5s. Ex-UAS trainees carry out their basic jet training at RAF Cranwell and their course lasts 31 weeks and includes 75 hours (this is the 'short' course with the 'long' course lasting 37 weeks covering 93 hours). During these basic courses not only flying is taught. The trainees also undergo a great deal of further general Service training but it must be emphasised at this point that *all* pilots for all types of aircraft used by the RAF go through this basic flying training on jet aircraft.

This all–jet basic flying training will change when the first of 130 Tucano turbo-prop trainers enters the flying training programme at an as yet unannounced date, probably some time during 1988.

It is only at the end of the first phase of their basic training that the specialist 'split' occurs. The split is into three groups, Group 1 is the fast jet stream, Group 2 the multi-engine stream and Group 3 is helicopters. All three Groups involve further flying training on the Jet Provost before the full basic training is completed. The Group 1 fast jet stream continues with a further 15 weeks and 57 flying hours on the Jet Provost T 5 for the 'long' course, or 13 weeks and 55 hours for the 'short' course. About one third of these basic courses comprises time spent flying solo and includes spells on instrument trainers on the ground. Much of the time is spent learning the necessary drills and procedures which cover every-

Right *A Hawk T 1 from No 4 FTS at RAF Valley flying over the ancient Caernarvon Castle.*

Below *RAF Finningley Jetstream on finals.*

299
XX299

thing from normal flight preparation to in-flight emergencies. There is very limited spare time for activities other than training and all the time the student pilots can expect to consider themselves as being constantly assessed. Anyone not making the grade at any stage will only rarely be given the chance to go over past ground again. Most slow learners will usually be transferred to another flying stream at best and the more normal is to transfer to some other aircrew branch such as training for Navigator. Some fail to the extent of leaving the Service, but by the time the basic stage is passed the early selection process should have cut these losses to a minimum.

With the basic stage behind them the Group 1 candidates then go back to RAF North Luffenham to convert their aeromedical knowledge to Hawk T 1 standards, for once that is behind them they are off to North Wales and Anglesey. There, at RAF Valley, the pilots undergo their Advanced Flying Training. Once the conversion to the Hawk has been made the training then becomes really hard for, with the conversion over, the trainees are expected to consider the mechanics of flying as second nature, and the flight training starts to take on a more aggressive nature. Low level flying along the Welsh mountain valleys commences and tactical formation flying, as opposed to the formal formation flying of the Jet Provost stages. The course at RAF Valley lasts a very active 22 weeks during which time 75 further flying hours will be entered into what are becoming increasingly worn flying log books.

With the successful completion of the Valley course, which includes a spell of survival training including a 'dump' in the sea and a helicopter winch out, a final series of formal tests should culminate in the award of the coveted Pilots' Wings—but the training is not yet over.

Then follows the Tactical Weapons Unit course held at either RAF Brawdy (No 2 TWU) or RAF Chivenor (No 1 TWU). Both units use the Hawk T 1. The TWU course lasts a hectic 18 weeks covering 57 more flying hours, during which time the pilots fire guns, drop bombs and generally learn to fly in an offensive environment. Much of the time is spent flying at low level, making use of what ground cover is available. The pilots often fly in pairs, taking turns to lead the other. Both offensive and defensive tactics are practised with the course culminating in an attack mission on a 'real' target.

With the successful completion of the TWU course, the pilot leaves the Support Command structure and passes to Strike Command to join an Operational Conversion Unit (OCU) where he will convert to his operational aircraft type. Group 1 pilots will be joining Tornado, Harrier, Phantom, Jaguar and Buccaneer units so they proceed to their various OCUs. There is no Tornado GR 1 OCU as such at present since most aircrew joining will be 'second tour' aircrew, but they pass through the Trinational Tornado Training Establishment RAF Cottesmore. (The Tornado Weapons Conversion Unit (TWCU) is at RAF Honington.) Jaguar conversion is carried out by No 226 OCU at RAF Lossiemouth, Tornado F2/F3 at No 229 OCU at RAF Coningsby and Phantom conversion at No 228 OCU, also at RAF Coningsby.

The OCUs not only carry out basic conversion training for an aircraft type but also provide refresher training for pilots who have been undergoing other duty tours on other aircraft types or who have been 'flying desks' for a tour. So the trainee pilot has to consider the OCU as merely one stage in his career to which he may return. While at the OCU he carries out all the various types of mission his aircraft type will be expected to carry out and he will spend a fair proportion of his time in the aircraft simulator, which also allows him to practise drill and procedures which would normally wreck an aircraft if they were carried out for 'real'. The actual time spent with the OCU depends on several factors but the longest is that for the Harrier (No 233 OCU) which lasts about six months at RAF Wittering. During this time the pace is relatively relaxed, compared with earlier courses. Harrier pilots have more than just flying the Harrier to get used to, as the aircraft also uses the vertical plane for flight so the complex Harrier simulator is used as much as possible in the early stages of conversion training. Pilots have to undergo at least three simulator 'missions' before they actually fly a real Harrier solo—earlier flights are carried out in the two-seat trainer Harrier T 4 while other OCUs also use two-seat trainer versions of their particular aircraft type. Buccaneer pilots may find themselves flying Hunter trainers with Buccaneer instrument panels to keep flying costs as low as possible.

Having completed the OCU portion of his lengthy course and his extensive training, the Group 1 fast jet pilot is ready to join his operational unit. He usually does so as a probationer to see whether or not he 'fits' the squadron to which he is assigned. After a period of mutual assessment the pilot should then be fully operational. By that stage he might already have flown as many as 375 flying hours on up to five types of aircraft and he will have cost the country a great deal of money.

Group 2 multi-engine pilots leave the basic flying

Above left *A Hawk T 1 from No 4 FTS at RAF Valley over Brittania Bridge, Bangor.*

Right *Sea King HAR 3 of the Sea King Training Unit (SKTU)*

training stage after 37 weeks of the 'long' course and 31 weeks of the 'short' course. The Group 2 trainee pilots have the extra future responsibility of becoming aircraft captains as well as pilots but at first they have to fly a further 27 hours on Jet Provost T 3s or T 5s on a course lasting eight weeks. The multi-engine training proper then begins at RAF Finningley using the Jetstream T 1. The Jetstream training takes 20 weeks during which time the trainee pilots fly 45 hours, at the end of which they are awarded their wings before proceeding to their appropriate OCUs.

Group 3 helicopter trainees also leave the basic course at the same time as the Group 2 trainees and continue to fly the Jet Provost T 3 for a further four hours in a short spell lasting only about a week. Then they transfer to the helicopter proper by travelling to RAF Shawbury in Shropshire to encounter the Gazelle HT 3. The Gazelle course lasts a busy 18 weeks during which time the trainees clock up 80 flying hours and, if successful, they then pass to the Wessex part of their training to fly a further 54 hours during a 12-week period. To this is added a further ten hours' Search and Rescue (SAR) training carried out over a period of a fortnight. Only then is the helicopter pilot awarded his Wings, ready to pass on to his helicopter OCU.

Navigators and other aircrew

RAF Navigators are trained at No 6 Flying Training School (FTS) at RAF Finningley, where they fly in both Jet Provosts and Dominie T 1s with some time spent in Jetstreams. They spend a great deal of flying time at both high and low altitudes with the full course lasting 14 months, at the end of which the trainee is awarded his Navigator's brevet. Further training then continues at the appropriate OCU.

RAF Finningley is also the destination for Air Engineers and Air Electronics Operators. Both join the station as trainee Sergeants, having completed a six-week-long Airmen Aircrew Initial Training Course, also held at RAF Finningley. This course is the equivalent of the officers' IOT. Once their flying training commences they fly alongside the navigators in Dominie T 1s and their full course lasts about a year.

Air Loadmaster training is carried out at the Air Loadmaster School and School of Parachute Training at RAF Brize Norton before proceeding to their appropriate OCU for the completion of their training.

Refresher and instructor training

As well as initial aircrew training, the RAF also carries out refresher training for aircrew who are returning to flying duties after spells of 'flying a desk' on some form of ground duty or other. Some of this may be carried out at an OCU if the period concerned has not been too long, but it is more usual for the officer concerned to be retrained at the Refresher Training School (RTS) at RAF Linton-on-Ouse. The refresher courses used to be carried out at RAF Leeming but that station has now been run down to allow its facilities to be prepared for the Tornado F 3, and its units have been distributed among several other stations.

One unit that has also been moved is the Royal Naval Elementary Flying Training Squadron (RNEFTS). This unit has been moved to RAF Topcliffe and there the RAF trains the Royal Navy's pilots to fly during a 56 flying hour, twenty-week course using Bulldog T 1s.

Another and much more august unit that has made the move from Leeming is the Central Flying School, or CFS, which now resides at RAF Scampton. The Central Flying School has the distinction of being the oldest military aviation establishment in the world (although other establishments overseas still try to dispute the fact). One of the main functions of the CFS is to train the instructors, who in their turn train the pilots of all three Services to fly. Many of these instructors are pilots who have excelled in their flying standards, both during their initial training and during their subsequent operational tours—a select few are taken direct from their initial flying training. Once qualified the instructors might find themselves training overseas air forces as well as the usual run of RAF students. They can rightfully regard themselves as something of an élite among airmen and in the past a CFS instructor's course has often been a stepping stone along the path to the higher ranks.

RAF Scampton also acts as the 'home' and administrative base of the Royal Air Force Aerobatic Team, the incomparable Red Arrows. The Red Arrows are officially part of the CFS but their duties take them all over the United Kingdom and on frequent trips abroad so that their Hawk T 1s are now familiar and well-remembered sights in many parts of the world.

RAF Barnesking

Life in the modern Royal Air Force is almost entirely based around the RAF Station, a variable-sized location and community from which the RAF will essay to combat. As the RAF Station is in many ways what the regiment is to the Army and the ship to the Royal Navy, it deserves study to show how it functions, how it is organised and how its day-to-day existence is administered. The problem with such a study is that no two RAF Stations are alike in anything other than very general outlines so in order to carry out any form of meaningful study it has been necessary to invent an RAF Station that encompasses the overall sense of how a station works. This fictitious station is located in Lincolnshire, one of the most RAF-orientated of English counties, and for our purposes it will be the home of two Tornado GR 1 squadrons with their own training establishment. The squadrons involved will also be fictitious and will be called No 888 Squadron and No 999 Squadron. The station will be called RAF Barnesking.

Location and surroundings

Most operational RAF Stations occupy a general area along the east and north-east of England with the extreme north and south being the preserves of the maritime-orientated squadrons. There is a concentration of stations in the north and central areas of Scotland but the bulk face the general area of the North Sea. Scattered all over the rest of the United Kingdom are the logistic, administrative and back-up units that are based on RAF stations without runways. These are the Maintenance Units, the training schools, stores units, depots and all the other establishments required to keep the flying stations manned and ready. The flying training establishments are generally situated to the west and south of the United Kingdom but the bulk are in Yorkshire.

Lincolnshire is dotted with RAF stations, one of which could be RAF Barnesking. Like most RAF stations RAF Barnesking is situated on flat ground well away from centres of population in a rural area centred on farming and with at least one sizeable village only a few miles away. The station has one main runway sited to take advantage of the prevailing winds, often roughly east-west, but some other stations have a second runway set at an angle to suit the dictates of the local situation. The station perimeter is long and irregular and of a nature that seems to have been chosen to invite infiltration. Overall, the site is open with no high ground or obstacles such as lines of electrical pylons or power station chimney stacks set too close.

The layout of the station was initially determined during the 1920s or 1930s and follows the general layout of what are now known as Trenchard stations. Considering their form was determined so long ago, most RAF stations have adapted well to modern requirements and would be recognisable still to past generations of airmen. The runway lies to one side of the station area with aircraft hard-standings arrayed along one side. The side opposite the hard-standings is given over to the fire services and fuel and ammunition dumps so that they are as far away as possible from the working and accommodation areas. The fuel and ammunition dumps are mainly underground or are at least protected by earth walls and banks.

Right in the centre of the hard-standing and almost at the centre of the station aircraft area is the airfraft control tower. This 'glass-house' is well provided with large windows which allow visibility over all the working and runway areas, and the height of the control building may be variable to suit the location. The radar associated with the control tower function may be well away from the flying area and may even be off the station proper in a small enclave, but most stations have their own radar on the perimeter.

Close by the hard-standings where the aircraft are prepared for their missions are the small buildings for the ground crew and their associated workshops and offices. Behind them and beyond a

system of aircraft access tracks are the main hangars of the station. The usual number of these prominent hangars is about four, set in an arc so that one bombing or strike run will not be able to hit them all. The hangars are tall structures with armoured blastproof access doors all around with further protection provided by the outside offices which are designed to protect the main structure by absorbing bomb blast from near misses. Apart from the aircraft shelter function, each hangar can be used as a maintenance and repair location and may be used in some cases for less aircraft-based uses such as a RAF Regiment base or a motor transport shelter.

However, RAF Barnesking, being a Tornado station, has extra aircraft shelters scattered all around its main flying area, each with access to the main runway. These shelters are known as HASs or Hardened Aircraft Shelters, and any station with HASs takes on an entirely new appearance from the old RAF stations. It would be easy to regard each HAS as a miniature fort, for their interior and general outline certainly provides such an impression. Each HAS is intended to house under complete protection one Tornado, its ground crew and all its necessary support equip-

Above left *A typical control tower scene during an NBC exercise.*

Left *Outside the Station Headquarters with the Station Commander's Cortina depicted by a Group Captain's pennant and one of the ubiquitous Minis.*

Below *Tornados being towed along one of the station 'peri tracks'.*

ment and supplies. In peaceful times they can usually accommodate two Tornados at a pinch. Each HAS is proof against attack of all kinds, apart from a direct hit by a nuclear weapon, and the seemingly haphazard layout of the HASs around the airfield is carefully planned so that one bombing run cannot knock out or hit more than one in a single attack run. Special blast doors and access doors are sealed against possible gas attack and a protected area on the side is large enough for a bowser or ammunition supply truck to drive into the HAS. The two squadrons each have their own squadron shelter complete with gas-locks and complete independence from the rest of the station if necessary. All communication links to the outside world and the rest of the station are completely protected but if necessary the squadron could function apart from the rest of the station.

Only a few United Kingdom RAF stations have HASs at present, but they are well established in RAF Germany. RAF Barnesking has 16 HASs, other stations having less and some more.

Away from the airfield area and behind the hangars is the main complex of the station. Here, scattered around an airfield access network of roads, are the main workshops, stores, offices and all the other many and various facilities needed to keep the station running. The main administrative building is usually near the main gate with its inevitable guardroom, but the main living areas and accommodations are in 'H' blocks to one side of the station parade ground. This in its turn is next to the main airmen's messing hall which may contain the NAAFI facilities. The Officer's Mess is well away to one side of the station area, usually on the perimeter with its own access approach to outside. It is the Officer's Mess that provides each RAF station with its name, for in nearly every case the station takes its name from the postal address of the Officer's Mess. This convention has produced many anomalies over the years, one which can be quoted being the late unlamented Radio School at RAF Yatesbury in Wiltshire. The village of Yatesbury was miles from the station but the Officer's Mess fell into the Yatesbury postal district and so RAF Yatesbury got its name.

Officers' and Airmen's Married Quarters are situated outside the station perimeter with perhaps an enclave inside the fence. The quarters have their own supermarket, school and sometimes their own medical centre, while transport is regularly laid on by local operators to the nearby towns. RAF Barnesking has its own cinema, as do most stations, and has its own central hall-cum-social centre. As with many other stations there is a public house and a garage within easy reach just outside the main gate and many families live off the station in the nearby villages. Local relations are well maintained to the extent that every year, operational commitments allowing, the local populace is invited to a 'Families Day' when the less sensitive part of RAF Barnesking is opened for a social, sports and fun day with maybe a small flying display laid on as well.

The area of RAF Barnesking can be measured in hundreds of acres/hectares so local defence is a problem. Normal policing is carried out by the RAF Police and their detachment of guard dogs which are kennelled as far away from other living accommodation as possible to reduce the nuisance of their incessant barking. The perimeter also houses other odd structures and stores areas with a few dispersal areas for aircraft and vehicles left over from an earlier era. In time of war defending such a farflung perimeter would be virtually impossible so RAF Barnesking has followed other Strike Command stations in having a centralised 'citadel' area that can be defended. This area encloses the main workshops, hangar and airfield area and there are some smaller defended areas among the administrative buildings. Barbed wire coils enclose the 'citadel' with moveable road blocks at each point, while a system of small sandbag pillboxes and sangars dotted around the place in the best defensive positions cover each road access point and hangar corner. Underground shelters are provided for ground-crew outside the main hangars and buildings, and some protection is provided to the station Medical Centre over and above that normally given.

The squadrons

As already mentioned, RAF Barnesking is home for two Tornado Squadrons, No 888 and No 999. Both squadrons operate under No 1 Group command and are detailed for strike missions into Eastern Germany and Poland in an emergency. Some personnel and aircraft may be detached to RAF Germany during the days of any build-up to hostilities.

Both squadrons are identical in their internal administration, make-up and personnel strengths. Being Tornado units, both are largely made up from 'second tour' aircrew mainly drawn from the old V-bomber or Buccaneer squadrons. Only a few navigators are first-tour personnel, while the ground crew consists mainly of experienced tradesmen or newly joined tradesmen who did well in their trade tests.

Each squadron is commanded by a Wing Commander. Under him are two Flight Commanders, each being a Squadron Leader. The

Squadron Commander also has a team of departmental leaders, these being Leaders for Airframes, Propulsion, Electronics, Weapons, Flight Guidance and Control Systems (FGCS), Automatic Navigation and Attack Controls (ANAC), and Support Communications. These leaders all report to the Squadron Commander on their particular responsibilities and there are rather more of them on Tornado squadrons, being an indication of the various systems involved in the highly complex aircraft. There is also a Training Officer function divided between two officers, one dealing with aircrew training and the other with groundcrew training.

Each Flight Commander, who may be either a navigator or more usually a pilot, has both an executive and an operational function. The executive function relates to the administrative running of the Flight and its personnel, while the operations aspect is the operational readiness of the Flight.

Each Tornado crew consists of a pilot and navigator who would normally always fly together. It would not automatically follow that they always flew in the same aircraft for that would depend on aircraft serviceability, but each HAS would contain one operationally-ready Tornado that had been prepared by the ground crew assigned to each HAS. Each HAS has a small internal office and crew room that is sound-proofed against the noises attendant on preparing an aircraft. These ground crew would normally be under the command of the Senior Engineering Officer (SENGO), who has under him a Junior Engineering Officer (JENGO), a Warrant Officer and two Flight Sergeants. The responsibilities of the SENGO should not be confused with those of the various system leaders for they are all aircrew with special responsibilities for their particular specialities within the squadron. Every officer on the squadron has some form of supernumary duty that might range from squadron Sports Officer to being in charge of squadron social activities.

Squadron life in the RAF is as hectic and full as it ever was both socially, in the sporting field and at work. The old social division between officers and other ranks, while still in being, is far less marked than it once was, although among the ground crew the once free and easy division between the various ranks is now far more marked than those of the old National Service times. While with the squadron, all personnel are expected to take part in as many activities as possible, facilities for which are amply provided on the station.

The number of aircraft on the squadron will vary somewhat from time to time depending on serviceability and squadron commitments elsewhere, ie, training or other operational detachments. Nominally the number of aircraft will be 12 or so but at times may be as many as 16 or as few as eight.

The Station administration

The Station Commander is usually a Group Captain but larger and more important stations may warrant an Air Commodore. The Station Commander will have risen to his position via aircrew training and the various Staff College courses so that, by the time he commands an RAF Station, he will have had wide experience of all aspects of the Service from squadron life to flying a desk at a headquarters somewhere or a spell in Whitehall. On the station he has his main office in the Station Headquarters, usually a Trenchard-period office block near the main gate, and he has his own staff car. These days it is almost unknown for him to have the personal aircraft that at one time would have been the best turned-out aircraft on the station.

Reporting directly to him, the Station Commander will have the two Commanding Officers of Nos 888 and 999 Squadrons. The other flying unit on RAF Barnesking is the training unit or OCU. (This OCU is as fictitious as the rest of the station and its squadrons but is included here to convey the administration of such a unit.) The OCU has three main sub-sections, one coming under a SENGO or Senior Engineering Officer. The second sub-section is the Simulator Unit for every OCU makes extensive use of the latest types of aircraft simulator and their extensive technologies. The third sub-section is the Standards Unit or Flight that not only sets the standards which the trainees have to attain, but also constantly reassesses operational requirements and amends the training system to meet new objectives.

Having digressed to the OCU, the Station Commander has three further commanders reporting directly to him. These are the OCs of the Operations Wing (Ops Wg), the Engineering Wing (Eng Wg) and the Administration Wing (Admin Wg). To take these three Wings in order, first comes the Operations Wing. In simple terms the OC Ops Wg is responsible for the general management of the airfield. The OC Ops Wg may have a number of Squadron Leaders reporting directly to him on their individual responsibilities. These responsibilities are Operations, Security, Intelligence and Planning, Flying Support and Air Traffic Control. RAF Barnesking is one of the stations that also has its own RAux AF Regiment station defence unit, the commander of which also reports to the OC

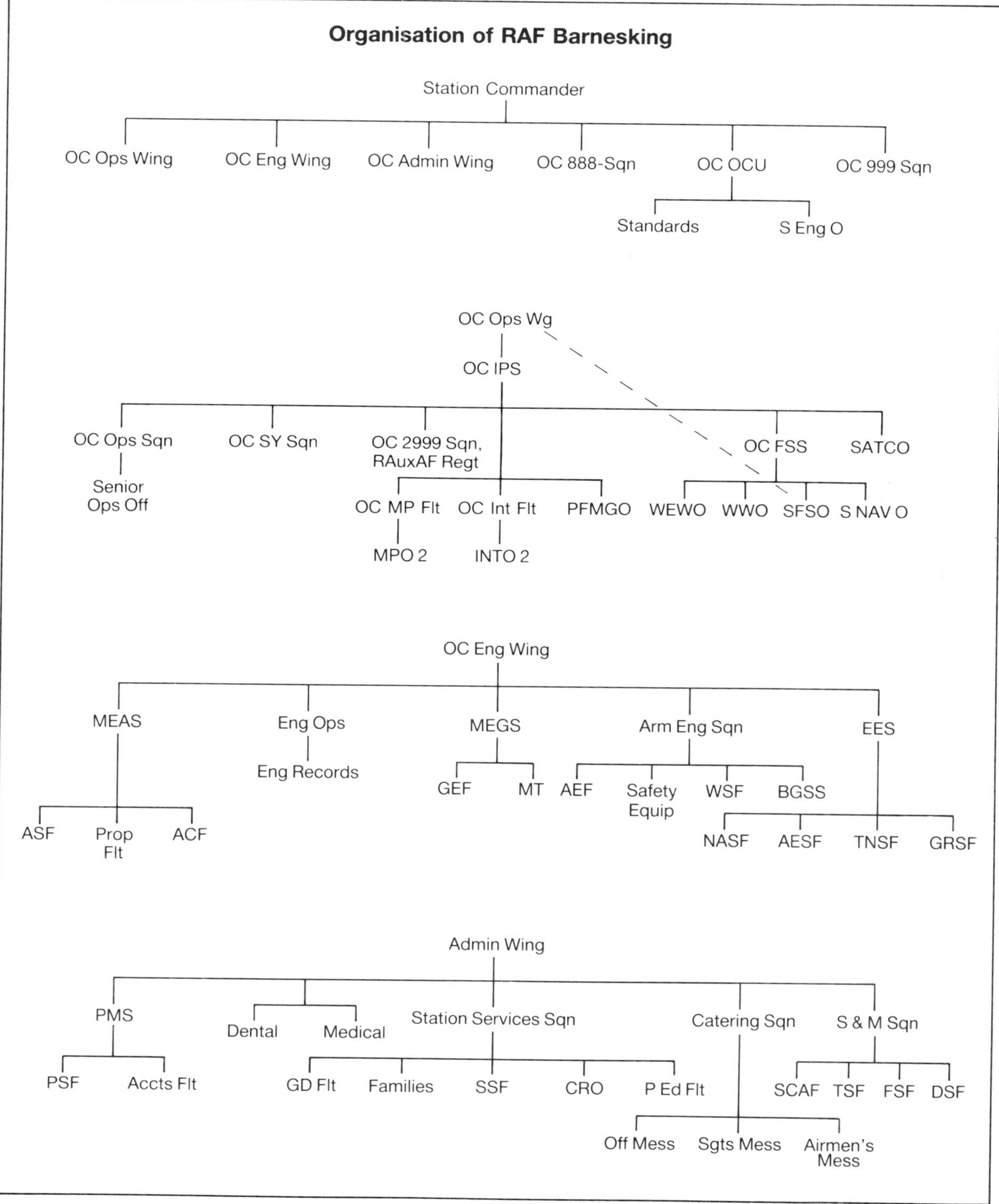
Organisation of RAF Barnesking
Station Commander
OC Ops Wing
OC Eng Wing
OC Admin Wing
OC 888-Sqn
OC OCU
OC 999 Sqn
Standards
S Eng O
OC Ops Wg
OC IPS
OC Ops Sqn
OC SY Sqn
OC 2999 Sqn, RAuxAF Regt
OC FSS
SATCO
Senior Ops Off
OC MP Flt
OC Int Flt
PFMGO
WEWO
WWO
SFSO
S NAV O
MPO 2
INTO 2
OC Eng Wing
MEAS
Eng Ops
MEGS
Arm Eng Sqn
EES
Eng Records
GEF
MT
AEF
Safety Equip
WSF
BGSS
ASF
Prop Flt
ACF
NASF
AESF
TNSF
GRSF
Admin Wing
PMS
Dental
Medical
Station Services Sqn
Catering Sqn
S & M Sqn
PSF
Accts Flt
GD Flt
Families
SSF
CRO
P Ed Flt
SCAF
TSF
FSF
DSF
Off Mess
Sgts Mess
Airmen's Mess

Ops Wg. The OC Ops Sqn is responsible for aircraft movements on the Station, the running and general functioning of the operations rooms and for the logging and general administration of flight planning and flight plans. To aid him in this task he has a Senior Operations Officer and three Operations Officers, plus a staff of a Sergeant and a number of airmen.

The Security Squadron (Sy Sqn) OC has under his command the three main functions of the RAF Police on the Station, together with the guard dogs and their handlers, the Fire Section and the RAF Regiment personnel who carry out not only the general Station security measures but also the Ground Defence training of all Station personnel. The OC Sy Sqn is usually a RAF Regiment officer.

On many operational stations the Intelligence and Planning Squadron is quite large in operational importance and manpower and is usually referred to as IPS. On a Tornado base the importance of this squadron is amplified for each squadron has its own particular sector along which it is expected to operate in time of war. The IPS therefore has to gather in all the information the squadrons might need in time of war such as the number and types of potential targets involved, the state of the local defences, the aircraft opposition they might anticipate, the paths of least risk to the targets, and so on. Thus the OC IPS has under him an OC Mission Plans Flight (OC MP Flt) with two Mission Planning Officers (MPOs) and a small staff of airmen. There is also an OC Intelligence Flight (OC Int Flt) who has the responsibility of compiling all the necessary intelligence information for the Station's resident units. The OC Int Flt has under him two Intelligence Officers (INTOs) and a small staff of airmen. Also reporting to the OC IPS is the Pre-Flight Message Generator Officer (PFMGO) who has the task of compiling and presenting all the information contained in a constant stream of pre-flight information orders relating to all sorts of things from low-level flight restrictions to alterations of hazard areas such as bird strike zones.

Also reporting to OC Ops is the OC Flying Support Squadron (FSS). As the name implies, this squadron provides all the various forms of support for the flying units and consists of a Senior Navigation Officer (S Nav O), a Wing Electronic Warfare Officer (WEWO), a Wing Weapon Officer (WWO) and a Station Safety Officer (SFSO). The SFSO is responsible for all aspects of safety, both on the ground and in the air, and to assist him in his responsibility he can report directly to the OC Ops if he feels the need to do so.

The Senior Air Traffic Control Officer (SATCO) also reports to OC Ops. His responsibilities may be quite wide on some Stations for in parts of the country where RAF and USAF Stations are set together, one Station may be responsible for the air traffic control of more than just its own air traffic alone. Some Stations control up to three others but more often than not the SATCO controls just his own base's air traffic. To provide an example of this multi-station responsibility, the SATCO at RAF Honington, a Tornado base, controls the air traffic not only for his own Station but also the air traffic using the USAF bases at nearby Mildenhall and Lakenheath. The SATCO may have some civilians on his staff.

Also under the direction and control of the OC Ops is the CO of the Station's resident Royal Auxiliary Air Force Regiment Squadron formed to provide some measure of local defence for the station and the local area. The Squadron is staffed by regular RAF Regiment officers who also lead a small cadre of instructors for the 140-strong unit. The bulk of the manpower is made up of volunteers from the local populace, including some of the local civilian women, who are mainly armed with light small-arms. Some of these RAux AF squadrons act as back-up for Rapier units. To date six squadrons have been formed (for further details see chapter on the RAF Regiment). (Although they are not in any way RAF units, some RAF bases act as the homes for what will eventually be eight Territorial Army airfield repair squadrons. These squadrons will be Royal Engineer units and will have the operational task of repairing damaged RAF airfields, especially runways, in rapid time following any enemy attacks. The first of these units is 277 Field Squadron (Airfield Damage Repair) Royal Engineers (Volunteers) which was formed at RAF Leuchars on March 26 1983.)

Following on from the IPS is the Engineering Wing (Eng Wg) commanded by the OC Eng Wg. The OC Eng Wg has under his command five sub-units, the first of which we will consider being the Mechanical Engineering Aircraft Squadron, or MEAS. This has three Flights, Aircraft Servicing Flight (ASF), Propulsion Flight (Prop Flt) and Aircraft Components Flight (ACF). These three Flights' functions are fairly self-explanatory with all three carrying out aircraft servicing up to major standards. Their work is based on one or more of the large Trenchard hangars on the stations with some sub-component servicing being carried out in other locations such as the large engine test shelters with their complex sound attenuation systems. Engineering Operation or Eng Ops is concerned mainly with the aircraft engines and the officer in charge is also responsible for the upkeep and administration of Engine Records.

Above *Inside the HAS with a Tornado being bombed up using a loading trolley.*

Below *A typical Hardened Aircraft Shelter (HAS) showing the end doors.*

MEGS is the Mechanical Engineering Ground Squadron and is split into two sub-units. One of these is the General Engineering Flight or GEF which deals with just about everything from electrical generators to aircraft power units (APUs) and even includes a woodworking staff. The MT Flight is familiar to everyone on any station for it is the Mechanical Transport Flight that deals with everything from aircrew buses to runway snow-clearing vehicles. Their remit includes such items as squadron hacks, fire-fighting vehicles, Station ambulances, runway sweepers and all the various fuel bowsers. The MT Flight also provides all the drivers for the station.

Reporting to the OC Eng Wg is the OC of the Armament Engineering Squadron (OC Arm Eng Sqn). As the name implies this squadron deals mainly with the weapons side of the station, including guns, bombs, rockets and missiles. These are primarily the responsibility of the AEF or Armament Engineering Flight which is responsible

On many airfields the problem of bird strikes is serious and many and various are the counter-measures taken to keep flocks of birds away from the areas where aircraft movements take place. This Land-Rover is one of them as it has a loudspeaker on the roof which broadcasts various bird distress calls to keep birds away. Other measures used include the use of maroons and tame kestrels.

for the maintenance and servicing of weapons and weapon systems. Once the weapons are serviceable they are passed to the Weapons Storage Flight (WSF) who look after their lethal charges in their various dumps, stores and bunkers. Also reporting to the OC Arm Eng Sqn is the Safety Equipment Section which looks after all aspects of flight safety equipment from parachutes to dinghys and flying clothing to NBC equipment.

On any station the Electrical Engineering Squadron (EES) is a fair-sized unit but the actual composition will vary according to the aircraft type based on the station. As RAF Barnesking is a Tornado base the EES is geared to deal with Tornado electrical systems and equipment but other aircraft bases will vary to suit their particular aircraft types. Thus the RAF Barnesking EES has a Navigation and Attack Systems Flight (NASF), an Avionics Electrical Systems Flight (AESF), a Tornado Navigation Systems Flight (TNSF) and a Ground Radio Servicing Flight (GRSF). The first three of these Flights relate directly to the Tornado aircraft but the GRSF is common to just about any Station as it is responsible for the telephone system and all the many and various beacons, radio links and other ground communication systems.

Common to any RAF Station is the Admin Wing that controls all the day-to-day activities of the airfield and its personnel. It is the Wing that feeds everyone, gets them paid, and finds somewhere for them to sleep as these are the three basic requirements that have to be carried out for all personnel in the RAF, whatever their rank or job. There are five main units who report to the OC Admin Wing, the first of which is the Personnel Management Squadron, or PMS. In the main this is tasked with the general record-keeping and accounts involved for all ranks on the Station and is divided into the Personnel Services Flight (PSF), dealing with documentation and records, and the

Accounts Flight (Accts Flt) dealing with all matters relating to pay and allowances.

Also reporting to the OC Admin Wg for functional matters is the Medical and Dental section which also has a responsibility to their own departments elsewhere away from the Station. On most airfields both are based in the Station Medical Centre where the Senior Medical Officer is a Wing Commander and the Senior Dental Officer is a Squadron Leader. Both have full facilities for their task, which includes the medical and dental care of the families on the station as well as the officers and all ranks; in some remote locations the SMC often provides medical care for some of the local populace at times. Most Stations have some facilities for emergency surgery but whenever possible serious cases are referred to the nearest RAF Hospital. For such emergencies the Station has its own ambulances.

The Station Services Squadron covers most of the day-to-day domestics of the station with the General Duties Flight (GD Flt) providing the manpower, including civilians for all the jobs that need to be done to keep the Station serviceable and presentable. The task under the control of the GD Flt include the never-ending grass cutting, the upkeep of the roads, all the painting chores, and so on. The Families Flight looks after all aspects of the various married quarters, while the Station Services Flight (SSF) is the 'works and bricks' department responsible for the fabric of the station buildings, usually passing some of the major or long-term programmes to outside contractors. Also reporting to the OC Station Services Squadron is the Community Relations Officer or CRO, an officer who comes into contact with all sectors of RAF Station life and is responsible for relations with the surrounding populace and the press and generally deals with community relations. He is the one who has to deal with the constant stream of complaints that flow into almost every RAF Station and relate to aircraft noise, local damage to property and structures and, more than ever these days, low-flying aircraft. The CRO also provides a local news service for the press, lays on local and other displays such as the various 'families days', and buys beers for journalists in the Officers Mess.

The Officers' Mess is under the control of the OC Catering Squadron, as is the Sergeants' Mess and the Airmen's Mess. Feeding the many mouths on any large RAF Station is a massive task that is the responsibility of a Squadron Leader.

Finally, there is the Supply and Movements Squadron (S & M Sqn) that deals with all matters relating to the supply of stores and all the many other items needed by any large community, and their subsequent carrying from one place to another. The control of this function is mainly the concern of the Supply Control and Accounts Flight (SCAF), a very busy unit that keeps all aspects of supply on the Station at an economic level, with the Accounts function dealing with levels and costing. The Technical Supply Flight (TSF) deals with all the many and various technical stores that might relate to anything on the Station from medical instruments to major aircraft parts. The TSF is the main stores department from which the Forward Supply Flight (FSF) takes the stores to where they are needed. On a Tornado Station this can be a fairly straightforward operation but on airfields dealing with helicopters or Harriers it can be much more complex when aircraft and units are detached or based at outlying locations. Last, but not least, is the Domestic Supply Flight (DSF), which deals with the essential but mundane chore of dealing with all matters relating to the stores required for barracks and offices, including furniture, cleaning materials, etc.

* * *

The above outline deals only with RAF Barnesking, a non-existent station thought up to provide a very general indication of how an RAF Station works, functions and exists on a day-to-day basis. Some of the units mentioned above may not appear on every RAF Station but most of them are typical and some RAF Stations may have units that are not mentioned above. These exceptions, one way or another, are mainly caused by the type of aircraft involved. For instance, a Chinook squadron has its own RAF Regiment contingent integral with its manpower structure but a Nimrod squadron would have no need of such an increment. Harrier squadrons have manpower alterations and units to deal with their particular mobility needs, while some RAF Stations have so many visiting aircraft that they need a permanent sub-unit (a Flight or even a Squadron) to handle them and provide servicing. Some Stations have sub-units that exist nowhere else in the Service, such as the Buccaneer Ground Servicing School under the control of the OC Arm Eng Sqn at RAF Lossiemouth. There could be many more such examples provided.

The RAF Regiment & RAF weapons

In very basic terms, the Royal Air Force Regiment exists to defend Royal Air Force bases from attack. As airfields are liable to attack both from the air and the ground, the Regiment is organised to combat both. To counter attack from the air, the Regiment has a number of low-level air defence (LLAD) squadrons equipped with the Rapier guided missile. To combat the ground threat, it is equipped with a mixture of Scorpion gun-armed light tanks and Spartan armoured personnel carriers. The two types of squadron operate in their unique role and are not interchangeable operationally, although personnel are often cross-posted and share many basic combat skills such as local and NBC defence.

The RAF Regiment has its own directorate and was originally formed as a Corps within the Royal Air Force. It therefore uses the same rank structure, chain of command and uniform regulations. Headquarters RAF Regiment is in Whitehall. Its commander is known as the Commandant-General, and he has to wear several hats. In addition to commanding the Regiment, he is also responsible for the Royal Air Force Police and Security Services and acts as Director Security and Royal Air Force Provost Marshal. The latter post involves the RAF Police and Security services who are, therefore, involved in the RAF Regiment command structure, as are the crash, rescue and fire personnel. In practice they operate independently of the Regiment.

HQ RAF Regiment does not have a direct command function for the squadrons in the field. What it does have is a policy and requirements function, both for men and equipment. HQ RAF Regiment has its own Headquarters Staff to study present and future requirements in its field and to advise and plan accordingly. Their directives are transmitted to the units operating under the auspices of Strike Command, RAF Germany, and to the RAF Regiment Depot at Catterick.

The Depot provides the background support for the Regiment. It is the location where all personnel, officers and airmen alike, for the Regiment are trained once they leave their initial Service training. The Depot also provides a home for the crash, rescue and fire services and continuation training for NCOs and officers, as well as that for the Rapier gunners and drivers and other personnel associated with the light armoured squadrons. The Depot has a Training Support Flight which supervises and administers all the training carried out in the Regiment and also provides some specialist personnel for other tasks.

Both Strike Command and RAF Germany have their own Command Regiment Officer who directly commands the units within his sphere of interest. Strike Command has both Rapier and light armoured squadrons under its control, spread between two Groups and an independent squadron. No 11 Group, involved as it is with the defence of the United Kingdom, has two LLAD squadrons, No 27 at RAF Leuchars and No 48 at Lossiemouth. No.1 Group has four light armoured (Lt Armd) squadrons split between two formations, 3 Wing based at RAF Catterick and 5 Wing based at Hullavington. 3 Wing commands 51 and 58 Squadrons; 5 Wing commands 15 Squadron and an unusual unit, No 2 (Para) Squadron. As the designation implies, No 2 (Para) has a paratroop capability. All the personnel in the unit are fully trained for the parachute role in case of some future non-NATO task (ie, it is not envisaged that they would be called upon to utilise this skill in a full war situation). The training carried out by No 2 (Para) Sqn is much the same as that carried out by the Army's Parachute Regiment but, as the squadron would be operating in an airfield defence role after any possible airborne operation, the physical requirements made of the airmen are not as exacting as those demanded by the Army's Paras.

Strike Command's independent squadron is No 34, based in the sun at RAF Akrotiri. Its primary role is to guard the sovereign base area in Cyprus but, in an emergency, it would be moved to RAF Germany when it would become a light armoured squadron. Its equipment for the armoured role is already stockpiled in Germany.

RAF Germany is divided into two Wings as far as the Regiment is concerned, one being No 4 which has four LLAD squadrons already in Germany. These are allocated among the four RAF Germany air bases with No 37 Squadron at Bruggen, No 26 at Laarbruch, No 16 at Wildenrath and No 63 at Gutersloh. 33 Wing has but one light armoured squadron under its control in time of peace. This is No 1, normally based at RAF Laarbruch. However, in time of war this would change rapidly. The light armoured squadrons of 3 and 5 Wings would move to RAF Germany and come under the control of 33 Wing, when they would be allocated among the 'Clutch' airfields near the German-Dutch border. There they would be joined by 34 Squadron from Cyprus if time allowed. No 1 Squadron would not stay at Laarbruch but would move forward into the 1 (BR) Corps area to provide protection for the Harrier squadron field sites. To round off the RAF Germany picture, as far as the RAF Regiment is concerned, mention must be made of the Queen's Colour Squadron which would form a Land Rover-based Field Squadron for the defence of RAF Gutersloh. In this they would be joined by men from the Training Support Flight at the RAF Regiment Depot at Catterick.

This relatively tidy picture of the major units in the RAF Regiment is somewhat clouded by the fact that all the units involved have to find men for commitments elsewhere. High on this list is the Falklands, and RAF Germany provides one of its

Right *A Spartan armoured personnel carrier of No 1 Squadron, RAF Regiment, in Germany—the Spartan is the most numerous of the armoured vehicles used by the Regiment.*

Below *RAF Regiment Scorpion light tank on exercises in Germany.*

4 Wing Rapier squadrons for a four-month tour on a rotation basis. The Regiment also has a role to play in defending RAF installations in Northern Ireland. This task is shared among the four light armoured squadrons of 3 and 5 Wing in the United Kingdom. On a rotation basis, they spend four months in the Province followed by a 12-month tour of duty back in the UK; some of these months have, however, to be spent in tuning-up for the tour in the Province. As if these two commitments were not enough, the Regiment also has to provide personnel to man the Rapier defences of the air base in Belize. Consequently, half of a United Kingdom LLAD squadron is in Belize at any one time on a three-month tour.

The light armoured squadrons each have a headquarters based around a single Sultan armoured command vehicle (ACV). Each headquarters has under its direct control an Engineering Flight based around a sole Samson armoured recovery vehicle (ARV). Each squadron has three Combat Flights, each with five Spartan armoured personnel carriers (APCs) carying a commander, driver and four or five men. A Support Flight is formed from six Scorpion light tanks (the Army refers to the Scorpion as a light reconnaissance vehicle but the Regiment uses the Scorpions in a light tank role). Each of the light armoured squadrons has a manpower strength of about 150 men and can operate as an independent unit for up to 14 days without support. Operationally, they would be used to deny the area around an RAF Germany airfield to an enemy. They would operate in teams of Spartans and Scorpions, patrolling the area with the rifle teams dismounting when required.

Each of the Rapier LLAD squadrons has a Headquarters Flight with its own Engineering Flight based around mobile workshops carried in container bodies on 4-tonne trucks. This headquarters controls eight Rapier fire units towed by 1-tonne Land Rovers with ¾-tonne Land Rovers in support. Each fire unit has an optical tracker with a DN 181 Blindfire radar in support when required. These fire units would not be located on the airfield in an emergency but would move out to preselected field sites that may be as far as 12-13 kilometres from the base itself in order to engage an enemy before he could deploy stand-off weapons or make an approach run. To do this the LLAD squadrons have to be able to defend themselves, practise a considerable level of fieldcraft and have the ability to operate under full NBC defence conditions. They also have to have a very high standard of aircraft recognition based on an initial 'friend or foe' identification before type

Above *A Rapier firing post in the Falklands* (Flt Lt T. Dean, No 37 Sqn, RAF Regt).

Right *The face of modern warfare—men of the RAF Regiment mount guard as a Rapier operator operates his Rapier optical tracker.*

Below *The Queen's Colour Squadron of the RAF Regiment mounting guard at Buckingham Palace.*

classification is attempted. Once in the field, Rapier fire units have to be maintained and supplied which involves yet more operational headaches; that the task can be accomplished was demonstrated ably by No 63 Squadron in the Falklands soon after the San Carlos landings.

Airfield defence is not the responsibility of the RAF Regiment alone. Any member of the Royal Air Force may expect to be called upon to grab a weapon and defend his locality. To this end he receives regular Ground Combat Training, administered and carried out by RAF Regiment instructors attached to every major station. In addition, some of the squadrons that operate in the field (such as the Chinook units) have their own RAF Regiment Flights which are an integral part of the squadron and whose personnel advise and administer the defence and security of the squadron's field locations. To round off the security aspect, the senior RAF Regiment officer on any Royal Air Force installation is usually the Security and Fire Officer as well.

The Royal Auxiliary Air Force Regiments will be dealt with under the chapter dealing with the Royal Auxiliary Air Force (see page 97).

A new responsibility for the RAF Regiment has been the formation of a new Wing, No 6, at RAF West Raynham to control the three RAF Regiment squadrons which will man the LLAD Rapiers used to defend some US Air Force bases in the United Kingdom. 6 Wing was formed in July 1983 and the first squadron, No 66, was formed at RAF West Raynham in November of the same year. No 19 was formed at RAF Brize Norton in mid-1984, to be followed during mid-1985 by No 20 at Honington. The US Air Force is providing the finance for these squadrons and their equipment. Normally the squadrons will remain on their parent bases, but in an emergency would move out to defend seven US Air Force bases. It is not possible to state which bases these include, but it is known that Cruise Missile bases will be involved.

The Queen's Colour Squadron has already been mentioned in connection with RAF Germany but

9 mm Pistol Automatic L9A1—the famous Browning pistol.

in normal circumstances its role is to escort the Queen's Colour of the Royal Air Force on ceremonial occasions. It also represents the Royal Air Force at many other ceremonial events such as the annual Cenotaph parade on Remembrance Day. From time to time it also provides the guard for Buckingham Palace or the Tower of London. Perhaps the Queen's Colour Squadron is best known to the public for the astonishing displays of continuity drill it performs at many public events such as the annual Royal Tournament. The Queen's Colour Squadron is based at RAF Uxbridge, just outside London, but it travels far and wide in the course of every year, somehow finding time to practise its war role as a Land Rover-based Field Squadron at RAF Gutersloh in RAF Germany.

The men of the RAF Regiment regard themselves as a unique bunch who have a very high esprit de corps. They train and work hard and their year is often full of movement which takes them to some remote locations, so they seldom have time to get bored. Their equipment is now the best there is for the role, so the RAF Regiment is set for a long and active life in the years to come.

Weapons of the RAF

The weapons included in this section are used throughout the RAF. Some of them are *not* used by the RAF Regiment (eg the L9A1 pistol) but the RAF Regiment does train other personnel to use them for station or other defence.

9 mm Pistol Automatic L9A1

Calibre 9 mm; **Length overall** 196 mm; **Length of barrel** 112 mm; **Weight empty** 0.88 kg; **Weight loaded** 1.01 kg; **Muzzle velocity** 354 m/s; **Magazine capacity** 13 rounds; **Rate of fire** Single-shot; **Maximum effective range** 40–50 m.

The L9A1 is now the only hand gun used by the Royal Air Force and is known almost universally as the 'Browning' after its designer. The first examples of this sturdy pistol were produced as far back as 1935 but it was not until the Army adopted the type as its service hand gun in 1961 that the Royal Air Force started to get rid of its old .38 Smith & Wesson revolvers and standardised on the L9A1.

The use of the L9A1 is mainly restricted to aircrew, who carry one when flying on operations where a hand gun might play a part in self defence or personal survival in the event of a forced landing, or by police units. The Royal Air Force Regiment does not normally use the L9A1. The strong construction of the L9A1 makes it a bit of a heavy handful for firing but with even a little practice it becomes an accurate-enough weapon at short ranges. The unusual 13-round magazine provides more than enough ammunition for normal emergency use.

Rifle 7.62 mm L1A1

Calibre 7.62 mm; **Length overall** 1.143 m; **Length of barrel** 0.5334 m; **Weight empty** 4.337 kg; **Weight loaded** 5.074 kg; **Muzzle velocity** 838 m/s; **Magazine capacity** 20 rounds; **Rate of fire** 40 rpm; **Maximum effective range** 600 m plus.

The L1A1 is the same weapon as the Army's L1A1 and is used not only by the RAF Regiment but by all other members of the Royal Air Force. All officers and airmen are trained in its use and it is also the weapon carried on parades. The L1A1 is a revised and 'British' version of the Belgian FN FAL (Fabrique Nationale Fusil Automatique Légèr) adopted for British service back in 1955. It is a gas-operated weapon that fires semi-automatically, requiring one pull of the trigger for every shot. The 7.62 mm × 51 NATO ammunition is carried

Sub-machine-gun 9 mm L2A3—the 'Sterling'.

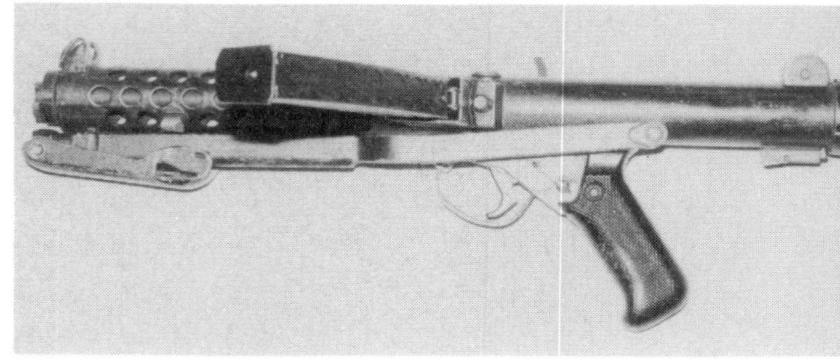

in 20-round box magazines. A bayonet can be fitted and the furniture (ie, the stock and butt) may be of either wood or black nylonite.

The L1A1 is a sound and sturdy weapon that has served well but its days with the RAF Regiment are now numbered as it is planned that it will be replaced in service by the 5.56 mm Individual Weapon (IW). However, it will be some time before the L1A1 passes from use with the rest of the Royal Air Force.

Sub-Machine Gun 9mm L2A3

Calibre 9 mm; **Length (butt folded)** 0.482 m; **Length (butt extended)** 0.69 m; **Length of barrel** 0.198 m; **Weight empty** 2.7 kg; **Weight loaded** 3.5 kg; **Muzzle velocity** 390 m/s; **Magazine capacity** 34 rounds; **Rate of fire (cyclic)** 550 rpm; **Rate of fire (practical)** 102 rpm; **Rate of fire (single shot)** 40 rpm; **Maximum effective range** 200 m.

Within the RAF Regiment the L2A3, often referred to as the 'Sterling', is used by senior NCOs and officers. It is a well-established weapon with a long development history stretching back to before 1945, but a weapon with an extremely robust and reliable mechanism that can absorb large amounts of hard use. Manufactured by the Sterling Armament Company Limited at Dagenham (hence the name 'Sterling'), the L2A3 is useful operationally at short ranges only but the folding butt makes the weapon an easy one to carry in confined spaces.

Like the L1A1 rifle, the L2A3 is now scheduled for replacement by the 5.56 mm IW.

5.56 mm Individual Weapon L85A1

Calibre 5.56 mm; **Length overall** 0.77 m; **Weight loaded** 4.68 kg; **Muzzle velocity** 900 m/s; **Magazine capacity** 30 rounds; **Rate of fire (cyclic)** 700–850 rpm; **Combat range** Up to 400 m (unconfirmed).

With the adoption of the 5.56 mm Individual Weapon (IW), the RAF Regiment has followed the lead of the Army in adopting the new NATO 5.56 mm round based on the Belgian SS109 cartridge. The adoption of a less powerful round than the existing NATO 7.62 mm × 51 cartridge has long been an Army wish but eventually the realisation of a protracted development programme and NATO trials has finally been achieved.

The IW is a product of Royal Ordnance Small Arms Division at Enfield Lock in Middlesex. It originally had a 4.85 mm calibre but, following the series of NATO trials, the Belgian cartridge was adopted instead and the IW has been re-engineered to adopt this ammunition. The IW is an unusual weapon in many ways, not the least of which is the adoption of a 'bull-pup' layout in which the trigger group is placed forward of the magazine. This allows the IW to be a compact weapon which is ideally suited to carrying and stowing in the close confines of APCs such as the Spartan. The layout also makes the weapon easy to handle and fire. The basic construction is steel with the main assemblies being stamped and welded. Machining has been kept to a minimum to reduce cost and

Left *A member of the RAF Regiment standing ready with his L1A1 7.62 mm rifle.*

Below *The 5.56 mm L85A1 which is destined to become the standard Individual Weapon for the RAF Regiment.*

ease production. This does not make the IW a shoddy weapon, for important items such as the optical sight have had no expense spared (if the optical sight becomes inoperative a small battle sight is provided over the sight housing, or the sight unit can be removed and replaced by conventional 'iron sights' carried in the pistol grip). After some deliberation, the original 20-round magazine has now been replaced by the 30-round magazine of the American M16 rifle, a magazine that is available all over the world. A small bayonet can be fitted to the IW muzzle which also has a fitting to enable rifle grenades to be fired.

The IW is easy to fire as the 5.56 mm round produces virtually no recoil and the weapon is simple to 'point' and handle. The exact operational range has not yet been announced but is believed to be of the order of 400 metres and below. At 400 metres the projectile can penetrate a steel helmet.

7.62 mm General Purpose Machine Gun L7A2

Calibre 7.62 mm; **Length as LMG** 1.232 m; **Length as HMG** 1.049 m; **Length of barrell** 0.629m; **Weight empty (LMG role)** 10.9 kg; **Weight loaded (LMG role)** 13.85 kg; **Weight of tripod** 13.64 kg; **Muzzle velocity** 838 m/s; **Type of feed** 100-round belt; **Rate of fire (cyclic)** 625–750 rpm; **Rate of fire in LMG role** 100 rpm; **Rate of fire in HMG role** 200 rpm; **Maximum effective range (LMG)** 800 m; **Maximum effective range (HMG)** 1,800 m.

The L7A2 General Purpose Machine-Gun, or GPMG, is used by the RAF Regiment in exactly the same roles as those used by the Army. The L7A2 can either be carried and used with a butt and a small bipod as a light machine-gun (LMG), or the butt may be removed and the weapon placed on a heavy buffered tripod in which form it can then be used as a heavy machine-gun (HMG). In both forms ammunition is fed into the weapon in 100-round belts of the same ammunition as that fired by the L1A1 rifle.

The GPMG is gas-operated, and it would be incorrect to state that it is a popular weapon. Being virtually machined from solid metal, it is heavy to carry, even in the light machine-gun role, and normally requires two men to service it, one of whom has to feed in the belts and carry extra ammunition. For all that, the GPMG is a reliable weapon that can pour out considerable amounts of supporting fire although, when fired for prolonged periods, the barrel can get very hot and thus has to be changed for a carried spare. Within the RAF Regiment, the GPMG is used mainly as a squad support weapon.

A variant of the basic L7A2 is the L37A1. This is basically an L7A2 converted for mounting on the commander's cupola of the Spartan and fitted with a chromed barrel to allow a greater proportion of tracer to be fired. The extra tracer enables the firer to follow more exactly the shot trajectory, as the L37A1 can be fired from inside the vehicle with the gunner using a periscopic sight. Fire corrections can be swiftly made by watching the path of the extra tracer rounds. Using a chromed barrel prevents the tracer elements from fouling the barrel too quickly. If required, the L37A1 can be dismounted from the Spartan cupola and converted back to the L7A2 configuration.

Another version of the basic L7A2 in service with the RAF Regiment is the L43A1. This is used on the Scorpion light tank as the co-axial weapon for the main 76 mm gun. It is used as an aiming device but is due to be replaced by a laser range-finder, and is thus retained as a co-axial weapon.

7.62 mm Machine Gun L4A4

Calibre 7.62 mm; **Length** 1.133 m; **Length of barrel** 0.536 m; **Weight empty** 9.96 kg; **Weight loaded** 10.68 kg; **Muzzle velocity** 869 m/s; **Magazine capacity** 30 rounds*; **Rate of fire (cyclic)** 500–575 rpm; **Rate of fire (practical)** 120 rpm; **Rate of fire (single shot)** 40 rpm; **Maximum effective range** 800 m.

*In an emergency the 20-round magazine of the L1A1 Rifle can be used.

The L4A4 machine gun is one of those weapons not normally used operationally by the RAF Regiment but it is still widely used for station

The L7A2 General Purpose Machine-Gun seen here mounted on a buffered tripod for use as a heavy machine-gun—the butt has been removed and the indirect-fire sight is fitted but the weapon is not loaded.

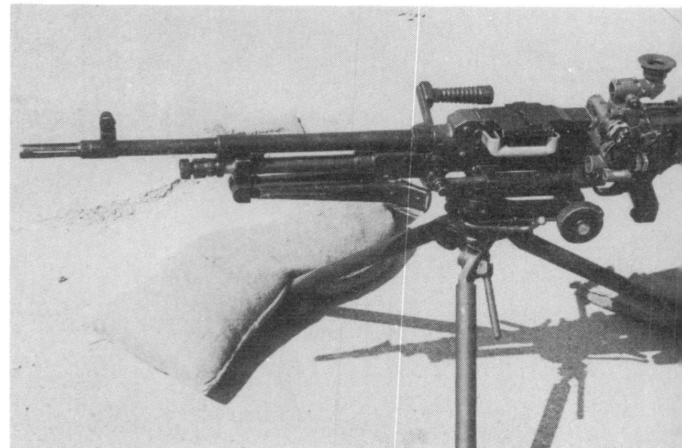

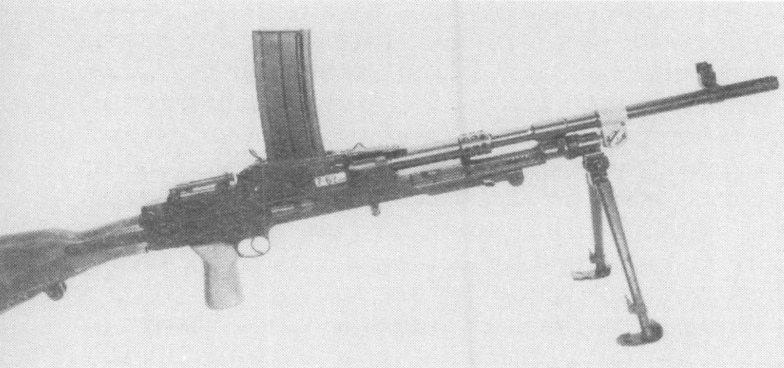

The 7.62 mm L4A4 machine gun, used throughout the RAF for local and other defence purposes.

defence and other such duties. The L4A4 is in fact the old Bren Gun updated to accommodate the 7.62 mm × 51 NATO cartridge. Compared to the old WW2 Bren Gun the L4A4 has a new barrel with a revised muzzle attachment and internal chromium plating to reduce wear (and to ensure that there is now rarely a need to change barrels in combat). Other changes are to the breech block and to the magazine (which can be replaced by the 20-round magazine of the L1A1 Rifle if required). Although its effectiveness in the role is doubtful, the L4A4 can be used to provide anti-aircraft fire from suitable mountings and it can also be used as a vehicle weapon. The L4A4 is still a good and handy machine gun which is well liked for its accuracy and ease of handling and there is, as yet, no sign of its being replaced by anything more modern.

51 mm Light Mortar L9A1

Calibre 51.25 mm; **Length of barrel overall** 0.75 m; **Outside barrel diameter** 55 mm; **Weight of barrel** 2.6 kg; **Weight of breech piece** 3.05 kg; **Weight complete (with sling)** 6.275 kg; **Rate of fire (normal)** 3 rpm for five minutes; **Rate of fire (rapid)** 8 rpm for two minutes; **Maximum range** 750 m; **Minimum range** 50 m; **Bomb weight (HE L1A1)** 1.025 kg; **Bomb weight (smoke L2A1)** 0.95 kg; **Bomb weight (Illuminating)** 0.825 kg.

The 51 mm mortar is now the only mortar used by the RAF Regiment as the 81 mm mortar went out of use when the light armoured squadrons were formed. The L9A1 mortar is exactly the same weapon as that used by the Army and is now being issued to all the light armoured squadrons. It is a versatile little weapon capable of lobbing small HE bombs for anti-personnel effects (the HE bomb body is serrated internally to produce the maximum anti-personnel effect) or firing illuminating bombs to produce enough light for other weapons such as the LAW 80 to see a target.

The L9A1 appears to be a simple weapon but is the result of a very protracted design and development programme that continued for over ten years. The weapon is now in production by Royal Ordnance at Nottingham. It has a steel barrel mounted on a base plate that incorporates a trigger mechanism and the weapon is normally carried using a sling with a separate satchel to carry the ammunition. The bomb is introduced into the barrel from the muzzel. Once the bomb has fallen to the base of the barrel, the mortar is aimed using a simple white line on the barrel for line laying and a Trilux illuminated drum sight for range. A lanyard-operated trigger mechanism fires the bomb. For use at short ranges an ingenious barrel insert is available. This allows the bomb's propellant gases to disperse within the barrel thus producing a lower pressure that lobs the bombs to a range as short as 50 metres. When not in use, the insert is carried under the muzzle cap inside the barrel.

The ammunition satchels each hold six bombs, individually cased in a waterproof tube. Available are HE, smoke and illuminating bombs.

LAW 80

Projectile calibre 94 mm; **Launcher length, extended** 1.5 m approx; **Launcher length, closed** 1 m approx; **Weight overall** 9.5 kg; **Weight of projectile** 4 kg; **Maximum range** 500 m; **Combat range** up to 300 m.

When LAW 80 is issued to the RAF Regiment during mid-1987 it will be as part of a massive issue programme that will see the weapon in use not only by the Regiment but by all the various branches of the Army and also the Royal Marines. LAW 80 is a very important anti-tank weapon for the British armed forces for it will provide every man with a means of defeating even the heaviest enemy armour.

The main components of LAW 80 showing the 94mm rocket, the extended launching tube and the spotting rifle underneath.

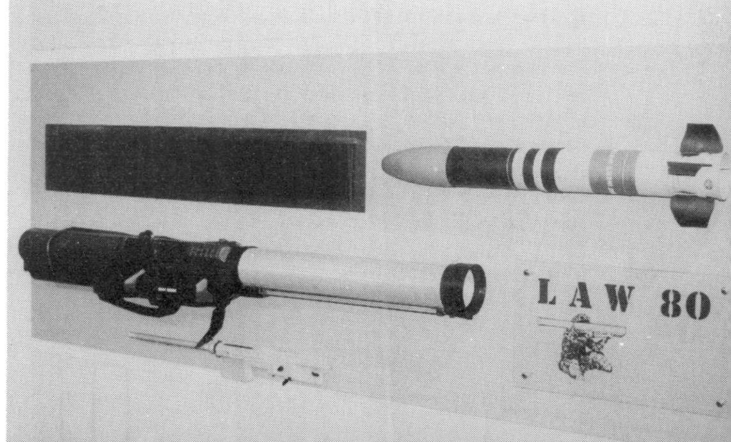

LAW 80 is a rocket-propelled anti-tank weapon that derives its name from Light Anti-armour Weapon 80. It has a 94 mm projectile warhead based on the high explosive anti-tank (HEAT) principle using a shaped warhead. LAW 80 will be issued as a normal piece of ammunition, albeit a bulky and heavy one for the average user, with the ends covered by bulky caps. Construction is basically from glass-reinforced plastic (grp) and there is a carrying handle that also acts as the firing grip.

To use LAW 80 the firer first removes the end covers. The telescopic tube is then extended and the firer takes aim through a small x1 optical sight. Once the target is in the sight, aiming can be confirmed by using an integral spotting rifle contained within the weapon.This spotting rifle is sealed, as is the rest of the weapon, and is provided with six rounds that produce a flash when they hit a hard target. Once the spotting flash confirms the target is within range and the sights are on target the main projectile is fired. It uses a short-burn rocket that is consumed within the length of the tube. If the weapon is not fired it can be folded again for re-use later. If it is fired the tube can be discarded. The projectile warhead is stated to be capable of penetrating the armour of the latest Soviet tanks, including the T-72.

When the first LAW 80s are issued to the RAF Regiment, their anti-armour potential will be considerably increased. Although no scale of issue has yet been announced it seems very likely that every RAF Regiment vehicle will carry at least one LAW 80 and in the fully operational vehicles this may well be increased.

Rapier

Weight at launch 42.6 kg; **Length of missile** 2.235 m; **Body diameter** 0.133 m; **Wing span** 0.381 m; **Maximum range** 6,800 m; **Maximum operational height** 3,000 m; **Maximum speed** Mach 2 plus; **Fire unit weight** 1,227 kg; **Fire unit length** 4.064 m; **Fire unit height** 2.134 m; **Fire unit width** 1.778 m; **Radar weight** 1,186 kg; **Radar length** 4.14 m; **Radar height (In action)** 3.378 m; **Radar height (travelling)** 2.032 m; **Radar width** 1.753 m; **Optical tracker weight** 119 kg; **Optical tracker height** 1.549 m; **Tripod diameter** 1.828 m; **Generator weight** 243 kg; **Generator length** 0.991 m; **Generator height** 0.914 m; **Generator width** 0.832 m.

The first Rapier units were issued to the RAF Regiment in 1971 and since then the missile has become the standard equipment of the Regiment's low level air defence (LLAD) squadrons. It has proved to be a highly successful ground-to-air missile and was 'combat proven' by the Army during the Falkland Islands campaign of 1982. That campaign proved to be invaluable as an operational test for Rapier and all manner of problems that would have otherwise arisen revealed themselves for public scrutiny. For all that, Rapier was responsible for some aircraft 'kills' and the opposition learned to keep away from areas where Rapiers were based.

Rapier is a towed air defence system based on either optical or automatic radar tracking. In the optical tracking mode, once the Rapier fire post has been set up (which usually takes about 15 minutes or more), a radar in the top of the fire post starts a 360 degree scan out to about 12 kilometres. Any approaching target is automatically given an IFF query signal and if the result is hostile the tracking unit operator is alerted to begin an optical search. The radar continues to track the target as well so that the firer has a choice of either an optical or an automatic launch sequence. With the optical launch the firer tracks the target and, after firing, uses the optical head and a small joystick to control the missile. On automatic, the radar goes through the guidance sequence with no further manual input. To assist in poor visibility or night engagements the Rapier fire unit can be augmented by a Blindfire (DN181) radar.

Operational experience has shown that the Rapier is rather prone to transit damage and to maintain the equipments in the field a large number of 'black boxes' have to be kept ready to

Right *The Rapier DN 181 Blindfire radar with an optical tracker in the background.*

Below *The complete Rapier surface-to-air missile system laid out for inspection with (foreground) the DN 181 Blindfire radar, (centre) the optical tracker and (rear) the fire unit.*

hand for possible use. The interior of the Rapier fire unit is a jungle of gyros, optical gadgetry and circuits and, once replaced, the entire fire post takes time to settle down and 'run-in' before maximum performance can be expected. The current generator has proved to be a considerable source of troubles and appears to be due for replacement as does the entire guidance system (which is scheduled to be considerably up-dated by micro-electronics and eventually the use of a laser-guidance system). For all this, Rapier is still an extremely accurate defence system. It has been sold widely overseas and has proved to be generally reliable. Certainly the Regiment has a considerable spares and maintenance back-up within each squadron. Based on 4-tonne trucks, there are two extensively-equipped workshops plus more equipment carried in trailers.

Each fire post is towed into action by two 1-tonne Land Rovers and a further ¾-tonne Land Rover. The first 1-tonne truck tows the basic fire unit and carries the optical tracker, three men and four missiles. The second 1-tonne truck tows the radar and carries two men and four more missiles. The ¾-tonne Land Rover carries another two men, all the stores and more missiles in a special trailer (the FV2412). Once on site, the fire unit and tracker are set up, plus the Blindfire radar if required, four missiles are loaded on to the fire unit, all the cables are connected, the generator is started and the various check procedures are gone through.

Once ready, the Rapier fire post can cover an area of sky about 100 square kilometres and up to a height of 3,000 metres. As each LLAD squadron has eight fire posts a great deal of sky can be covered, enabling each squadron to deploy away from its base, ready to defend against enemy aircraft using stand-off weapons or aircraft about to commence an attack run. Each squadron has its own supply network for extra missiles and spare parts but once established at field sites they have to operate virtually independently. As used by the Regiment, Rapier has virtually no overhead cover against attack and as each fire post covers a minimum 30 metres' radius, local defence can be a problem. In some cases extra local defence will be provided by detachments from the light armoured squadron but normally each LLAD squadron has to look after itself. They are all equipped and trained to operate under NBC conditions.

The newly-formed 6 Wing squadrons for the defence of United Kingdom US Air Force bases are established exactly the same as existing LLAD squadrons and will operate along the same lines.

FV101 Scorpion

Armament 1 × 76 mm L23A1 gun; 1 × 7.62 mm L43A1 machine-gun; 2 × 3-or 4-barrel smoke dischargers; **Crew** 3; **Weight in action** 7,938 kg; **Length overall** 4.788 m; **Length of hull** 4.572 m; **Height** 2.102 m; **Width (overall)** 2.235 m; **Width (over tracks)** 2.134 m; **Track width** 0.432 m; **Ground clearance (approx)** 0.356 m; **Maximum road speed** 80.5 km/h; **Range (roads)** 644 km; **Engine type** Jaguar J60 No 1 Mark 100B; **Engine power** 190 bhp; **Engine capacity** 4.235 litres; **Fuel capacity** 423 litres; **Ammunition capacity** 76 mm—40 rounds, 7.62 mm—3,000 rounds; **Main armament elevation** −10° to +35°; **Main armament traverse** 360°.

The RAF Regiment acquires much of its equipment direct through Army sources and thus takes on many weapons and vehicles that are designed primarily for Army use. The Scorpion is a case in point, for the RAF Regiment's Scorpions differ in few ways from their Army equivalents. The Army intended the Scorpion as a light reconnaissance vehicle, for which it is ideally suited, but the Regiment uses it as a light tank although there are now few light tanks left in service anywhere. In this role, the Scorpion's 76 mm gun is used for the direct

Above *RAF Regiment Scorpion.*

Left *An RAF Regiment Scorpion guarding a Harrier hide with its 76 mm main gun.*

Below left *A Spartan APC of No 1 Squadron, RAF Regiment, on exercises in Germany.*

Below *Each RAF Regiment Light Armoured Squadron has a Sultan armoured command vehicle which acts as its headquarters vehicle—it can be recognised by the raised roof which is higher than that of the Spartan.*

fire support of the Combat Flights of the Light Armoured Squadrons. The L23A1 is a good gun that fires a useful range of ammunition, but its efficiency against main battle tanks is at best doubtful. Against the light reconnaissance vehicles and armoured personnel carriers it is likely to encounter it would be far more successful.

The Scorpion was the first of a line of vehicles intended for general Army use. It is light, fast, very nippy across country and easy to conceal. Its crew comprises a driver, commander and a gunner. The driver is on the left next to the Jaguar 4.2-litre engine while the commander and gunner are in the turret. The turret houses the L23A1 gun which can fire HE, HESH and smoke. The usual anti-armour round is HESH, the projectile of which weighs 5.39 kg with a maximum direct range of 2,200 metres. Ranging is assisted by user tracer fired from the co-axial L43A1 machine-gun, a derivative of the L7A2 GPMG, but this system is scheduled to be replaced by a laser rangefinder. The main gun can also fire illuminating projectiles to light up targets at night and Canister may be used to break up infantry squads at very short ranges (about 100 metres).

Each Light Armoured Squadron has six Scorpions. Normally they would operate in ones or twos as part of a support team for the Spartans.

FV103 Spartan

Armament 1 × 7.62 mm L37A1 machine-gun; 2 × 4-barrel smoke dischargers; **Crew** 2 or 3 + 4 or 5; **Weight in action** 8,172 kg; **Length overall** 4.93 m; **Height** 2.26 m; **Width (overall)** 2.242 m; **Width (over tracks)** 2.134 m; **Track width** 0.432 m; **Ground clearance (approx)** 0.356 m; **Maximum road speed** 80.5 km/h; **Range (roads)** 483 km; **Engine type** Jaguar J60 No 1 Mark 100B; **Engine power** 190 bhp; **Engine capacity** 4.235 litres; **Fuel capacity** 386 litres; **Ammunition capacity** 7.62 mm—3,000 rounds.

The Spartan is the RAF Regiment's armoured personnel carrier (APC) and forms the backbone of the Light Armoured Squadrons. Each Spartan can carry four or five fully armed men ready to act as infantry, while the driver and commander may stay with the vehicle—on occasion a further signaller or other man may also stay with the vehicle. The Spartan is really a lightly-armoured box on tracks and there is no provision for the men to fight from inside the vehicle. Only the commander is equipped with a 7.62 mm L37A1 machine-gun on his cupola; this machine-gun can be aimed and fired with all the hatches closed, either for local defence or extra fire support in an infantry attack.

The Spartan has many components in common with the Scorpion, including the engine, suspension and controls. This considerably assists maintenance and logistic support. The layout at the front is much the same as on the Scorpion as the driver sits to the left of the Jaguar engine. Behind him is the commander's cupola which is well provided with vision blocks and the machine-gun mounting. To the right of the cupola is a second but smaller roof hatch, and there is a much larger roof hatch to the rear, over the main personnel compartment. Inside this compartment is seating for the main squad plus racks and stowage for their kit and pots and pans. The interior is rather crowded and access is via a door in the rear of the main hull.

Each Combat Flight has five Spartans so there are 15 in each light armoured squadron.

FV105 Sultan

Armament 1 × 7.62 mm L7A2 machine-gun; 2 × 4-barrel smoke dischargers; **Crew** 5 or 6; **Weight in action** 8,664 kg; **Length overall** 4.8 m; **Height overall** 2.559 m; **Height (top of hull)** 2.026 m; **Width overall** 2.242 m; **Width (over tracks)** 2.134 m; **Track width** 0.432 m; **Ground clearance (approx)** 0.356 m; **Penthouse length** 2.591 m; **Penthouse height** 2.235 m; **Penthouse width** 2.134 m; **Maximum road speed** 72.5 km/h; **Range (roads)** 483 km; **Engine type** Jaguar J60 No 1 Mark 100B; **Engine power** 190 bhp; **Engine capacity** 4.235 litres; **Fuel capacity** 395 litres; **Ammunition capacity** 7.62 mm—2,000 rounds.

The Sultan is virtually a Spartan with a heightened roof to improve internal capacity for the armoured command vehicle (ACV) role. Sultan has to carry the bulk of the Light Armoured Squadron headquarters staff, including the Commanding Officer, and is thus well equipped with such items as extra radios, map boards, planning boards and all the other paraphernalia associated with the command role. The Sultan interior is thus rather crowded and when possible some of these functions and personnel are moved out of the vehicle under the cover of a penthouse awning that is usually carried on the Sultan's front hull. This not only gives everyone more room but provides some accommodation for the people who have to come and go from any headquarters. The extra internal compartment space is partially taken up by air conditioning but there is room for the command staff to carry all their kit and paperwork in racks and some stowage spaces, and room has to be found for personal weapons and the 7.62 mm L7A2 GPMG used for local defence—there is a pintle on the roof for this.

FV101 Scorpion
1:76 scale

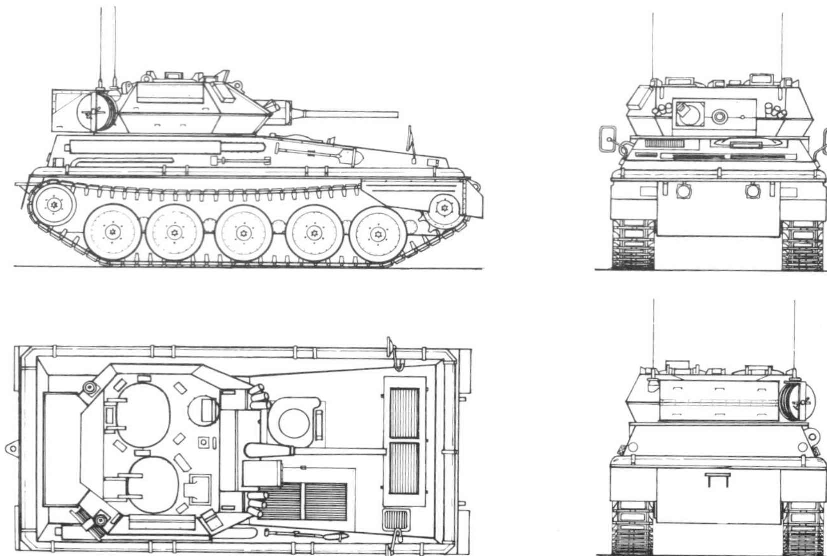

FV103 Spartan
1:76 scale

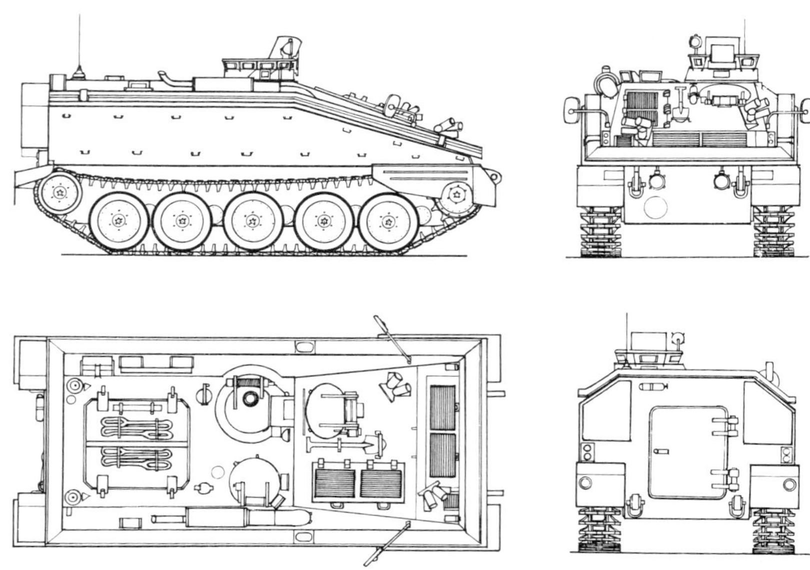

FV105 Sultan
1:76 scale

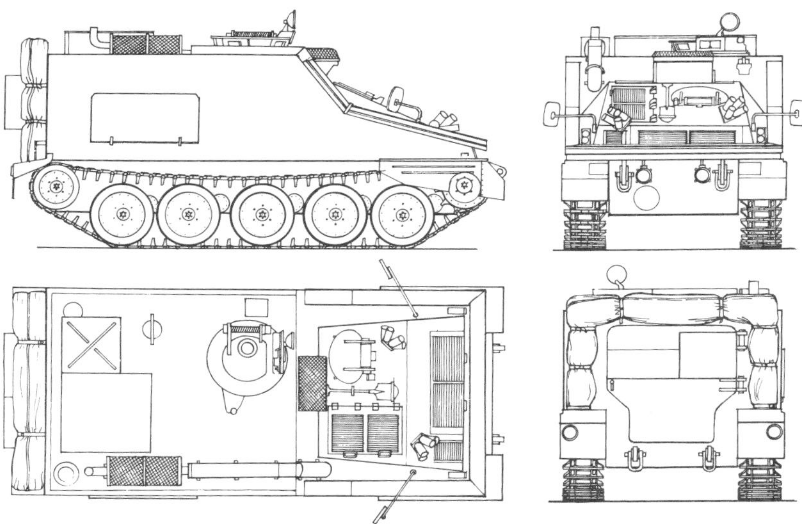

FV106 Samson
1:76 scale

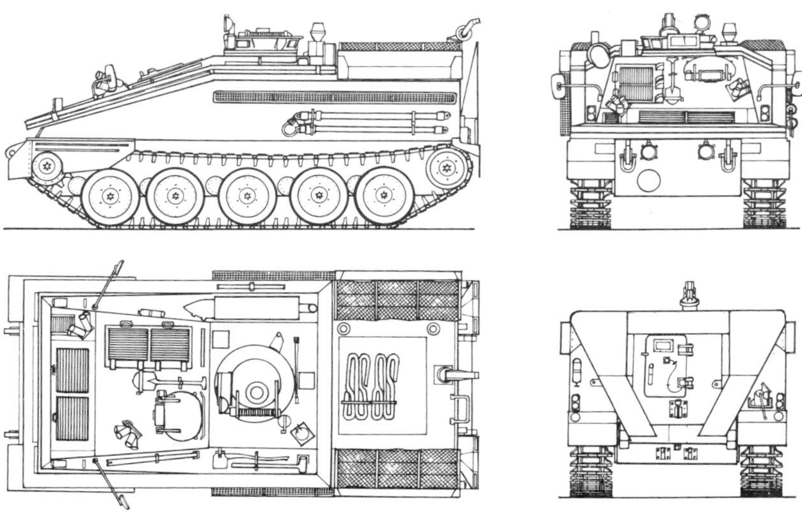

FV106 Samson

Armament 1 × 7.62 mm L7A2 machine-gun; 2 × 4-barrel smoke dischargers; **Crew** 3 or 4; **Weight in action** 8,738 kg; **Length overall** 5.004 m; **Length of hull** 4.788 m; **Height overall** 2.254 m; **Height (top of hull)** 1.718 m; **Width overall** 2.43 m; **Width (over tracks)** 2.134 m; **Track width** 0.432 m; **Ground clearance (approx)** 0.356 m; **Maximum road speed** 72.5 km/h; **Range (roads)** 438 km; **Engine type** Jaguar J60 No 1 Mark 100B; **Engine power** 190 bhp; **Engine capacity** 4.235 litres; **Fuel capacity** 404.5 litres; **Ammunition capacity** 7.62 mm—2,000 rounds.

At first sight Samson appears to be a Spartan but a closer examination will reveal the large spades on

Above right *Rear view of an RAF Regiment Light Armoured Squadron Samson recovery vehicle.*

Right *Side view of Samson showing side stowage.*

Below *Members of the RAF Regiment dismounted from their Spartan APC (in the background) and carrying (left) a L7A2 GPMG and (right) a L1A1 7.62 mm rifle.*

the rear and some other less obvious differences. Samson is the armoured recovery vehicle (ARV) member of the Scorpion family and is included in the Light Armoured Squadron to provide technical assistance to keep the other vehicles in the squadron in action. For this it is equipped with a winch with a possible pull of up to 12 tons, a small jib crane, recovery equipment such as blocks and tackle, and all the various tools required for engine and vehicle repair, right down to a vice secured to the hull rear. Internally Samson is rather cramped as the winch takes up much of the space so most of the equipment is carried externally on racks and in various extra stowage bins. In the recovery role the pulling power of the winch is considerably increased by lowering the large spades at the rear and reversing the vehicle up and over them. This then provides a much more stable pulling platform for the winch, which can then pull a weight more than that of the Samson itself.

Each Light Armoured Squadron has one Samson which is the base vehicle for the squadron's Engineering Flight, directly under the control of the Headquarters Flight.

FV107 Scimitar

Armament 1 × 30 mm Rarden L21 Gun, 1 × 7.62 mm L37A1 Machine Gun and 2 × 4-barrel smoke dischargers; **Crew** 3; **Weight in action** 7,750 kg; **Length overall** 4.985 m; **Length of hull** 4.572 m; **Height** 2.096 m; **Width** (overall) 2.242 m; **Width** (over tracks) 2.134 m; **Track width** 0.432 m; **Ground clearance** (approx) 0.356 m; **Maximum road speed** 80.5 km/h; **Range** (roads) 644 km; **Engine type** Jaguar J60 No 1 Mk 100B; **Engine power** 190 bhp; **Engine capacity** 4.235 litres; **Fuel capacity** 423 litres; **Ammunition capacity** 30 mm–165 rounds, 7.62 mm–3,000 rounds; **Main armament elevation** −10° to +35°; **Main armament traverse** 360°.

The FV107 Scimitar is not used by the RAF Regiment but by personnel assigned to Explosive Ordnance Disposal (EOD) duties. In the aftermath of an air attack on an air base it is virtually certain that the surface of the airfield and its approaches will be left littered with time-fuzed bomblets and unexploded bombs. The task of the EOD personnel is to reconnoitre the airfield, assess damage and work out clearance priorities, in co-operation with any Royal Engineer airfield damage repair squadrons that are on the station. EOD clearance on RAF property is a job for RAF personnel and that is where the Scimitars come in.

The Scimitars enable the EOD personnel to at least move around the airfield in relative safety but that is not their main task. Their main purpose is to use their 30 mm Rarden cannon to crack open the cases of unexploded bombs using armour-

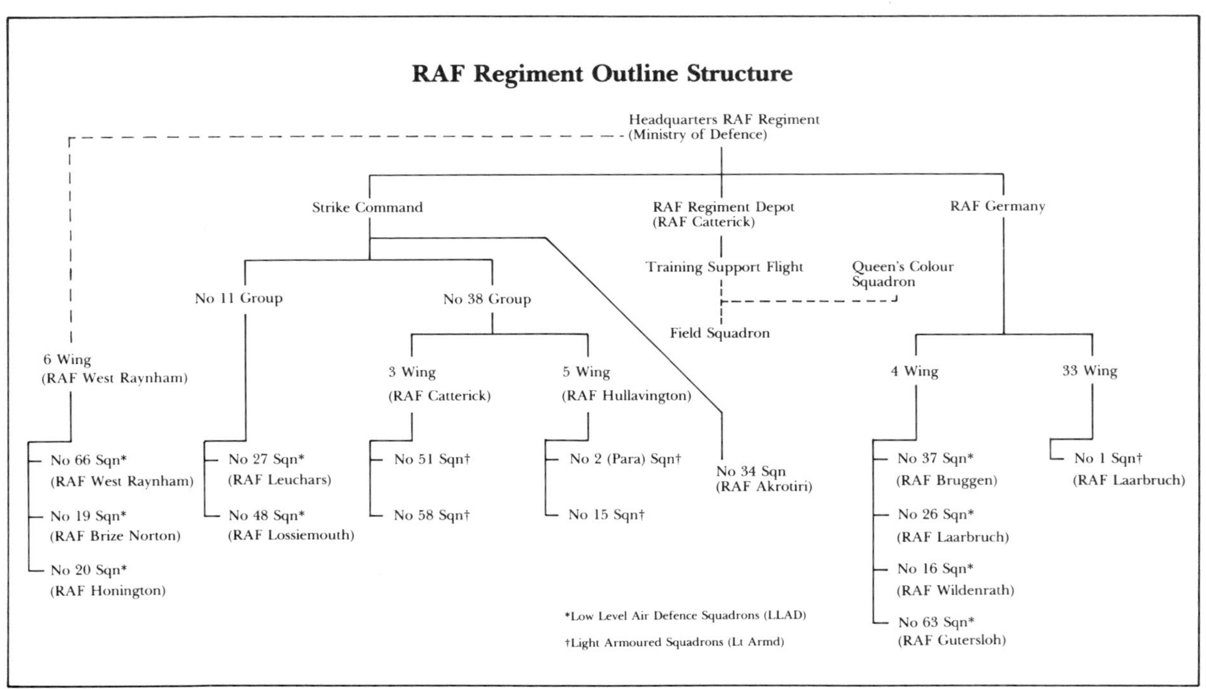

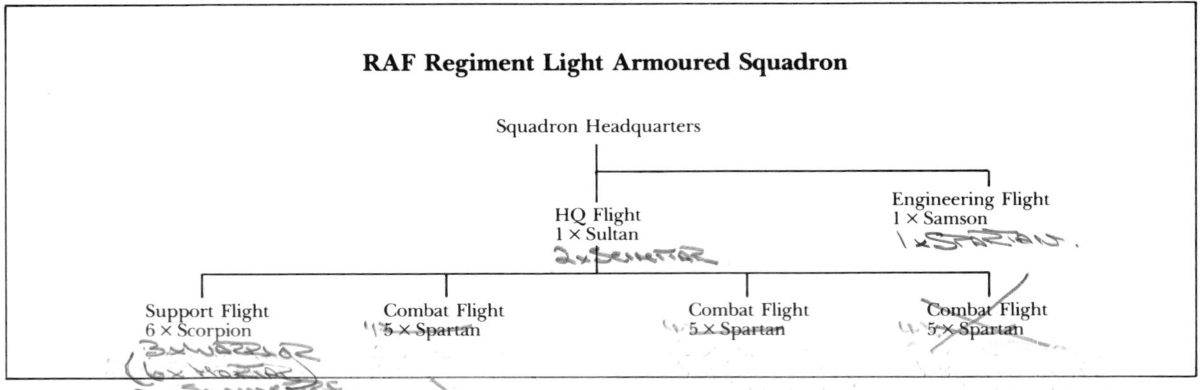

piercing ammunition and set fire to the contents with a tracer—the explosive contents of the bomb can then burn harmlessly. This sounds an unsafe thing to do but if the bomb should detonate in the process the EOD personnel will be relatively safe as they will be some distance away and within the protection of the Scimitar's armour. The Rarden cannon could also be used to detonate bomblets in critical positions. These measures are carried out purely to get an airfield back into commission after an attack. If time and other circumstances allowed, more conventional clearance measures would be used.

The FV107 Scimitar used by the RAF is exactly the same as the vehicles used for reconnaissance by the Army, although a few RAF modifications might be introduced to suit the airfield environment. The vehicle is essentially the same as the FV101 Scorpion with the 30 mm Rarden cannon taking the place of the Scorpion's 76 mm gun. It is anticipated that only one Scimitar will be issued to an airfield that is high on the attack-expected priority list, ie, RAF Germany and some attack/strike bases in the United Kingdom.

Women in the RAF

When the Royal Air Force was formed on April 1 1918, women were already an integral element in the personnel of the Service. Before 1920 no less than 32,000 women served in the ranks in all manner of trades from mechanics to drivers. Alongside them were the members of the Royal Air Force Nursing Service. Today, the nurses serve as part of Princess Mary's Royal Air Force Nursing Service (PMRAFNS) and the mechanics as part of the Women's Royal Air Force (WRAF). This chapter will take a short look at their roles and present-day organisation within the Royal Air Force.

Members of the WRAF and PMRAFNS today have completely equal status with the men within the Service. They have equal career opportunities, they train alongside the men and they get their full share of promotions, assignments and opportunities. The only restriction placed upon their duties is that they would not undertake any combatant duties and this is reflected in the fact that only very basic weapon training, if any, is provided other than small-bore rifle shooting. Having said this, women are nevertheless expected to be able to conduct themselves sensibly in combat situations and for their own safety take part in full NBC defence exercises. Thus are the boundaries between combatant duties and defensive measures becoming increasingly blurred.

Members of the womens' services can expect to spend a fair portion of their time on overseas postings, although some trades will be restricted to the United Kingdom. At the present time women are serving in Gibraltar, Cyprus, Hong Kong, West Germany, Holland and Belgium. One lucky officer is stationed in Washington, DC.

Women's Royal Air Force

The starting age for joining the Women's Royal Air Force is 17 for airwomen and 18 for officers. The officers start their service life at the Initial Officer Training wing of the Royal Air Force College at RAF Cranwell. They train alongside their male colleagues and are part and parcel of their entry, undertaking all sections and tasks on the course. From there they then pass out from the course together with their newly awarded commissions to their specialist training. Women officers have open to them a number of possible career paths in various specialities. Two of these come under the General Duties (Ground) Branch. One of these is Aircraft Control and the other Fighter Control. The role of women in the Photographic Interpretation Branch is well established, and their role in the Engineer Branch is now becoming an important part of that speciality. In the Engineer Branch officers can specialise in mechanical or electrical engineering and can thus find themselves part of the Engineering Wing on any station.

In the Supply Branch, women serve as an integral part of the Royal Air Force's logistic structure. In the Administrative Branch they have the choice of various specialisations. They can specialise in the secretarial skills which might include personnel management, service accounting and unit administrative organisation, recruit and specialist training, recruiting, and even intelligence and cryptography. Also part of the Administrative Branch are education, catering and physical education. Small numbers of professionally qualified women are also employed as medical and dental officers.

Airwomen commence their Service careers at the Royal Air Force School of Recruit Training at RAF Swinderby. Here they pass through a 5½-week course which includes the usual 'square-bashing' and other basic Service skills and knowledge, and from there they pass to their specialist training at the usual trade schools where they are trained alongside the airmen.

The number of trades open to airwomen is wide and varied. Eagerly sought after are the places in the aircraft engineering and electronic engineering trades, but the number of places is usually limited.

Left *Air Traffic Controllers on duty at RAF Gibraltar.*

Below right *A WRAF technician working alongside her male colleagues at RAF Linton-on-Ouse.*

In the mechanical transport field airwomen can become drivers, mechanics and operators of the large fleets of vehicles used by the Royal Air Force. Air Traffic Control is another skill open to airwomen and this can entail clerical work in operations rooms and Air Traffic Control units. As part of the General Service branch, airwomen can become involved in general Station administration, personnel welfare and physical fitness training. Into this bracket comes the General Service training of recruits. In telecommunications airwomen can train as telegraph and telephone operators. They can also train as operators for the various radar and other equipments used by the Service as part of the fighter control and radar reporting systems. Airwomen can also train to maintain and service safety equipment such as flying suits, dinghies and survival equipment, and within this speciality comes the care and application of the paint finishes of aircraft.

Photography is an airwoman trade, not so much in the actual taking of the pictures, although that is a possibility, but in the care and maintenance of the aircraft cameras, the assembling of photographic mosaics, film processing, printing and copying. This may involve the operating of offset printing equipment and the filing of print libraries.

In the medical and dental fields, airwomen may train for clerical and administration work in the various hospitals and Station medical centres. The dental trades may involve some surgery duties including oral hygiene and preventive dentistry. Airwomen can also train for the clerical, secretarial and statistical fields, a general administrative support function which can include work study and computer programming. This support function is carried over to the Supply and Movements Branch where airwomen carry out all manner of tasks from clerical to the actual storing and handling of supplies.

Historically, airwomen have always been well established in the Catering Branch and still are. These days they can be responsible not only for the day-to-day catering for Stations or units but may also be involved with special diets for hospitals or training, and they may also be involved in the day-to-day domestic running of messes.

There is also a women's branch of the Royal Air Force Police and they are involved not only with the usual disciplines of the WRAF but also of all aspects of the RAF Police and their duties.

One of the most sought-after trades in the WRAF is that of Air Loadmaster. This trade involves a great deal of travel but also a great deal of responsibility, and there are relatively few places available. The job involves all aspects of loading and weight distribution of transport aircraft and on trooping flights involves the supervision of the cabin services.

Some of the above trades are carried out by what are known as local service airwomen. These airwomen are recruited by some of the larger established stations from the local populace and may even 'work from home'. They are not normally posted away from their local unit.

On all Stations, WRAF personnel have their own quarters but usually mess with their male colleagues. They do have some special facilities of their own and their accommodation is not usually as spartan as that endured by airmen at some locations, but they still have the opportunity to take part in the various adventure and recreation training courses that are held from time to time.

Princess Mary's Royal Air Force Nursing Service

The PMRAFNS has both male and female members but this section will deal primarily with the female nursing staff. A small number of qualified State Enrolled Nurses (SEN) can join the Service but most entrants join as unqualified recruits from the age of 17 onwards. After joining they pass through the recruit training school at RAF Hereford alongside their WRAF colleagues and then pass to the next stage of their basic training (men pass through the normal RAF Swinderby 'square-bashing' course). This next stage is a 2½-week course at RAF Halton and is a special safety and first aid course. From there the nurse training proper commences.

There are two nurse training hospitals in the United Kingdom. One is Princess Alexandra's Hospital, RAF Wroughton in Wiltshire, and the other the RAF Hospital, Ely, near Cambridge. In addition, every year a number of pupil nurses start their training at the RAF Hospital, Wegburg, in West Germany. Each hospital has a School of Nursing at which an initial four-week basic course is held. From then onwards the routine settles down to training on the wards followed by further classroom training. Some of the training will be carried out in civilian hospitals and other establishments. All this training can lead to the award of SEN qualifications and, at the end of training, the qualified nurse may be posted to one of the RAF hospitals or to a Station medical centre.

Once SEN Training is complete there is still the opportunity to train for further qualifications such as a SEN (Mental) certificate, the course for which is carried out at the Princess Alexandra's Hospital,

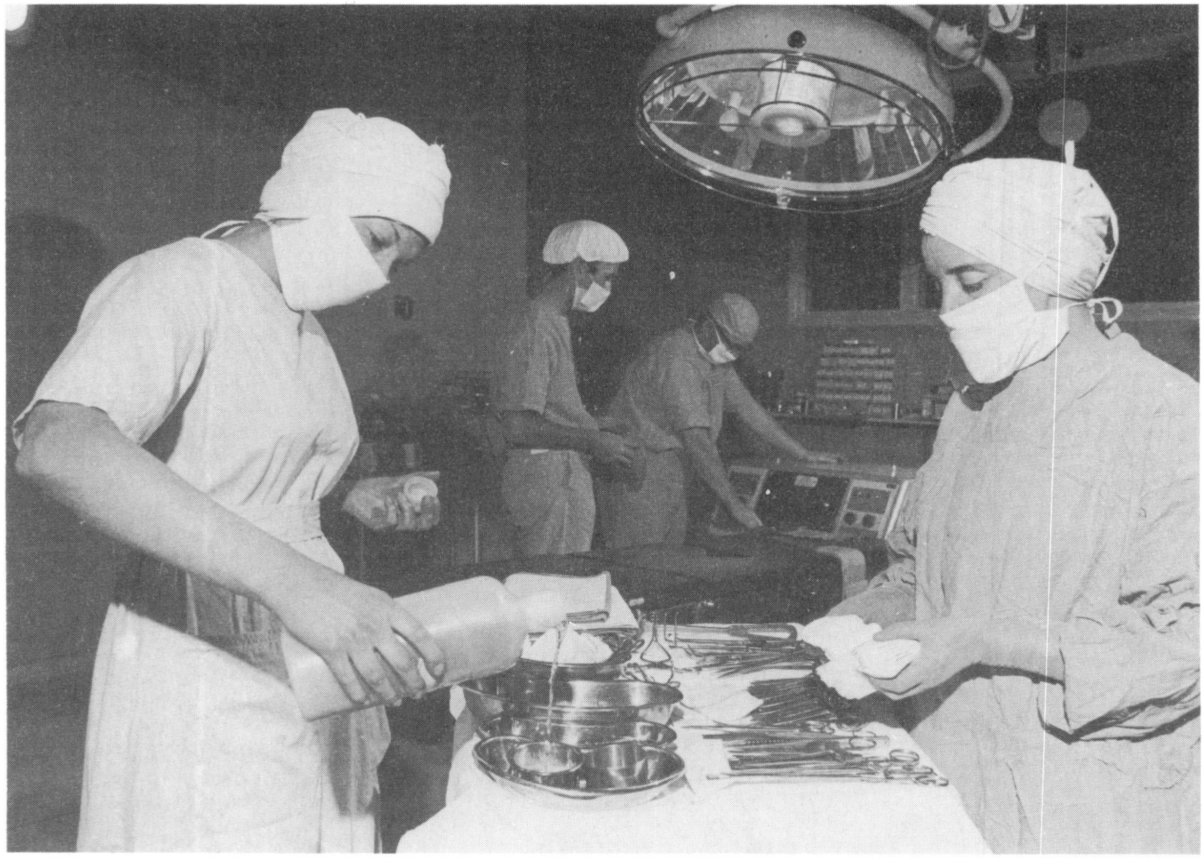

Nursing Staff at Princess Mary's Royal Air Force Nursing Service preparing for an operation.

RAF Wroughton, or in aeromedical nursing to serve as a Flight Nursing Attendant on one of the many aeromedical flights carried out by No 1 Group. The Aeromedical Unit is based at RAF Brize Norton.

Royal Auxiliary Air Force

Some 140 airwomen serve in the Royal Auxiliary Air Force at the Maritime Headquarters Units of No 18 Group. There are three of these units at RAF Northwood, RAF Pitreavie and RAF Mount Batten.

The Royal Auxiliary Air Force and Royal Auxiliary Air Force Regiment

The Royal Auxiliary Air Force had a fine record during World War 2 but in the post-war years it was gradually phased out until it became a virtual dead letter. The only units bearing the name were a small unit who are still part of the Joint Services Headquarters at Northwood and a small band of airmen and airwomen who serve in the Maritime Headquarters Units of No 18 Group. These cadres kept the name of the Royal Auxiliary Air Force (RAuxAF) in being for many years but things are changing again and the RAuxAF is now growing in numbers once more.

There are several reasons for this renewed growth. Perhaps the most important of them is that the regular Royal Air Force's manpower levels are now maintained at the minimum possible limit and in many aspects are below that limit. While spending and other limitations dictate that it would not be possible to maintain full-time personnel to carry out many important tasks it would be very possible to use part-time personnel to carry out those duties in a time of emergency.

These duties vary from flying to local defence. At first sight the use of part-time aircrew to fly many of the advanced aircraft the RAF now uses would seem to be something of an anomaly but there are many flying roles that part-timers could undertake. There is a large pool of trained aircrew, many of them ex-RAF, flying commercial jet aircraft that are not far removed from several types of aircraft now in service—the VC 10 and Tristar immediately spring to mind. Many of those aircrew would no doubt welcome a change from the candy floss airline and other everyday traffic they have to fly, and their commercial flying routines ensure that they have plenty of rest or free time in which to undertake the odd spot of flying with the RAF and keep their hand in with Service disciplines and methods.

RAuxAF personnel are not all aircrew. There are plans to recruit ground personnel to undertake a number of duties that will free permanent personnel to undertake more important duties elsewhere. These duties include such tasks as plotting, communication staff, clerical personnel and so forth and may eventually include Explosive Ordnance Disposal (EOD) personnel.

There are plans to raise the number of personnel in the RAuxAF to around 5,000 although this figure may not be reached for some time. There are some active auxiliary units already in being. One of them is 4624 Squadron RAuxAF based at RAF Brize Norton which acts as a Movements Squadron.

There are also the guard personnel who provide local defence for a number of bases within the United Kingdom. These units are formed by part-time members of the Royal Auxiliary Air Force Regiment (RAuxAF Regt) who come from all walks of life and include in their ranks women as well as men. In an emergency they would take over the bulk of the ground defence and guard duties at various United Kingdom bases and by so doing free full-time trained personnel to carry out their intended duties.

These ground defence Field Squadrons are equipped with Land Rovers and 4-tonne trucks for local transport and are armed up to full RAF Regiment standards with rifles, GPMGs, light mortars and some anti-tank weapons. The squadrons each have four flights; two mobile Field Flights that carry out much of the active patrolling and two Rifle Flights for more static guard duties. There is also a Headquarters Flight in which the women volunteers serve.

Squadrons formed so far include the following:

No 2503 (County of Lincoln) Field Squadron, RAuxAF Regt (V), RAF Scampton
No 2620 (County of Norfolk) Field Squadron, RAuxAF Regt (V), RAF Marham
No 2622 (Highland) Field Squadron, RAuxAF Regt (V), RAF Lossiemouth
No 2623 (East Anglian) Field Squadron, RAuxAF

An Oerlikon twin 35mm GDF-002 automatic anti-aircraft gun emplaced ready for firing.

Regt (V), RAF Honington
No 2624 (County of Oxford) Field Squadron, RAuxAF Regt (V), RAF Brize Norton
No 2625 (County of Cornwall) Field Squadron, RAuxAF Regt (V), RAF St Mawgan
No 2729 (City of Lincoln) Squadron, RAuxAF Regt (V), RAF Waddington

The latter squadron is of particular interest as it has rather more than usual guard duties. It is an air defence squadron equipped with anti-aircraft guns captured from the Argentinians during the Falkland Islands campaign of 1982. So many guns were captured, to say nothing of the associated Skyguard fire control radars and 35 mm ammunition, that the weapons have been adopted as airfield defence guns and issued to the RAuxAF Regt. Towed by Bedford TM 4-4 trucks these weapons are operationally deployed not only at RAF Waddington itself but over the surrounding area. It seems very likely that a second anti-aircraft gun squadron will be formed as there are still a number of ex-Argentinian guns to hand, but this would mean the purchase of more Contraves Skyguard radars.

The guns involved are Oerlikon twin-barrelled 35 mm GDF-002 automatic guns, originally produced in Switzerland and refurbished after their capture by the British Manufacturing and Research Company at Grantham. They are somewhat large and heavy weapons (weight when travelling fully equipped is 6,700 kg) but each barrel has a cyclic rate of fire of 550 rounds a minute and ammunition is fed into the weapon from containers holding 56 rounds each. The maximum effective range of each weapon is about 4,000 metres, with fire control carried out by Contraves Skyguard radars that acquire and track prospective targets. The ammunition fired is of the fixed-round type and the muzzle velocity is 1,175 metres a second. Different types of projectile can be fired, usually a variety of high explosives with incendiary elements or delayed action fuzes—the average projectile weight is around 0.55 kg and a complete round weighs around 1.58 kg.

It is anticipated that more ground defence field squadrons will be formed by the RAuxAF Regt. The main problem for such squadrons is that they are called upon to defend airfields that are often in remote and low-populated areas where prospective recruits are somewhat thin on the ground. For example it took the RAF Lossiemouth squadron three years to come up to full strength. This is not the case everywhere and in many cases recruiting is no real problem.

The Royal Observer Corps

Although strictly speaking the Royal Observer Corps (ROC) is no longer an integral part of the Royal Air Force, the ties with the Service remain strong. The Commandant of the ROC is a serving Royal Air Force officer and Royal Air Force uniforms are worn, with some changes of insignia such as the cap badge, black beret and midnight blue rank braid on the officers' uniform. The ROC is now the field force of the United Kingdom Warning and Monitoring Organisation, which is run by the Home Office. As the field force of the UKWMO, the ROC has functions related to the threat of nuclear warfare. The Corps is responsible for reporting the actual explosion of nuclear devices and provides data that can be used to estimate their exact location and power. It forms part of the organisation that provides warnings to the public to take cover in the period just before an attack and carries out the subsequent monitoring and reporting of the arrival and strength of the residual effects of a nuclear explosion, ie, the 'fall out'. From this monitoring, warnings can be provided for the general public and Service organisations.

This grim-sounding task is one that the ROC has assumed with its usual quiet and thorough efficiency and enthusiasm. The Corps has been in existence since 1925 and throughout that time it has given yeoman service to the nation from the early days of aircraft reporting down to today's patient routines. The Corps is a volunteer organisation with its own command structure of spare-time officers and a small cadre of wholetime officers. The enthusiasm generated for the task is one that has to be experienced to be fully appreciated.

In outlining the work and role of the ROC it is perhaps best to start from the 'nerve ends' of the organisation and work inwards.

The front line of the ROC can be described as the 870 monitoring posts spread throughout the United Kingdom at intervals of 16 to 20 kilometres or so. Each of the monitoring posts has a complement of ten volunteer Observers with a Chief Observer to administer the post and its premises. To back him up there is a Leading Observer who usually handles the training side. The post itself is an underground chamber that contains all the necessary instruments and communications equipment along with the supplies to allow the operational crew of three to survive underground for two weeks. Using the instruments provided, the crew can monitor and report on all the effects of a nuclear attack. Communications to higher levels are via dedicated land lines and radio relays. For administrative and reporting purposes the posts are grouped in 'clusters' of three or four posts.

The 870 monitoring posts report their data to 25 Sector and Group Controls, again housed in premises usually set below ground, protected by layers of concrete and earth. Inside these controls the data from the monitoring posts are collated and assessed before being passed on to 'customers'. Each Control is responsible for the clusters in its local area who report to it and in turn reports to a Sector Control which is responsible for four Group Controls. The locations of the Sector Controls and their Group Controls are as follows:

Metropolitan Sector Control, Horsham: Maidstone Group Control; Oxford Group Control; Colchester Group Control; Winchester Group Control.

Southern Sector Control, Bristol: Yeovil Group Control; Exeter Group Control; South Wales Group Control; Shrewsbury Group Control.

Midland Sector Control, Lincoln: Norwich Group Control; Bedford Group Control; Coventry Group Control; York Group Control.

Western Sector Control, Preston: North Wales Group Control; Carlisle Group Control; Durham Group Control; Belfast Group Control.

Caledonian Sector Control, Dundee: Edinburgh Group Control; Ayr Group Control; Aberdeen Group Control; Inverness Group Control.

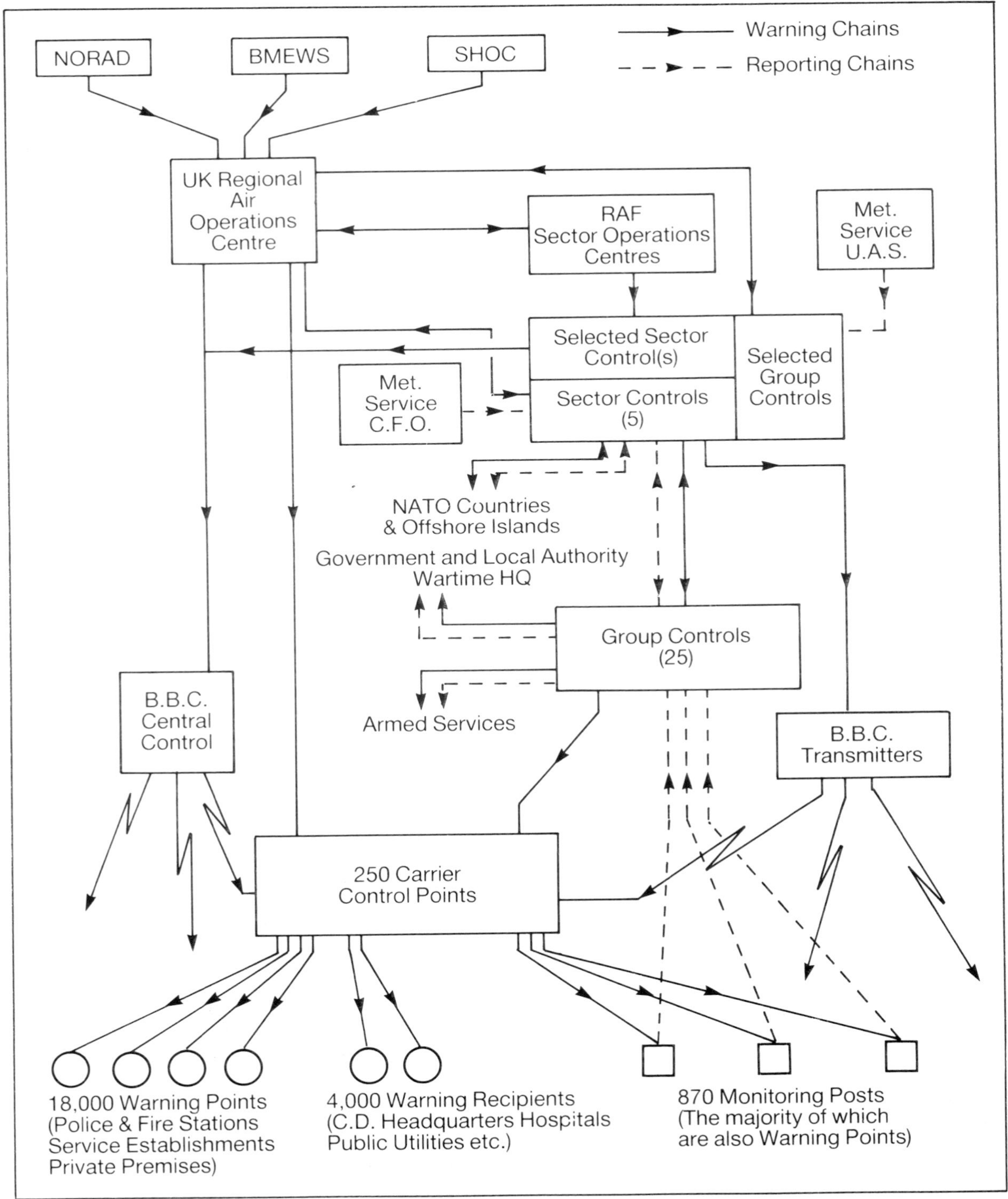

Warning Chains
Reporting Chains
NORAD
BMEWS
SHOC
UK Regional Air Operations Centre
RAF Sector Operations Centres
Met. Service U.A.S.
Selected Sector Control(s)
Sector Controls (5)
Selected Group Controls
Met. Service C.F.O.
NATO Countries & Offshore Islands
Government and Local Authority Wartime HQ
Group Controls (25)
Armed Services
B.B.C. Central Control
B.B.C. Transmitters
250 Carrier Control Points
18,000 Warning Points (Police & Fire Stations Service Establishments Private Premises)
4,000 Warning Recipients (C.D. Headquarters Hospitals Public Utilities etc.)
870 Monitoring Posts (The majority of which are also Warning Points)

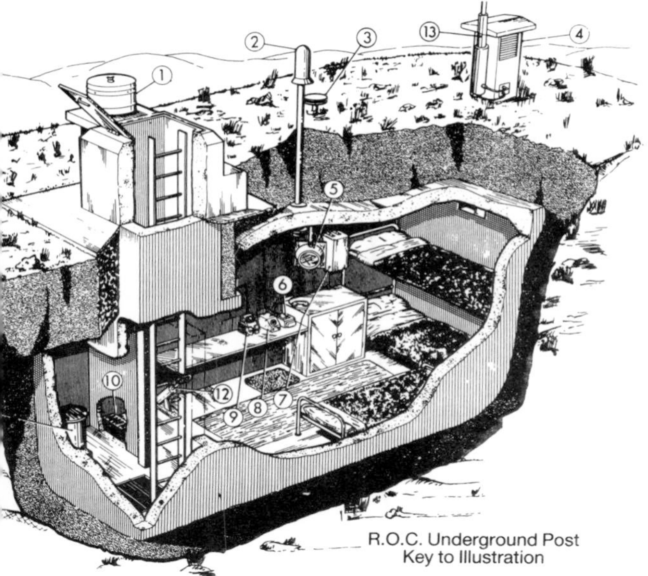

R.O.C. Underground Post
Key to Illustration

1. Ground Zero Indicator
2. Survey Meter Sensing Head
3. Bomb Power Indicator Sensing Head
4. Air Vent
5. Bomb Power Indicator
6. Fixed Survey Meter
7. Stand-By Radio Set
8. Tele-talk Set
9. Carrier Receiver
10. 12 Volt Battery
11. Chemical Closet
12. Pump for Pneumatic Aerial
13. Pneumatic Aerial

Each UKWMO Control is located at an ROC Group Headquarters which manages and trains the spare time members of the ROC.

The Controls would be very busy places during a nuclear attack as from them emanates almost all the various types of warnings that the public and the Armed Services and public authorities would require. Using a complex and involved communication network (shown in the nearby flow chart), the Sector Controls can issue warnings of attack direct to the BBC for broadcasting on all radio and television channels. The Controls can also provide warnings to what are known as Carrier Control Points, locations from which warnings of attack and the approach of fallout can be given to the local populace (these locations may range from local police stations to pubs).

Within this warning system the primary information and subsequent monitoring comes from the personnel of the Royal Observer Corps working in UKWMO monitoring posts and Controls. Warnings of attack on the United Kingdom may come from several points but the confirmation that a nuclear attack has taken place comes from the UKWMO. To back up this confirmation further instruments known as 'AWDREY' are placed at various locations throughout the United Kingdom, always at Controls, and these have sufficient range to analyse the peculiar nuclear explosion radiation side-effects anywhere over the country and can provide an almost immediate data feed-out to give the necessary confirmation. The warning chain includes the monitoring posts which can provide warning of attack using the familiar sirens and the approach of fallout using maroons.

This book is no place to go into all the various intricacies of the instruments and operating procedures used. At present the ROC/UKWMO is being equipped with new radiation instruments, and communications at all levels are constantly being revised and improved. Recent innovations have included telegraph systems and new private wires. The main point to be stressed is that ROC personnel man the formations of the United Kingdom Warning and Monitoring Organisation which obtains vital data without which the United Kingdom would be at a distinct disadvantage in the event of a nuclear attack. Thus anybody joining the ROC will be carrying out a useful and worthwhile job.

The age limits for joining are between 16 and 55 and both men and women are welcomed. Once enrolled, training is carried out locally and each Observer has to attend not less than 26 two-hourly training meetings each year and some four or five weekend exercises. Most years an annual training camp is held but attendance is voluntary, although usually oversubscribed. The annual camp is usually held at a Royal Air Force Station. A uniform is provided free and there is a system of allowances for travelling. Each year a proficiency test is held to assess training levels and standards. As can be expected, the preponderance of monitoring posts means that there are more post personnel than Group or Sector personnel, but wherever possible Observers are recruited to the unit nearest to their homes.

There is much more to the ROC than outlined above. For instance, additional special training courses are sometimes run in various Government and Service establishments and the art of aircraft recognition is still kept alive by the ROC, although at present there is no operational requirement—but there might be one day and therefore those skills have to be retained. There is a thriving social side to the Corps at every level and each year there are social meetings of all kinds.

The Headquarters of the ROC is at Bentley Priory, near Stanmore in Middlesex.

RAF aircraft and weapons

The Royal Air Force uses a very simple method of designating the aircraft put under its charge. It quite simply refers to them by a given name, eg, Victor, Tornado and so on. The only problem with this system is that it makes few allowances for the same aircraft either being equipped to carry out more than one role or being used in service with more than one equipment 'fit' or configuration. Consequently, the Royal Air Force provides each aircraft name with a capital code letter which provides an indication of the aircraft's function, eg, F, C, T, etc. A listing of these letters and their functions is provided below. Each letter is associated with a code number, eg, C1, C2, etc. In full, these should be written as C Mark 2 but in practice the 'Mark' is often dropped. These Mark numbers may refer to major alterations to the basic aircraft such as an uprated engine or change of wing shape, but many aircraft in service never alter from their original Mark number 1. Sometimes a suffix might be added to the Mark number, such as (T) or (P). These suffixes are not often used and in these instances refer to (Trainer) and (Probe) with the latter denoting the addition of an in-flight refuelling probe.

AEW	Airborne Early Warning
B	Bomber
C	Cargo transport
CC	Transport fitted with VIP interior
E	Electronics
F	Fighter
FGA	Fighter Ground Attack
FGR	Fighter Ground Attack Reconnaissance
GR	Ground Attack Reconnaissance
HAR	Helicopter Air Rescue
HC	Helicopter transport
HCC	Helicopter transport with VIP interior
HT	Helicopter Trainer
K	Tanker
KC	Tanker/transport
MR	Maritime Reconnaissance
PR	Photographic Reconnaissance
R	Reconnaissance
S	Strike
T	Trainer
TT	Target Tug
U	Unmanned drone
W	Weather aircraft

Tornado GR 1 of the TWCU fitted with practice bomb panniers.

Tornado GR Mark 1 and **GR Mark 1 (T)**

Crew 2; **Span (swept)** 8.6 m; **Span (open)** 13.91 m; **Length** 16.72 m; **Height** 5.95 m; **Max take-off weight** 27,215 kg; **Max weapon load** approx 9,000 kg; **Max speed clean** Mach 2.2; **Max ferry range** 3,890 km; **Armament** 2 × 27 mm Mauser cannon, three weapon points under fuselage, four weapon points under wings; **Engines** 2 × Turbo-Union RB199-34R Mk 101.

The Tornado is a tri-national aircraft project that has both benefited and suffered from all that international aircraft development programmes entail. The benefits have come from the spreading of the development load among three highly technical nations, but the suffering has come from the seemingly inevitable cost escalations that such programmes bring in their wake. What was once supposed to be a complex but reasonably inexpensive aircraft has become a technological accomplishment costing millions of pounds sterling for an individual sample. Not all of this cost escalation has been caused by the tripartite arrangement between the United Kingdom, West Germany and Italy, for some has been caused by the financial inflation of recent years and much of it has been caused by the imposition of an almost impossible flight operations envelope on to a single aircraft and its electronics.

In simple terms the Tornado GR 1 has to be capable of penetrating the formidable air defences of the Warsaw Pact nations and field forces and attacking their vital rear areas. It must be able to do this with a wide array of weapons at any time and in all weathers. Put in that simple form the task does not sound too bad but in practice it is one that would daunt any designer. Tornado has to be able to fly to its pin-pointed target across some of the most difficult flying terrain in the world, which may vary from the wide open plains of Northern Europe that are so amenable to modern air defence ground systems, to the closely wooded mountains and valleys of south Germany and Poland. It must be further stressed that these missions will have to be flown in weather conditions that might vary from the brilliant clarity of a summer day or the clag of industrially-polluted skies to heavy snow at the dead of night. To cap it all, the need to evade the Warsaw Pact defensive systems dictates that this flying has to be done at high speeds at operational altitudes of about 50 metres or less. If all that were not enough, each mission must be virtually certain of hitting and destroying its target, no matter how small or well hidden, for in today's air warfare scenario there will probably be no time or capability for a second chance.

The need for a new type of aeroplane to cover this type of mission had been forecast long before the tri-partite agreements were formulated during the late 1960s. To design and develop the new aircraft, a consortium of companies was formed under the name of Panavia and the project was given the general name of MRCA—Multi-Role Combat Aircraft—for, in addition to the interdiction/strike role, the MRCA was to be all things to all men in that it was also to be an interceptor, a reconnaissance platform and be amenable to being used as its own conversion trainer. After a period of time this array of operational tasks was found to be too wide even for the MRCA project and the interception aspect was ruled out, only to be continued in a new and specialised form for the RAF alone as the ADV (see separate entry).

Panavia was formed from three main parent companies—British Aerospace, Messerschmitt-Bölkow-Blohm and Aeritalia. Inevitably from these three companies sprang a whole stream of contractors and sub-contractors involved with the project and the various development establishments in all three countries. The original intention was that each nation would specialise in one particular aspect of the project's development but it was not long before these aspects overlapped. What had once been intended as a single-source weapon system became fragmented into three national programmes each geared to its own national requirement. The duplication grew to the extent that each nation now has its own weapons 'fit' but this disparity should not be over-emphasised. Today the operational crews from all three nations involved all train and work together in harmony and it is only when the three air force tactical

Tornado GR 1 making for home as the evening shadows lengthen—a photo which helped earn Sergeant Brian Lawrence the title RAF Photographer of the Year.

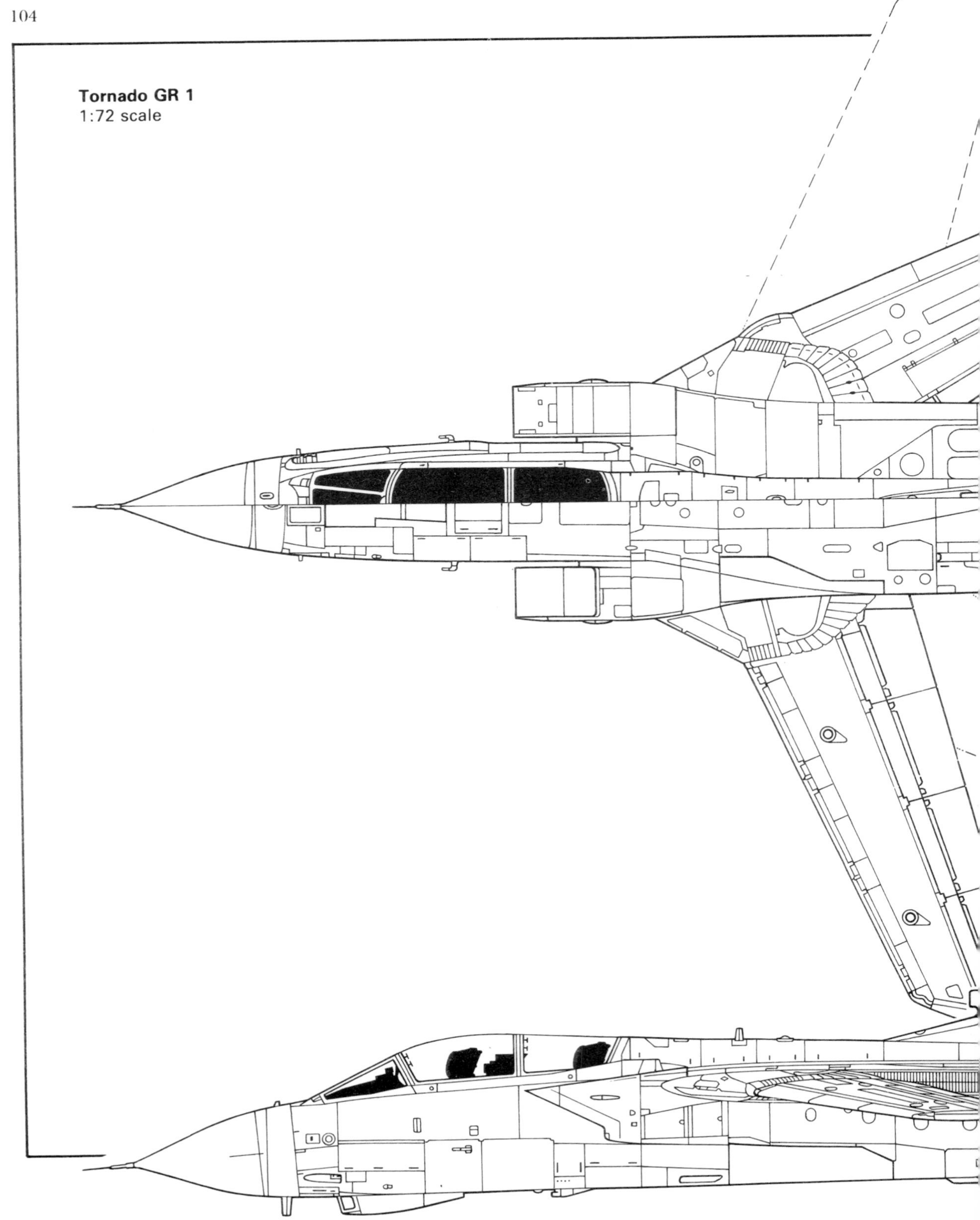
Tornado GR 1
1:72 scale

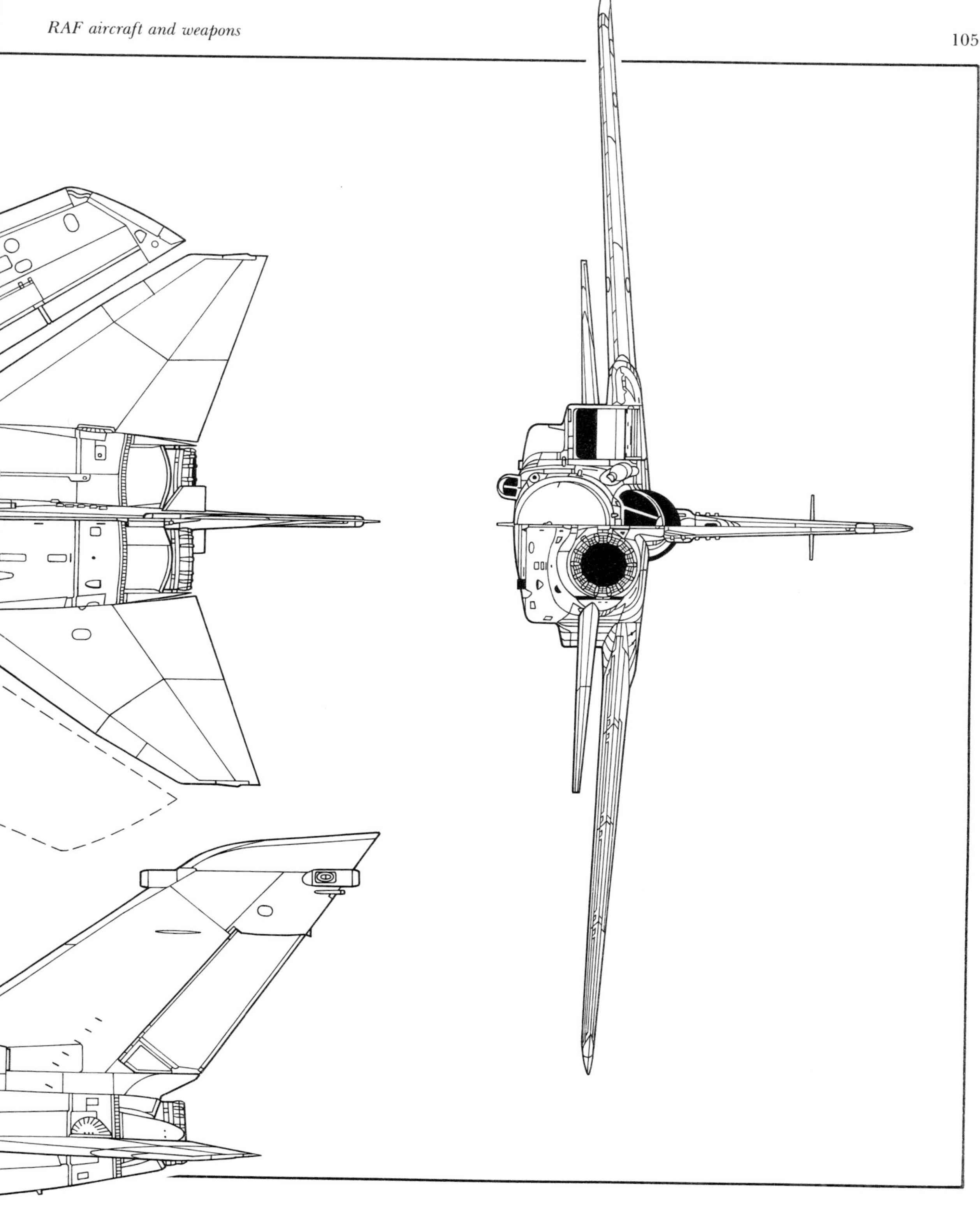

arrangements are compared that the differences can be seen.

The design stages of the MRCA were long and involved and it was not until August 14 1974 that the first prototype flew in West Germany. The second prototype flew from the British Aerospace airfield at Warton, Lancashire (the main British airfield for the British production effort) soon afterwards. The rest of the prototypes followed from then onwards, seemingly every few months although sometimes the intervals were longer. These pre-production aircraft each had their own particular part to play in the flight development programme as some were used solely for exploration of handling and flight envelope investigations while others were devoted to testing and developing the electronics. Others were used for weapon development and some are still being used for flight testing all manner of items from yet more control electronics to carbon fibre sub-assemblies and flight control areas.

From the airframe point of view, the Tornado is a surprisingly orthodox design apart from the shoulder-mounted swing wings, but today these are no novelty. The Tornado's swing wings pivot from a leading edge angle of 25 degrees when fully forward to a sweep of 60 degrees when the wings are swept backwards into the fuselage sides, in which configuration the wing and tail surfaces seemingly combine to form a distinctive delta shape. Titanium alloys are extensively used in the wing structure which is remarkably strong, not only to accommodate the considerable stresses involved in high speed flight at very low altitudes, but also to carry the weapon loads involved. The Tornado has two weapon hardpoints on each wing, each being able to swivel to suit the angle of wing sweep. These weapon stations can carry a wide array of weaponry from Sidewinder air-to-air missiles, JP 233 airfield attack munitions (under fuselage only), cluster bombs, ECM pods, flare pods, Paveway laser-guided bombs and retarded bombs through to nuclear devices. Similar weapon loads can be fitted to the three underfuselage weapon stations. However, one load that will not be carried by Royal Air Force Tornados for some time is the special reconnaissance pod developed for the aircraft.

It is in electronics that the Tornado really becomes such a highly-advanced airborne weapons system, for the Tornado bristles with all manner of modern technological wonders. The flight control system is made up from a number of components including a Marconi Avionics/Bodenseewerk triplex command stability augmentation system (CSAS) using fly-by-wire and auto-stabilisation, both of which can lighten the pilot's load considerably. Two self-monitoring digital computers control the autopilot and flight director (APFD). There is also a terrain-following system. These components can be used in a variety of modes. The APFD can operate to provide pre-selected flight attitude, heading or barometric height hold and a pre-selected airspeed hold by using an autothrottle. The flight director can be used with, or as a back-up to, the autopilot to provide automatic approach, terrain-following and radio height-holding modes among other choices. The navigation and attack system includes a Texas Instruments multi-mode forward-looking radar, a three-axis digital inertial navigation system (DINS) with a combined radar display, a filtered Doppler radar system used for navigation accuracy, several digital computers, a radio altimeter, a nose-mounted laser ranger and target-seeker, and various cockpit tabular displays. Reeled off in the above fashion the list seems endless but what it boils down to as far as the aircrew are concerned is that much of their operational tasks are carried out accurately and virtually automatically to the point where they can take off and from then on the aircraft itself can carry out its attack mission with no inputs from the aircrew other than checking and small corrections.

Above *Line-up of Tornado tails at the TWCU, RAF Honington.*

Below right *Tornado GR 1 on finals — another Brian Lawrence photo.*

The navigation and attack system is one that can be virtually carried out from the safety of the squadron HAS. Inside the operations centre the navigator for a mission can use a small computer to record the aircraft flight path, mission attack headings and weapon control and release. This is done in conjunction with special maps on which are very carefully surveyed co-ordinate locations. Using a small sensor head connected to the computer, the navigator identifies these points to the computer using the device's keyboard. Flight

abort a mission. The accuracy of the electronics is almost unbelievable. Some training missions using ML Aviation CBLS 200 Practice Bomb Carriers have ranged the length of the United Kingdom to approach bombing ranges from all manner of headings and consistently achieve hits within 10 m or so of the chosen targets using all manner of release methods from simple bombing runs to toss-bombing. The main point to emphasise is that all this electronic control enables the aircraft to perform consistently under all weather conditions from bright sunlight to dense snow at the dead of night. Crews have already carried out low-altitude missions using the terrain-following systems only.

The first Service unit using Tornados was the Tri-national Tornado Training Establishment (TTTE) at RAF Cottesmore. The first aircraft were delivered to the TTTE in July 1980 and about 50 Tornados will eventually be used among the four sub-units within the TTTE (including an OCU). As the name implies, the TTTE is an international unit used to train the aircrew from West Germany and Italy as well as those for the Royal Air Force. All the Tornados on the TTTE have an operational role if required, including the paths and headings are then entered into the computer along with weapon loads and release points, target information, return paths and areas to avoid en route. The computer, known as the cassette preparation ground station (CPGS), then provides the navigator with a standard-looking tape cassette and a 'hard' paper copy of all the mission flight information it contains, which he can use as a check list during the mission. The tape is inserted into the Tornado electronics and from then on, once the aircraft is airborne, it is flown by its electronics systems, all of which are interconnected to form a flying system that can operate at speeds and in conditions where the human Mark 1 brain would be hard put to assimilate and control all the many inputs and stresses involved. The electronics can guide the aircraft to the attack heading, carry out the actual attack with the aircraft's own weapon control system selecting the weapons to be used, release them at the critical time and then guide the aircraft away from the target area to a high-speed, low-altitude return home. All this time the pilot and navigator can but monitor and check the systems, although at any time they can intervene to change a programme or

dual-control pilot training aircraft known as the GR 1 (T) which will also be used by squadrons. Royal Air Force crews, once their conversion at the TTTE is complete, will then proceed to the Tornado Weapons Conversion Unit (TWCU) at RAF Honington. As its name implies, this unit is responsible for converting the aircrew to the 'British' weaponry carried by the Royal Air Force Tornado GR 1s. The strength of the TWCU is 22 aircraft. A further development unit is the Tornado Operational Evaluation Unit at Boscombe Down. This was formed during 1983 and comprises four aircraft which are used to evaluate Tornado operational tactics and methods.

The first Royal Air Force Tornado squadron was No 9 at RAF Honington, which was officially formed in June 1982 although aircraft deliveries had commenced six months earlier. The second unit was the famous 617 Squadron (the 'Dam-Busters'), formed during early 1983 at RAF Marham. The third squadron was No 27. As more Tornado GR 1s join the Royal Air Force they will gradually assume more and more roles.

By the time the full strength of 220 Tornado GR 1s are delivered, the Tornado will be the Royal Air Force's most important single aircraft type, especially in RAF Germany. It will be virtually the only strike component of No 1 Group and some will be used by No 18 Group as well. The Tornado is already committed to being the main strike aircraft that will see the Royal Air Force through into the 21st century, and current development programmes will ensure that yet more versions and variants will appear to make the Tornado one of the most potent and flexible aircraft of its type for decades to come.

Buccaneer S Mark 2

Crew 2; **Span** 13.41 m; **Length** 19.33 m; **Height** 4.95 m; **Max take-off weight** 28,123 kg; **Max speed** 1,040 km/h; **Armament** iron or smart bombs, rocket pods, Bullpup, Martell or Sea Eagle missiles, AIM-9 Sidewinder missiles; **Engines** 2 × Rolls-Royce Spey RB 168-1A turbofans.

The Buccaneer seems set to become one of the Royal Air Force's most enduring strike aircraft, for the Buccaneer S2 had its operational debut in July 1970 and there is still no sign of its being removed from use for many years to come. The Buccaneer had its origins in the advanced NA39 concept back in the mid-1950s and was originally intended to be a naval strike aircraft. The Royal Air Force only became involved with it after the cancellation of the TSR 2 strike aircraft project, ordering a batch of Buccaneer S 2s in its place. In many ways they have had little cause to regret the order for the Buccaneer has given sterling service and has proved to be a versatile weapon mount.

One oddity regarding the Buccaneer is that, almost alone among modern strike aircraft, it retains a bomb bay. This is a carry-over from naval origins, but the rotary form of the bay makes it ideal for the high speed and low level tactics the Royal Air Force has to employ over Europe. The bay has an internal capacity of 1,814 kg of weapons, which may be conventional 'iron' bombs or laser-guided 'smart' bombs, although the latter are often mounted on the four wing pylons, each of which can carry up to 1,360 kg. The wing pylons are the obvious carriage points for the many types of missiles used by Buccaneer squadrons. Bullpup and Martel are two but the future will be with the Sea Eagle, of which more below. For self-defence the Buccaneer S 2 can carry the AIM-9 Sidewinder and a full ECM suite is usually fitted.

With the loss of conventional aircraft carriers for the Fleet Air Arm, the Royal Air Force has taken over many ex-Royal Navy Buccaneers. This has led to some confusion with the Buccaneer designations. The key is the use of the television-equipped Martel missile. The Buccaneer S 2A cannot use the Martel, the S 2B can; the suffixes S 2C and S 2D are the same for ex-Royal Navy Buccaneers. To confuse matters further, the Royal Air Force uses

Buccaneer S 2 of 208 Squadron, now based at RAF Lossiemouth for operations with the Sea Eagle anti-ship missile.

The Buccaneer S 2 armed with Sea Eagle anti-ship missiles.

only the S 2A and S 2B designations but to make life simpler all round the use of the Buccaneer S 2A, the non-Martel versions, is largely confined to the OCU, No 237.

With the replacement of the RAF Germany Buccaneers by Tornados the main location for Buccaneers is now RAF Lossiemouth. Lossiemouth is the home of No 237 OCU and two squadrons, Nos 12 and 208, and their aircraft are part of No 18 Group, having an anti-shipping role armed with Sea Eagle or Martel missiles. The aircraft involved with these units, a total of sixty in all, have undergone an extensive refit for their anti-shipping role and apart from the new missile-associated equipment they have been fitted with new inertial navigation systems (the Ferranti FIN 1063), Blue Parrot attack radar and new electronic warfare black boxes. The basic airframe has also undergone extensive testing and rebuilding to ensure that the Buccaneers will be able to maintain their anti-shipping role for many years to come. In this role their main weapon will be the potent Sea Eagle missile with its powerful explosive warhead (reported to weigh over 150 kg) and range of up to 100 kilometres.

At one point there was talk of Tornados taking over the anti-shipping role but this does not now seem likely to happen for some time to come, if ever. Instead the Buccaneers will serve on in the environment for which they were originally designed, namely anti-shipping operations carried out at low level over the grey wastes of the North Atlantic and North Sea.

Buccaneer S 2
1:72 scale

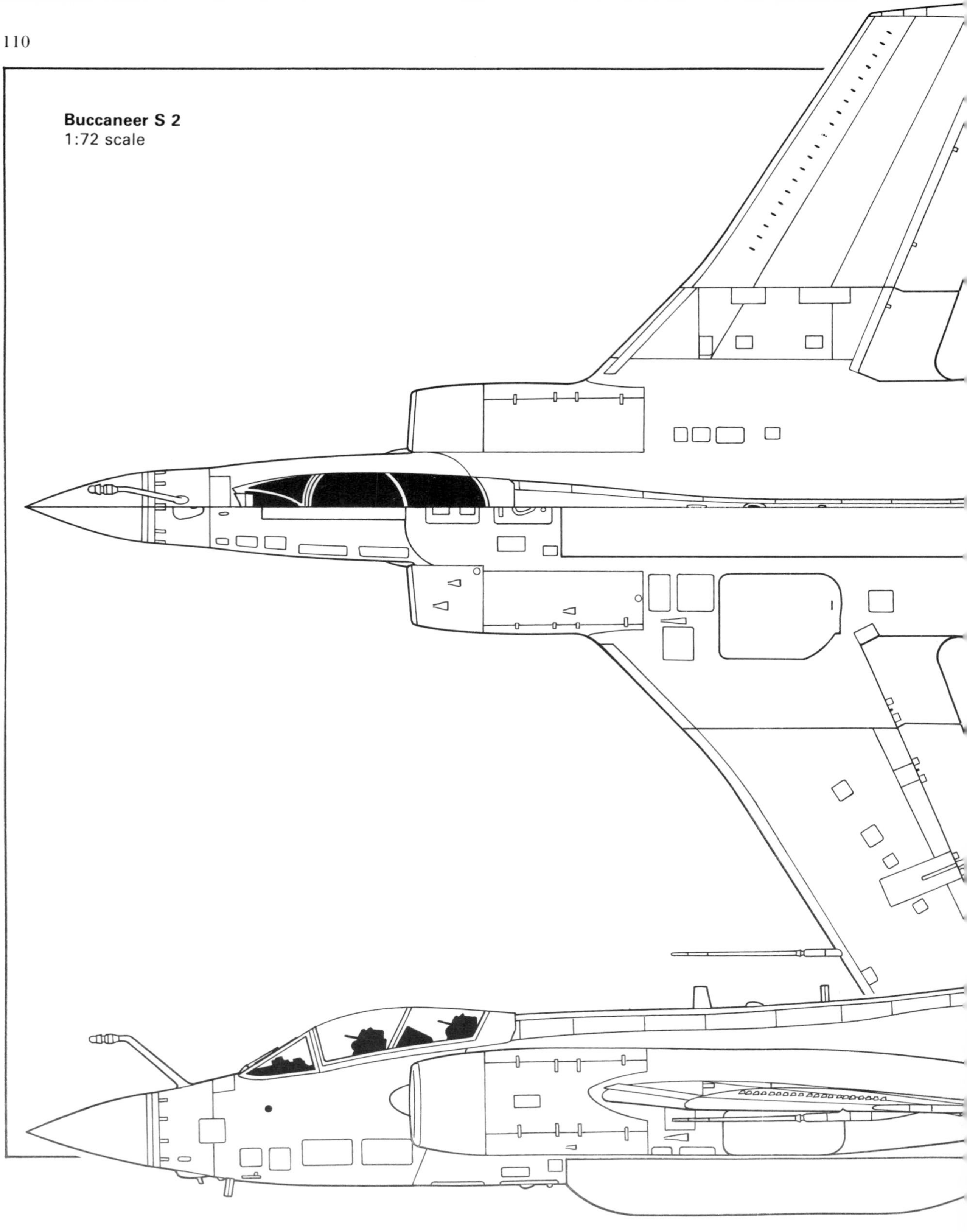

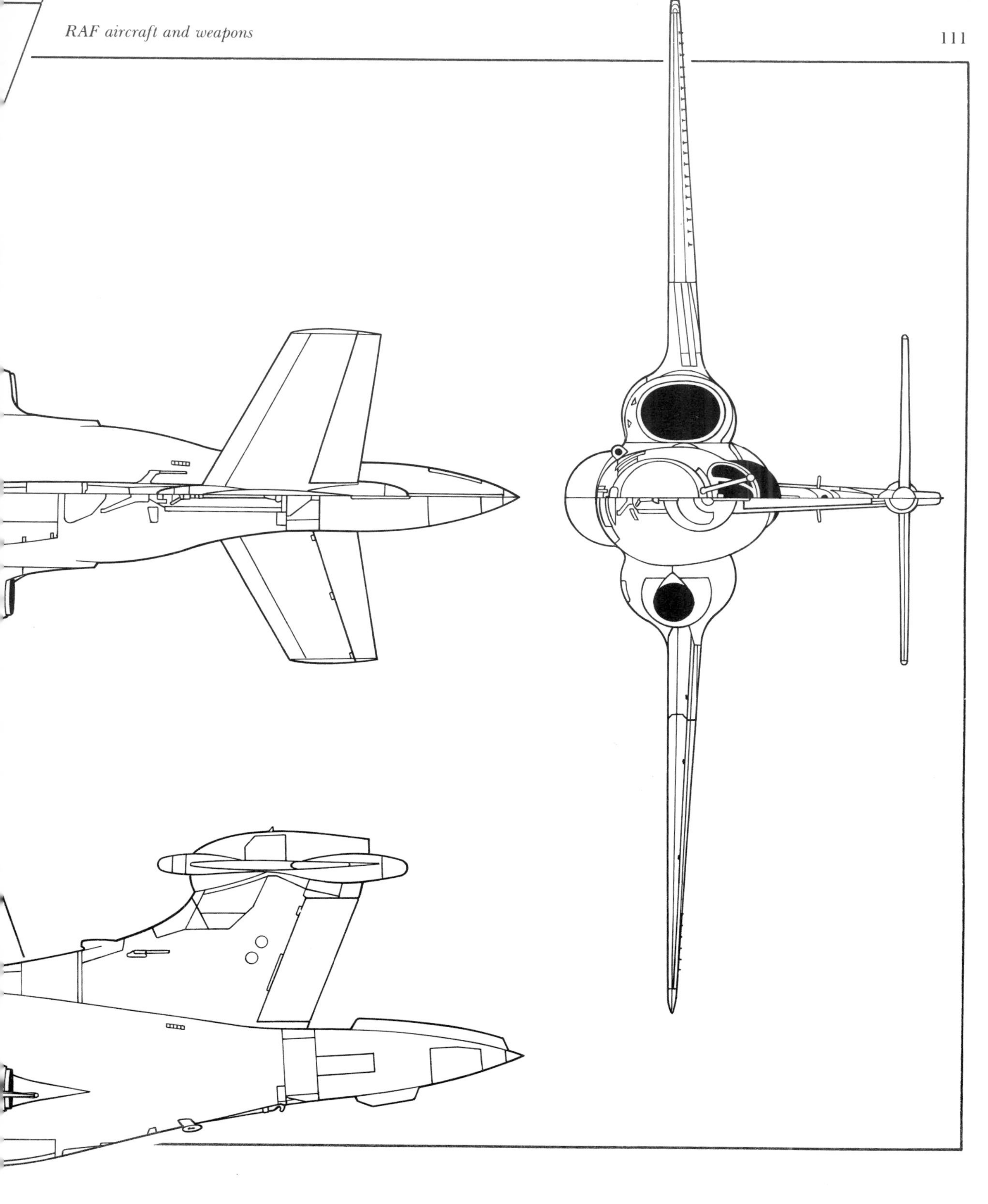

Harrier GR Mark 3, T Mark 4 and T Mark 4A

Crew (GR 3) 1; **Crew (T 2A, 4, 4A)** 2; **Span, normal** 7.7 m; **Span, ferry** 9.04 m; **Length (GR 3 laser nose)** 14.27 m; **Length (two-seaters)** 17 m; **Height (GR 3)** 3.45 m; **Height (two-seaters)** 4.17 m; **Max take-off weight, GR 3** 11,340 kg plus; **Max speed** 1,186 km/h; **Armament** 2 × 30 mm Aden guns in pods, one underfuselage weapon station, four underwing weapon stations; **Engine** 1 × Rolls-Royce Pegasus Mk 103S.

Today the Harrier still retains that odd attraction for everyone that it has had ever since its fore-bearer, the Hawker P 1127, made its first tottering vertical take-offs. To this day the Harrier and its derivatives are still the only viable vertical take-off aircraft using vectored thrust and the type remains one of real feathers in the Royal Air Force's cap. The uniqueness of the Harrier is one of the mysteries of the modern aviation world, for the overall concept seems to offer so many attractions that one can only wonder why so few other designers have adopted the concept.

The P 1127 made its first attempts at flight way back in October 1960. From these first early attempts came the realisation that the vertical take-off aircraft was a feasible concept and increasing amounts of money and facilities were devoted to the project, much of the money coming from the United States. From the P 1127 came the Kestrel and from there came the first Harrier, with the first GR 1 flying on December 28 1967. In all 120 single-seat Harriers were produced for the RAF.

Once the Harrier was in service it became the subject of all manner of trials and developments ranging from equipment trials to tactical experi-mentation. It soon became apparent that flying the Harrier, especially in the tricky transition phase from forward to vertical flight, and vice versa, was no easy matter, as many pilots have found to their cost, especially in the United States. Another drawback has always been that the Harrier lacks combat range without external tankage or in-flight refuelling, and the design has always tended to be under-powered. This fact has been partially remedied by the retrofitting of the more powerful Pegasus Mk 103 to replace the Mk 102 and produce the Harrier GR 3, the type now mainly in service.

A two-seat Harrier was an obvious addition to the range, the first of them flying on April 24 1969. These two-seaters differ from the single-seat version in several ways, the most obvious being the increase in fuselage length to accommodate the extra seat, although the tail surfaces have been enlarged also. The early model was the Harrier T 2 but this was re-engined with the Pegasus

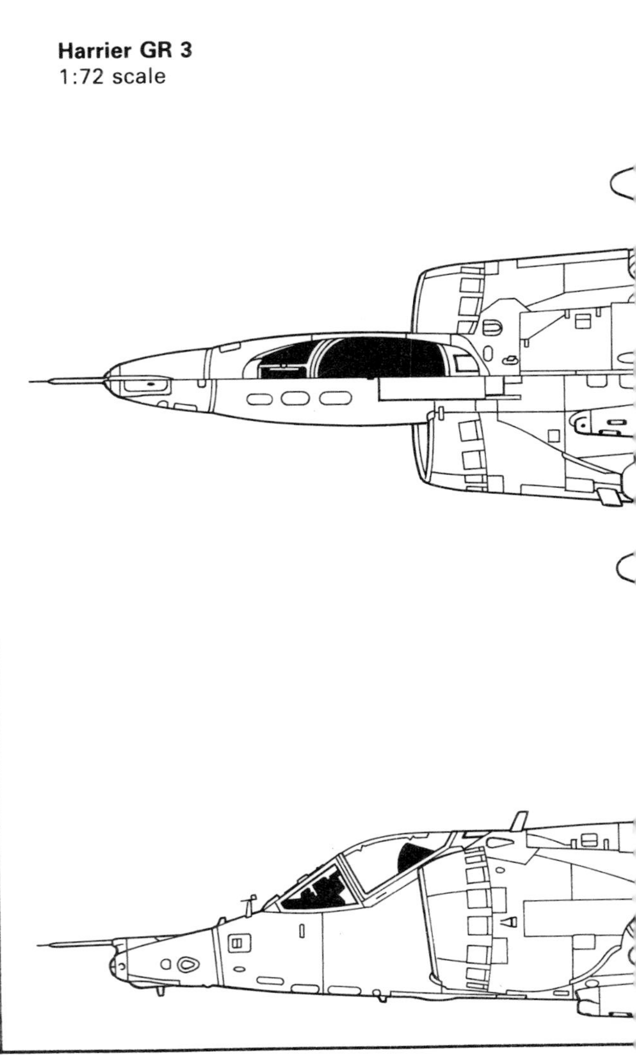

Harrier GR 3
1:72 scale

Mk 102 to produce the T 2A and the T 4 is the same type equipped with the Pegasus Mk 103. The Harrier T 4A is a two-seat Harrier built from new with the Pegasus Mk 103.

With the Harrier proving itself in the Falklands, there is now a renewed interest in the type as evinced even before the South Atlantic blow-up by the introduction of the Anglo-American variant, the GR 5 (for which there is a separate entry). In the Falklands campaign the Harrier not only operated from aircraft carriers and was ferried over huge distances but it also acted as an interceptor and was very successful in the role. It carried out numerous ground strike missions for the loss of only three aircraft. The campaign involved just about every facet of the Harrier's considerable flight envelope and operational capability. The almost universal use of a short rolling take-off to increase weapon load and reduce fuel consumption was adopted, and the aircraft were then able to make maximum use of their considerable weapon power, augmented for the interception role by the addition of AIM-9L Sidewinders on the wing pylons. The lessons of the Falkland Islands

Left *Harrier GR 3 operating at its usual low level.*

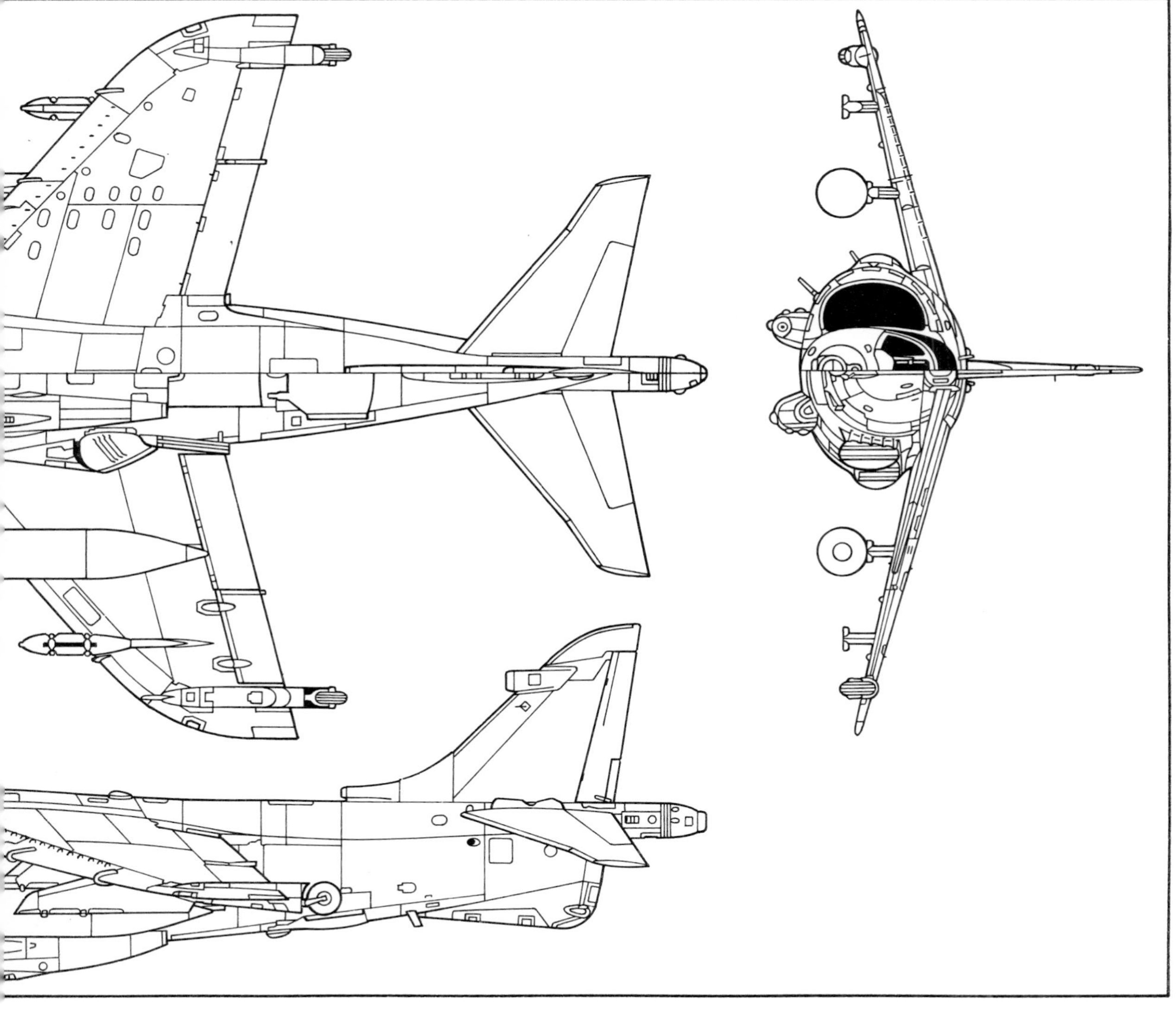

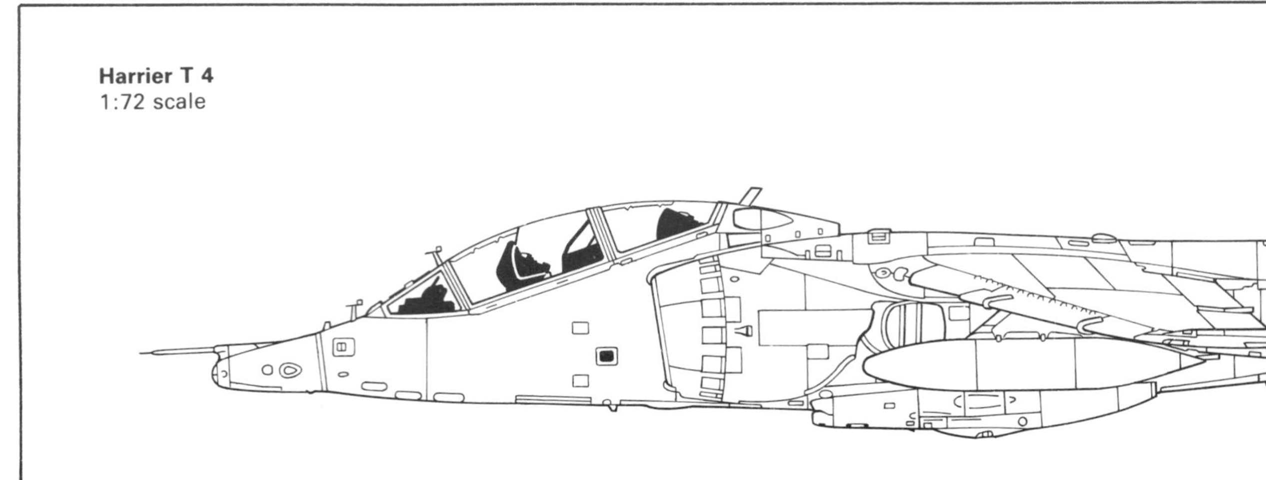

Left *Harrier T 4 of 233 OCU at RAF Wittering.*

campaign are still being sifted and analysed but one thing which has already emerged is that the Harrier came through with flying colours.

Despite the use of the Harrier for dog-fighting, it should be remembered that its prime operational role is that of ground attack and strike in support of ground forces. In this role the squadrons operate close to the forward edge of the battle area (FEBA) from field sites. No 1 Squadron could find itself operating almost anywhere in the world as it provides support for 5 Airborne Brigade. It was in this role that No 1 Squadron became the first Royal Air Force unit to become involved in the Falkland Islands campaign. The two RAF Gutersloh squadrons, Nos 3 and 4, would provide strike support for 1 (BR) Corps generally and for this purpose would be dispersed to field sites away from the base. Some of these sites will have been pre-surveyed and pre-prepared but operational situations may necessitate the squadrons using improvised sites. Indications from exercises are that the two squadrons would be dispersed to six sites, each for six or so aircraft. A central logistical depot would be established from which fuel, weapons and all the essentials would be dispensed using about 400 trucks and other vehicles, but each site would normally keep supplies for two days' operations at any one time. The Army would be involved in the supply operations and some infantry units may be used in perimeter defence along with RAF Regiment personnel. Each site would have limited repair and maintenance facilities. Two of the sites would be commanded by the two Squadron Leaders with their Flight Commanders in charge of the other four sites. The exact requirements for operating sites are imprecise but some natural cover would be essential, preferably near a flat area for the actual take-offs and landings and close to a good road network for the supplies

The Harrier is designed to operate under such field conditions and is equipped accordingly with a robust undercarriage. The shoulder-mounted wings are used to carry the weapon load or drop tanks and a point to be emphasised is that the Harrier has no internal weapon or ECM capacity, all loads being carried slung under the wings or from the single under-fuselage station. The latter is often used to carry two 30 mm Aden guns in a faired pack that also contains the ammunition, but the same station can be used to carry a five-camera

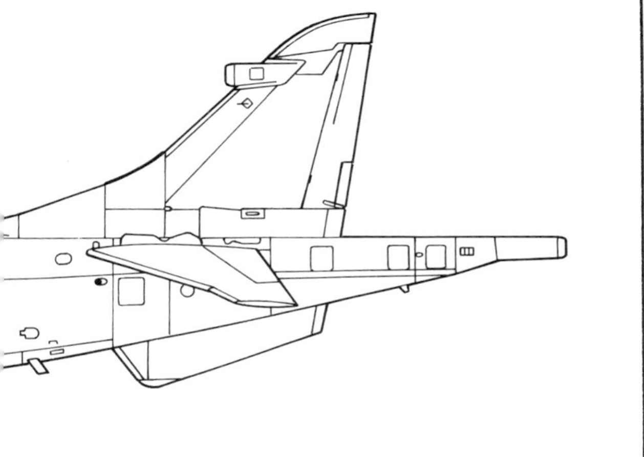

reconnaissance pack. Each of the inboard wing stations has a weight capacity of 910 kg while the outboard stations can carry up to 295 kg each. The normal operational weapon load is a maximum of 2,270 kg, although this can be exceeded. To fly useful distances with these weights the Harrier has to adopt a STOL rather than a VTOL mode. In flight the weapons are released using an aiming computer and for the acquisition of precise ground targets most Harriers are now fitted with a laser ranger and marked target seeker (LRMTS) in an extended nose (some two-seaters have been retro-fitted as well). Overall flight management is aided by an inertial navigation and attack system (INAS) and a head-up display (HUD). Add the usual communications and homing devices and the cockpit of the Harrier GR 3 becomes a very crowded and cramped area. Pride of place in the tiny cock-pit goes to the combined throttle/vector control lever that provides the Harrier with its unique take-off and landing method. As is now widely known, the same control imparts to the Harrier a remarkable dog-fighting capability with the use of the vectoring control to induce 'Viffing' (Vectoring in Forward Flight), a manouevre no conventional aircraft can match. The two-seater Harriers have a full operational capability.

Conversion training to the Harrier is carried out at No 233 OCU at RAF Wittering. A flight of four Harriers known as 1417 Flight operates from the main airfield in Belize.

Left *Harrier GR 3 with Sidewinders.*

Below *Unimog tractor towing No 1 Squadron Harrier GR 3.*

Harriers of No 1417 Flight operating in Belize.

When the Harrier GR 5 enters service it is scheduled to replace the GR 3s now in Germany. The ex-No 3 and -4 Squadron aircraft will then probably return to RAF Wittering where they may undergo a gradual programme of updating with improved avionics, fitted ECM and other changes.

The Harrier in all its forms is a remarkable aircraft whose operation provides the Royal Air Force with a reservoir of skilled and experienced personnel ready to assume the next generation of V/STOL aircraft in the form of the Harrier GR 5. This aircraft will have considerable all-round performance and capability attributes but this must not hide the fact that the current Harrier is a unique type of aircraft with an excellent in-service and combat record. It may be somewhat tricky to fly and it may lack range alongside comparable types of orthodox aircraft, but it has proved itself to be capable of operating from both field sites and carrier decks under all conditions and is now 'combat proven'.

Harrier GR Mark 5

Crew 1; **Span** 9.25 m; **Length** 14.12 m; **Height** 3.55 m; **Max take-off weight (STO)** 13,494 kg; **Max speed** 1,083 km/h; **Armament** 2 × 25 mm Aden guns, one under-fuselage weapon station, six underwing weapon stations; **Engine** 1 × Rolls-Royce Pegasus 11-21 Mark 103.

When considering the adoption of an American-based design variant of the Harrier as the next generation of V/STOL strike aircraft for the Royal Air Force, it would be well to remember that much of the financing of the early P 1127 and the Kestrel was funded from American Service sources. The Americans have adopted the V/STOL concept heartily and have gained considerable experience with their US Marine Corps AV-8As, the American version of the Harrier. At one time before 1973, a combined United Kingdom and American design team spent a considerable amount of effort in attempting to define an 'international' generation of aircraft to follow on from the original Harriers, but the team broke up in the face of what seemed to be differing operational requirements. Since then British Aerospace at Kingston, Surrey, and McDonnell Douglas at St Louis, Missouri, have gone along their separate design paths, but both wished to retain the overall form of the Harrier engine and airframe to keep down development costs and time scales.

Both manufacturers worked towards a form of aircraft with increased weapon-carrying ability and

Harriers proceed where other aircraft fear to tread.

agility for the ground strike and support role. To this end they both worked towards a new 'big wing' Harrier with a more powerful engine that would be able to carry an increased load and yet have a good turn rate. The British designers worked on a greatly increased wing area approach while in general terms the Americans used an improved aerodynamic approach using advanced materials.

When the choice of the Harrier follow-on aircraft became necessary during 1981, the Royal Air Force decided on the American design which became the Harrier GR 5. The decision was not purely political for early forecasts indicated that, while the US Marine Corps would require no less than 257 of the new design, designated by them the AV-8B, the Royal Air Force would require only 60. Also, by the time the two designs were substantially complete, there was little to choose between them, although the GR 5 will be somewhat slower in maximum level speed than the Harrier GR 3. Where the American design does score is in overall performance.

The Harrier GR 5 programme is now an international project. McDonnell Douglas now undertakes some 60 per cent of the project and British Aerospace 40 per cent of the airframe, and the Americans will undertake some 25 per cent of the engine manufacture by value. All Harrier GR 5s for the Royal Air Force will be assembled in the United Kingdom.

The main changes from earlier Harriers in the GR 5 version are many. The wings have increased area with larger flaps and with a super-critical section. Composite materials have been used extensively to save weight and the number of wing weapon stations has been increased from four to six altogether. The air intakes have been increased in size to improve the mass of air being put through the engine, which has numerous internal and external alterations to improve handling and efficiency close to the ground. To take the increased weights, the undercarriage has been strengthened. Changes have been made to the forward fuselage and nose contours and the latter will be able to accommodate a combined laser and video sensor unit or a foward looking camera array. A new electronics 'fit' will be the Hughes Angle Rate Bombing System, and a full authority digital electronic control (FADEC) is already under test for the Pegasus engine.

The first test aircraft were converted AV-8As and the first 'all AV-8B' prototypes were flying by the middle of 1982. Deliveries of the Harrier GR 5 began in the middle of 1986 but these were two development aircraft to be used for weapon trials as the Royal Air Force weapon requirements are different from those of the US Marine Corps. A fatigue test airframe will be used to check out the aircraft for clearance in the low level flight envelope that most Harrier GR 5s will be expected to operate within, ie, low level over the Central European area since most Harrier GR 5s are expected to be based in Germany.

The weapons carried by the Harrier GR 5 are expected to be much the same as those carried on the GR 3 but with the possible addition of the JP 233 and some missiles such as Mavericks. The four inboard wing stations on the GR 5 can be used to carry fuel drop-tanks and the under-fuselage gun packs are carried separate from the central weapon-carrying station. Guns carried by the Royal Air Force GR 5s will be 25 mm Adens.

The New Harrier GR 5.

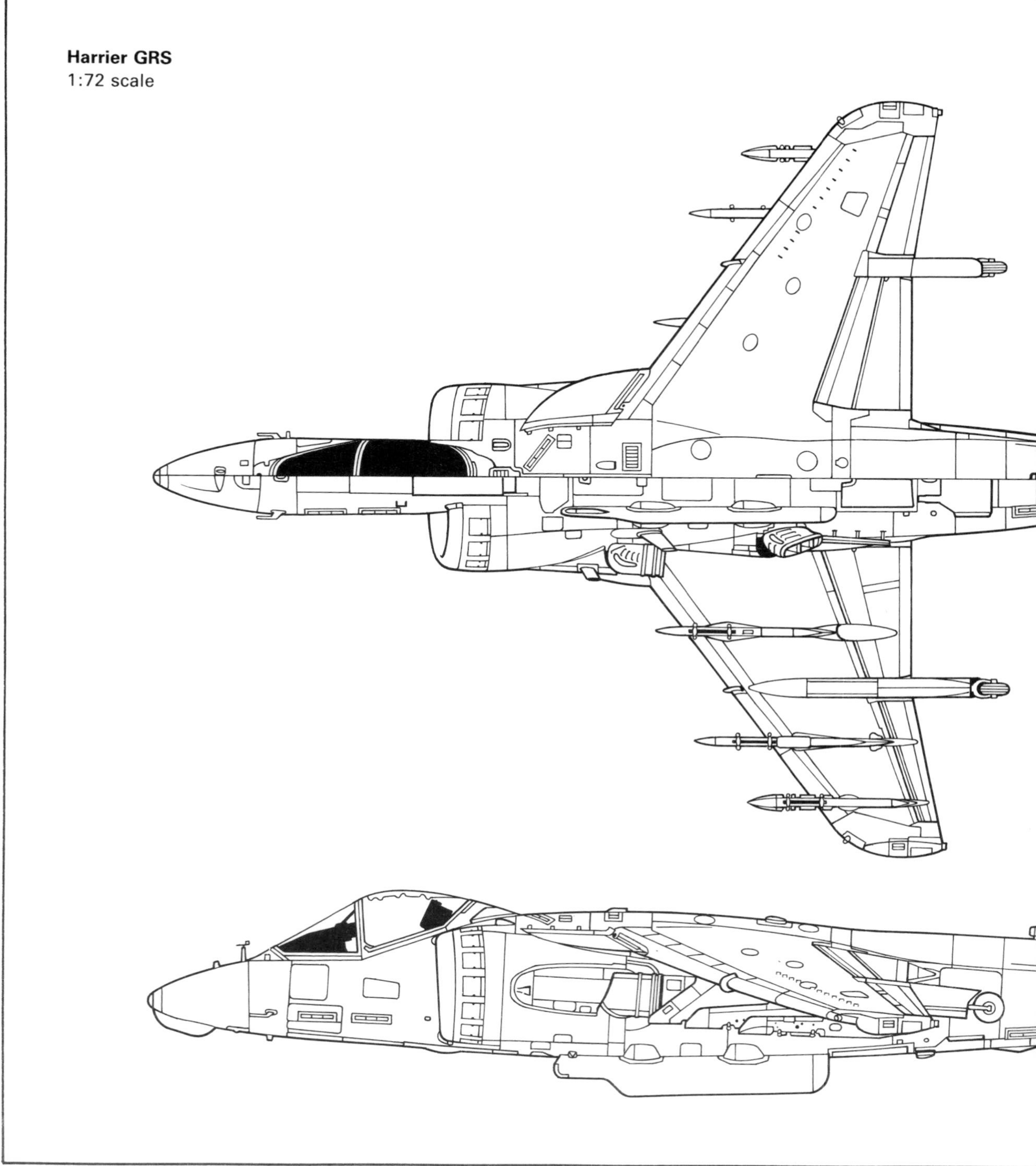
Harrier GR5
1:72 scale

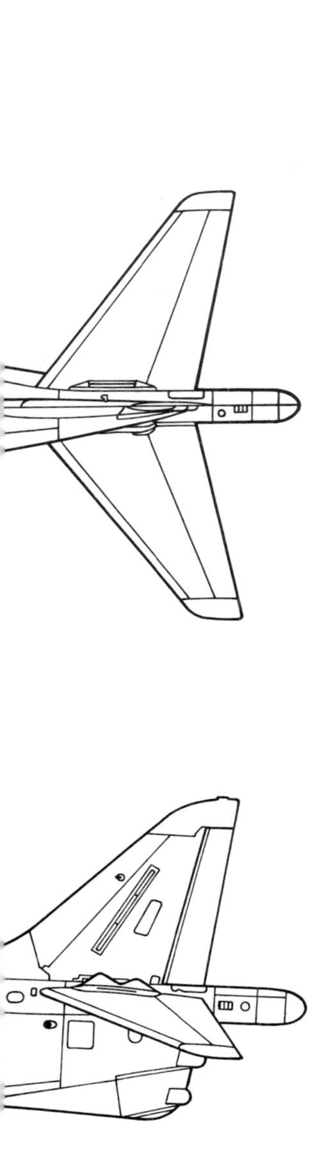

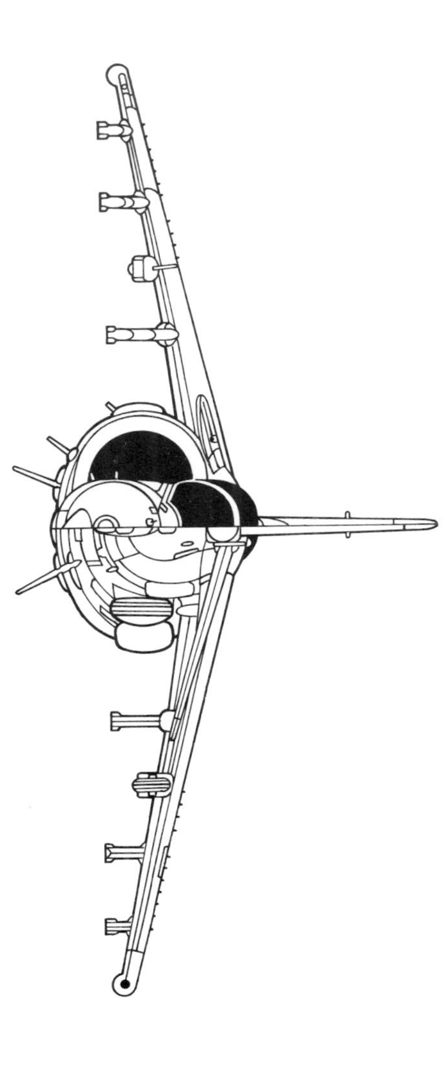

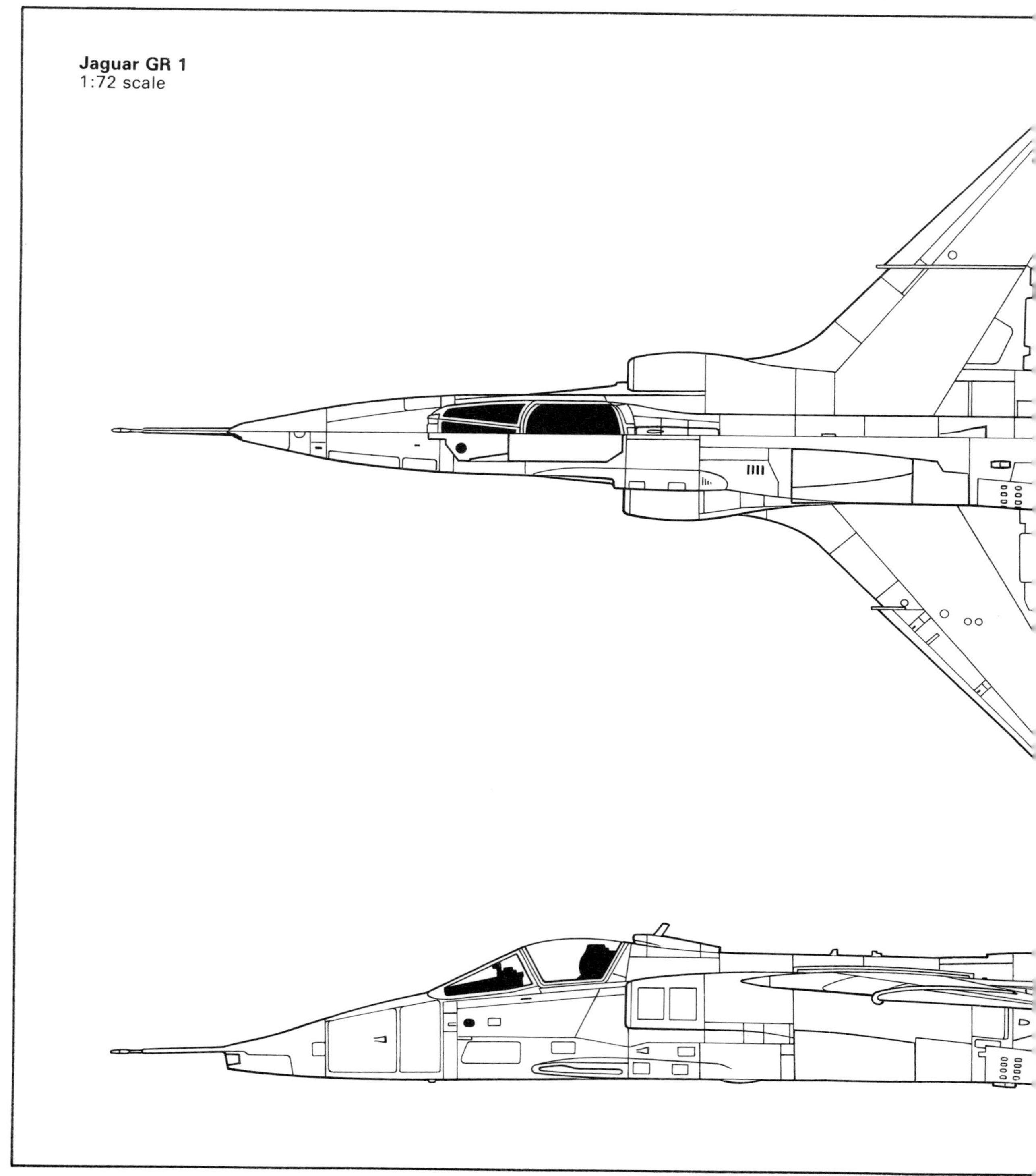
Jaguar GR 1
1:72 scale

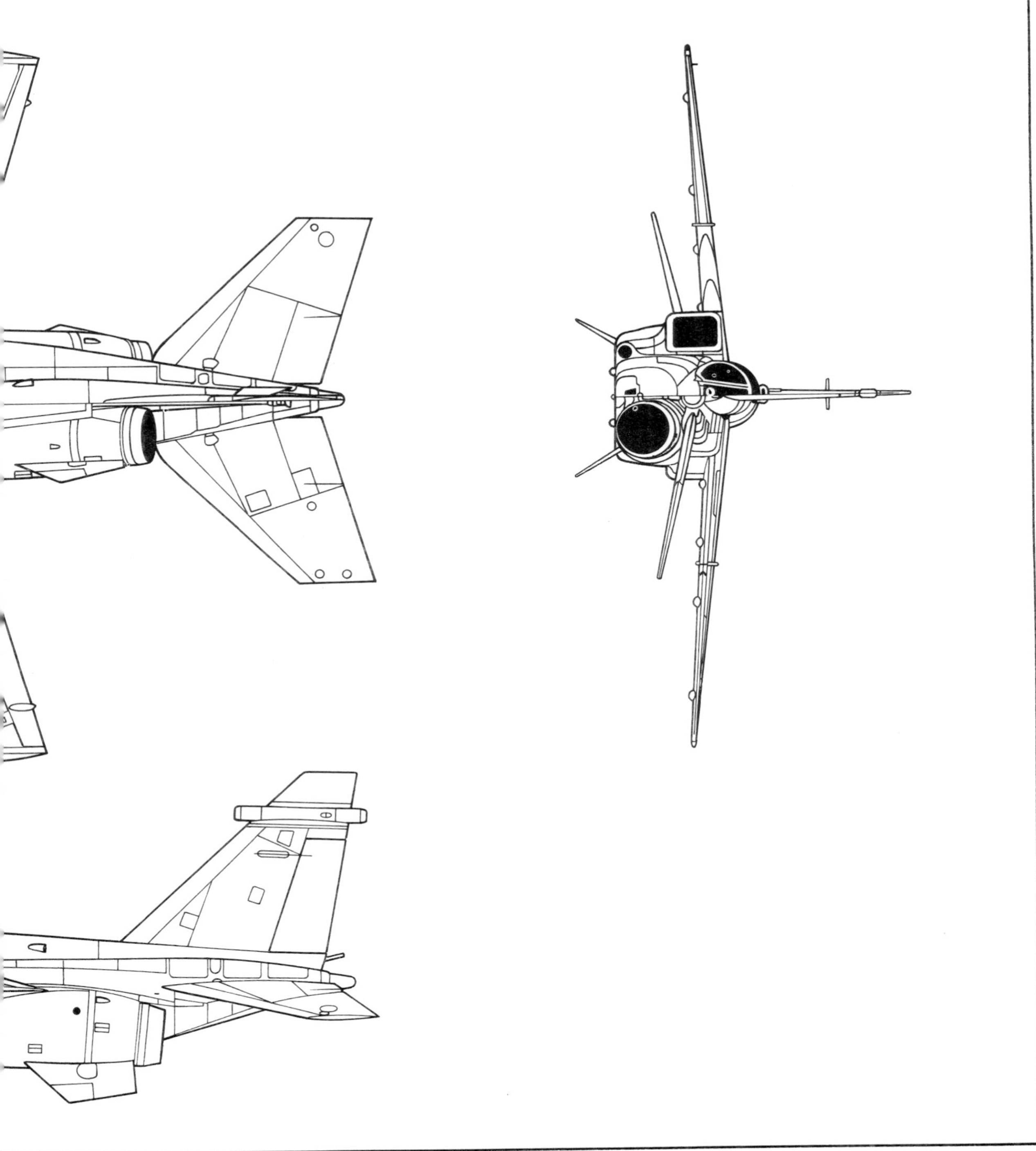

Jaguar GR Mark 1 and T Mark 2

Crew (GR 1) 1; **Crew (GR 2)** 2; **Span** 8.69 m; **Length (GR 1)** 15.52 m; **Length (T 2)** 16.42 m; **Height** 4.89 m; **Max take-off weight** 10,954 kg; **Max speed** 1,350 km/h; **Armament** 2 × 30 mm Aden (GR 1), 1 × 30 mm Aden (T 2), Martel, BL755, retarded and free-fall bombs, rockets; **Engines** 2 × Rolls-Royce Turbomeca Adour Mk 104s.

In contrast to many international collaboration projects involving the aerospace industries, the Jaguar programme has been a shining example of simple and easy working together to produce an excellent end product. The Jaguar project began in 1965 as the result of the realisation that both the Royal Air Force and the French Armée de l'Air had a common requirement for a tactical support aircraft and advanced trainer. In 1966 British Aerospace and Breguet combined to form a new company known usually as Sepecat (Société Européenne de Production de L'Avion E.C.A.T.), and using a Breguet design as a basis went on to develop the aircraft now known as the Jaguar. The individual requirements of the two national air forces led to the inevitable slight differences between types and the Royal Air Force eventually took over two designs, the Jaguar S and the Jaguar B.

The first Jaguar S made its maiden flight on October 12 1969. Since then 165 have been delivered to the Royal Air Force where they are known as the Jaguar GR 1. The Jaguar GR 1 is a single-seat strike aircraft used for the direct tactical support of ground forces and as such is well

supplied with a weapon lifting capacity using three main weapon stations, one under the fuselage centre-line and one under each wing. The GR 1 has two 30 mm Aden guns mounted under the aircraft just behind the cockpit area. Each of the weapon points can carry up to 1,134 kg of offensive stores or fuel drop-tanks. To assist in the accurate weapons delivery required by modern forces, the Jaguar GR 1 has two systems for weapon guidance. The most obvious one visually is the chisel-shaped nose section that accommodates the main sensor for the Laser Ranging and Marked Target Seeker

Above left *Jaguar GR 1 of No 226 (Jaguar) OCU at RAF Lossiemouth demonstrating the full range of ordnance it can carry.*

Above *Jaguar GR 1 of No 6 Squadron, RAF Coltishall.*

Left *Loading up a Jaguar GR 1 in its HAS under NBC conditions.*

to be used in conjunction with ground-based laser target designators. These devices enable the Jaguar GR 1 to be guided to a ground target by ground observers even when the pilot cannot see the target at all. The second system is the digital inertial navigation and weapon-aiming system, or NAVWASS, that is currently being replaced by a newer Ferranti FIN 1064 updated system. Using this system the pilot is provided with target navigation and track information on a head-up display (HUD) that can guide him to the target almost automatically. The Jaguar GR 1 can also be used for photo-reconnaissance and in this role is fitted with a camera 'nose' and pods.

The Jaguar B first flew on August 30 1971 and is now the Jaguar T 2, a two-seater with the occupants seated in tandem. A total of 38 were built. The Jaguar T 2 was primarily intended for use as an advanced training aircraft but while it is used as such by the Jaguar OCU, numbers are also issued to nearly every Jaguar squadron for refresher and check training purposes. The T 2 can also have a full operational role for it retains all the weapon-carrying capability and electronics of the GR 1 version, apart from the laser system, although only one 30 mm Aden gun is mounted.

Jaguars are intended to be used operationally at low altitudes where they operate under defensive radar cover, releasing their weapons very close to their intended targets. To do this successfully they have to be fast, very agile and very tough and the Jaguar is all these things. Their weapon loads can be quite considerable with up to eight 1,000 lb bombs being carried on some missions. These bombs may be free-fall or retarded, with the BL 755 cluster bomb being very useful for all manner of attacks. If required the Jaguar can carry nuclear stores.

The Jaguar OCU is 226 (Jaguar) OCU at RAF Lossiemouth in Scotland. United Kingdom squadrons are based in one location at RAF Coltishall, the home of Nos 6, 41 and 54 Squadrons. Of these No 41 Squadron is employed as a re-

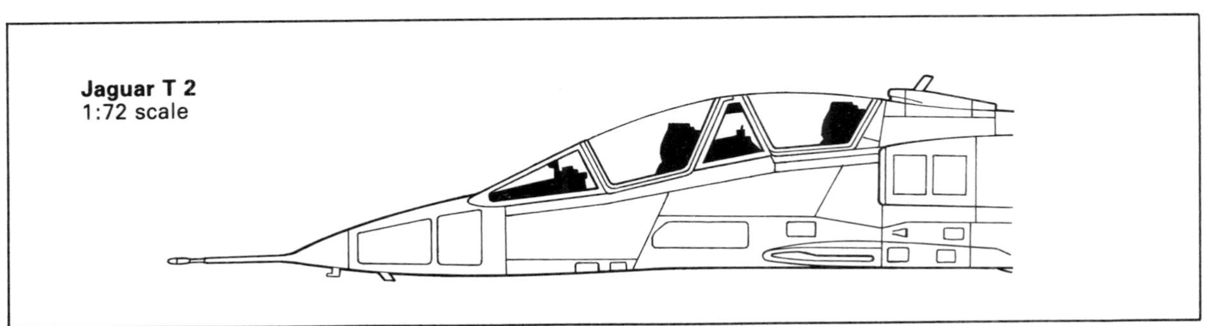

Above *Jaguar T 2 of No 20 Squadron, RAF Bruggen.*

Left *Jaguar GR 1 with under-fuselage camera pack.*

connaissance unit. The only other Jaguar squadron operates under the control of RAF Germany. No 2 Squadron based at RAF Laarbruch operates in the reconnaissance role. In an emergency the OCU would assume a full operational role.

The Canberras

Crew 2 or 3; **Span** 19.5 m; **Length** 19.96 m; **Height**

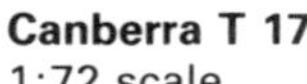

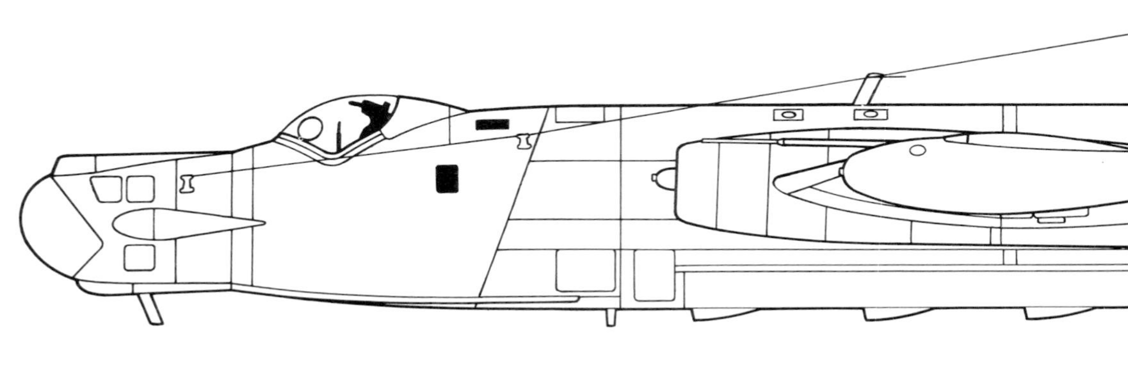

4.77 m; **Max take-off weight** 56,250 kg; **Max speed** 834 km/h; **Armament** now nil; **Engines** 2 × Rolls-Royce Avon 109s or 206s.

While the Canberra is still in service many years after the first B 2 was delivered to the Royal Air Force way back in 1951, it no longer has a front-line role. Today the remaining Canberras are used almost entirely in the support role, although no doubt from time to time a photo-reconnaissance example is used to take the odd survey or mapping photograph.

The Canberra has had a remarkable operational career with the Royal Air Force, a career that has seen operational bombing at Suez, record-gaining long-distance journeys, a lengthy spell in the long-range interdiction role, and many long sojourns as reliable but effective research platforms. As a bomber it for long provided the back-up to the less numerous but more glamourous V-bomber force, although in its latter days as a bomber its operational role was reduced to being little more than a 'spoof' force to soak up enemy defensive counter-measures. However, the Canberra still has a useful performance, and in the high-altitude role the Canberra PR 9 variant, with its up-rated engines and increased wing area, is still a very useful reconnaissance tool—in fact the Royal Air Force has retained five of them in use and they will be around for a long while yet.

Canberra TT 17 of 360 Squadron, RAF Wyton, on detachment in Gibraltar during April 1980 to take part in Exercise Open Gate.

Today all the Royal Air Force Canberras are based at one location, RAF Wyton, as part of No 18 Group. RAF Wyton is the home of the Canberra OCU, No 231 plus No 100 and No 360 Squadrons. Between them these three units use a variety of Canberra marks including the B 3, T 4, B 6, PR 9, E 15, T 17 and TT 18. Most of these aircraft have been what can only be referred to as rebuilt at the BAe facility at Samlesbury, near Preston, and they can all be expected to remain in service for many years to come. (A long-standing in-Service joke is that the initials 'MRCA' originally meant 'Must Refurbish Canberra Again'!)

No 231 OCU trains the aircrews not only for the Royal Air Force Canberras but also for those of the Royal Navy. Most of these are based at RNAS Yeovilton and are manned by civilian personnel.

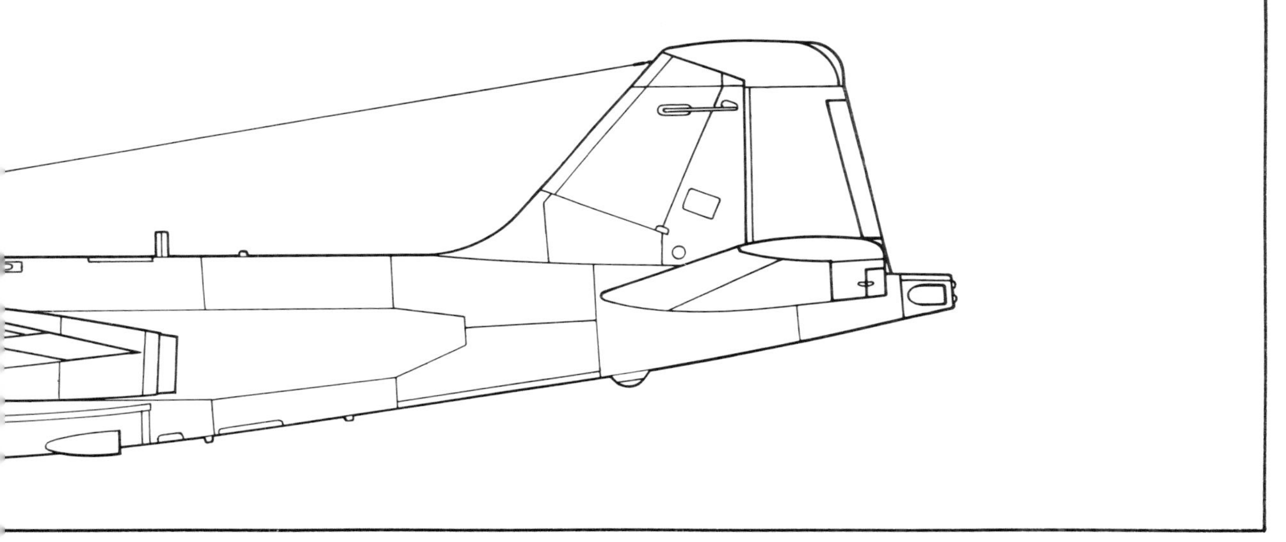

Canberra PR9
1:72 scale

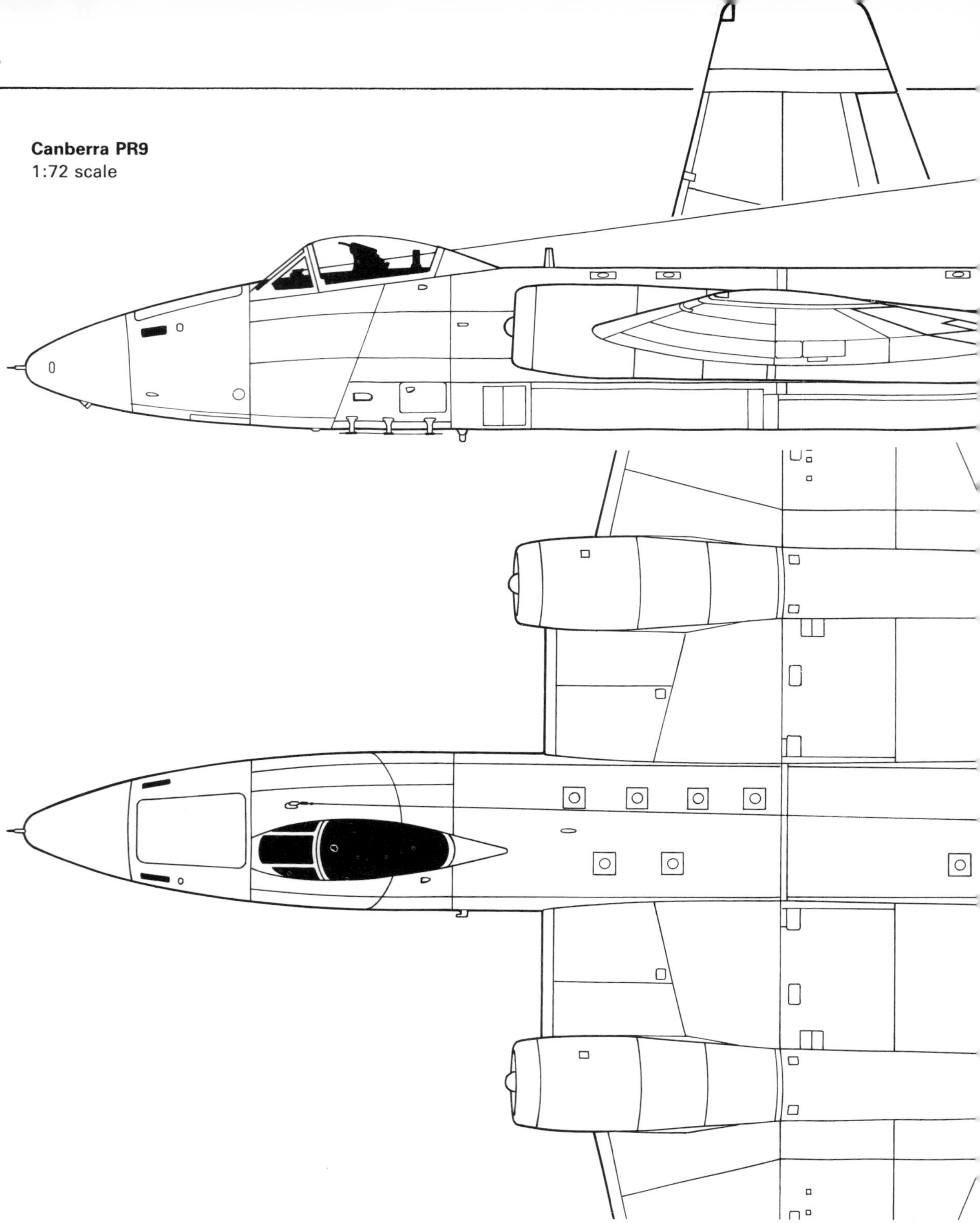

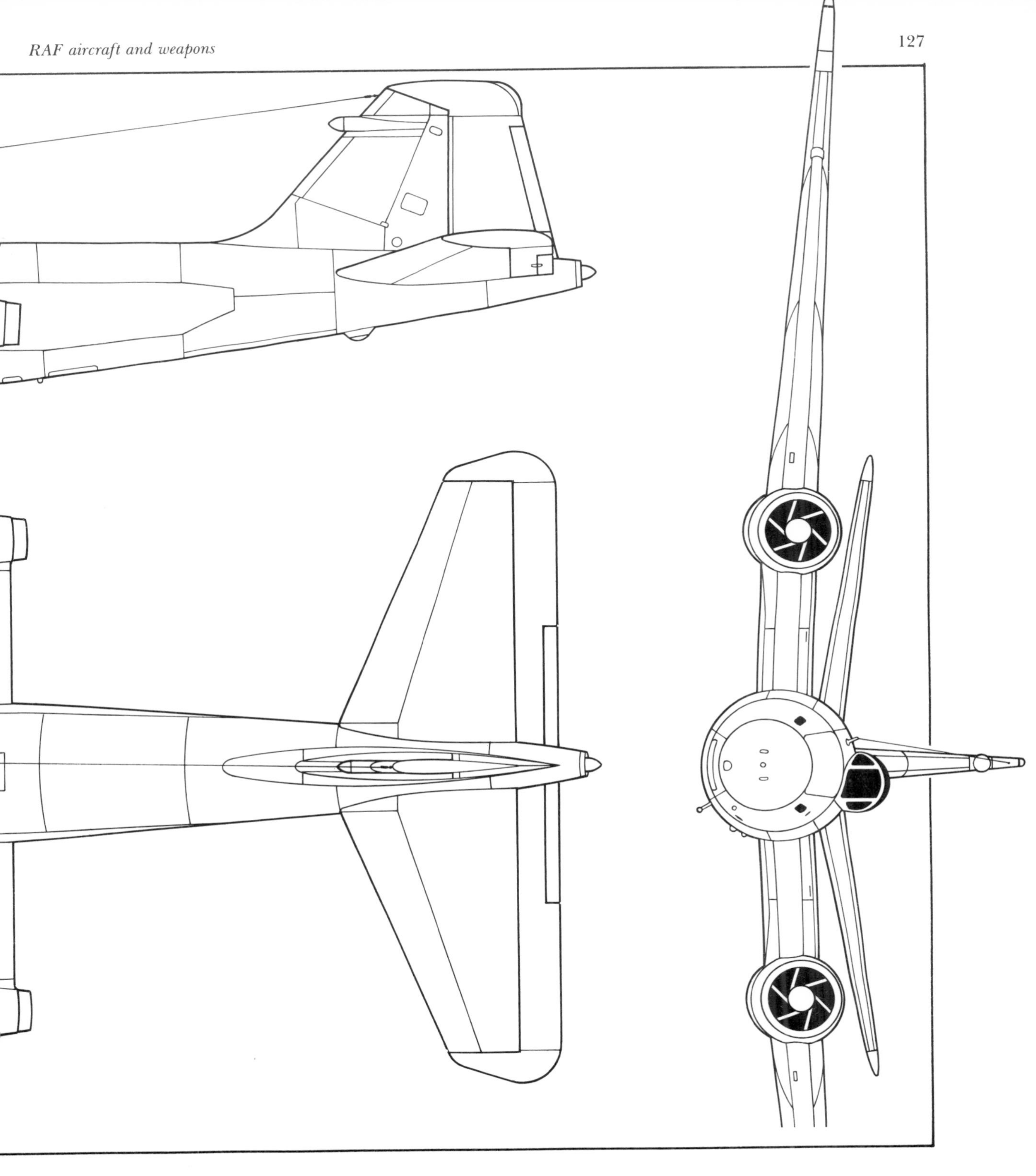

Loading a Window radar-jamming foil container into the wingtip pod of a No 360 Squadron Canberra T 17.

The OCU operates other marks as well but the main type is the Canberra T 4, a trainer version with two pilot positions side-by-side under the cockpit canopy and carrying a third crew member behind them.

No 100 Squadron uses a variety of Canberra marks ranging from the elderly B 2 which now has only a banner-towing function to perform for air-to-air cannon-firing practice. The Canberra E 15 is a high-altitude target aircraft used for the training of interceptor units. Another target aircraft is the Canberra TT 18 which is used to pull Rushton-type targets behind the aircraft from winches under each wing. These units are used by the Royal Navy and by Royal Artillery Rapier SAM units training on the Outer Hebrides ranges.

No 360 Squadron is an unusual unit in several ways, one being that it is an inter-Service squadron operated by Royal Air Force and Royal Navy personnel. It operates yet another Canberra mark, the T 17, the most easily recognisable of the remaining Canberra variants as it features a large nose section liberally studded with bulges and small radomes. The Canberra T 17 is intended for use as a radar and ECM source to train the radar operators and systems to work in the face of enemy electronic counter-measures, and is used not only by ground-based radar stations but also by airborne radar users such as the Shackleton AEW 2s. Such a useful training tool is required not only by the Royal Air Force but also by the Royal Navy, hence the inter-Service squadron manning.

Also at RAF Wyton is 1 Photographic Reconnaissance Unit (1 PRU) equipped with the last few Canberra PR 9s. These aircraft were among the most advanced of all the Canberra marks and feature a lengthened wing span (20.32 m) plus enlarged wing roots to enable the aircraft to gain high altitudes, and up-rated Avon 206 engines. They have fighter-type cockpit canopies in place of the Canberra's more usual bubble canopies and the crew is normally limited to two. Numerous cameras and other photographic sensors are carried in what was once the bomb bay area and under the forward fuselage. The Canberra PR 9 was designed for long range strategic reconnaissance at high altitude but the introduction of the space satellite and other technological novelties has tended to reduce the importance of the PR 9 in its design role. These days 1 PRU spends much of its time taking high altitude photographs for cartographic purposes, with the Director of Military Survey being a prime customer. To this end a section of Royal Engineer specialists, 1 Air Survey Liaison Section, is based alongside 1 PRU at RAF Wyton.

So the elderly Canberra will be around for a long time to come. It has given sterling front-line service in the past and there is no reason to think that in the support role it will be any less successful.

Tornado F Mark 2 and F Mark 3

Crew 2; **Span (swept)** 8.6 m; **Span (open)** 13.91 m; **Length** 18.082 m; **Height** 5.95 m; **Max take-off**

weight 27,986 kg; **Max weapon load** 8,500 kg; **Max speed clean** Mach 2.2; **Max endurance (no in-flight refuelling)** 2 hours; **Armament** 1 × 27 mm Mauser cannon, 4 × Sky Flash, 2 × Sidewinder; **Engines** (F Mark 3) 2 × Turbo-Union RB199-34R Mk 104s.

The Tornado GR 1 has an air combat capability but it is first and foremost a strike aircraft; self-defence weapons are limited to the two Mauser 27 mm cannon and any Sidewinder missiles that might be carried. When the Panavia team were putting the design of the Tornado together it became apparent that the Royal Air Force has a particular air defence task that is not shared by the other Panavia nations (West Germany and Italy), something that led to the introduction of an all-British Air Defence Variant (ADV) of the Tornado that was introduced for the United Kingdom alone. In 1971 an Air Staff Target (AST 395) was issued to cover the development of the ADV and in 1976 authorization for full scale development was provided. The first prototype flew in March 1984 and ever since then aircraft of one standard or another have been rolling off the production lines.

The Royal Air Force has ordered 165 Tornado ADVs. The first eighteen delivered have RB199-34R Mk 103 engines—these are the Tornado F 2. Subsequent batches are powered by the RB199-34R Mk 104 which has extended afterburner nozzles, leading to the designation Tornado F 3. The F 3s also have automatic wing sweep and a system known as the automatic manouevre device system for use during combat. Aircraft that reach the squadrons will be of the F 3 standard with the F 2s being retained by No 229 OCU at RAF Coningsby in Lincolnshire.

In time the Tornado F 3 will be the main equipment of No 11 Group. It will also be the most powerful interceptor and air defence aircraft the Royal Air Force has ever possessed for the Tornado F 3 is no mere local defence fighter. It can operate to long ranges over the North Sea and with in-flight refuelling can remain aloft for extended periods to allow it to operate over distances that range from Iceland and the Baltic to the English Channel; it can even play its part in the air defence of Central Europe and defend the United Kingdom's maritime forces. Its Foxhunter radar fire control system allows it to track targets flying at either extreme altitude or right down on the deck and it can track several targets at once. It can operate under extreme electronic warfare

Tornado F 2 prototype carrying four Sky Flash missiles.

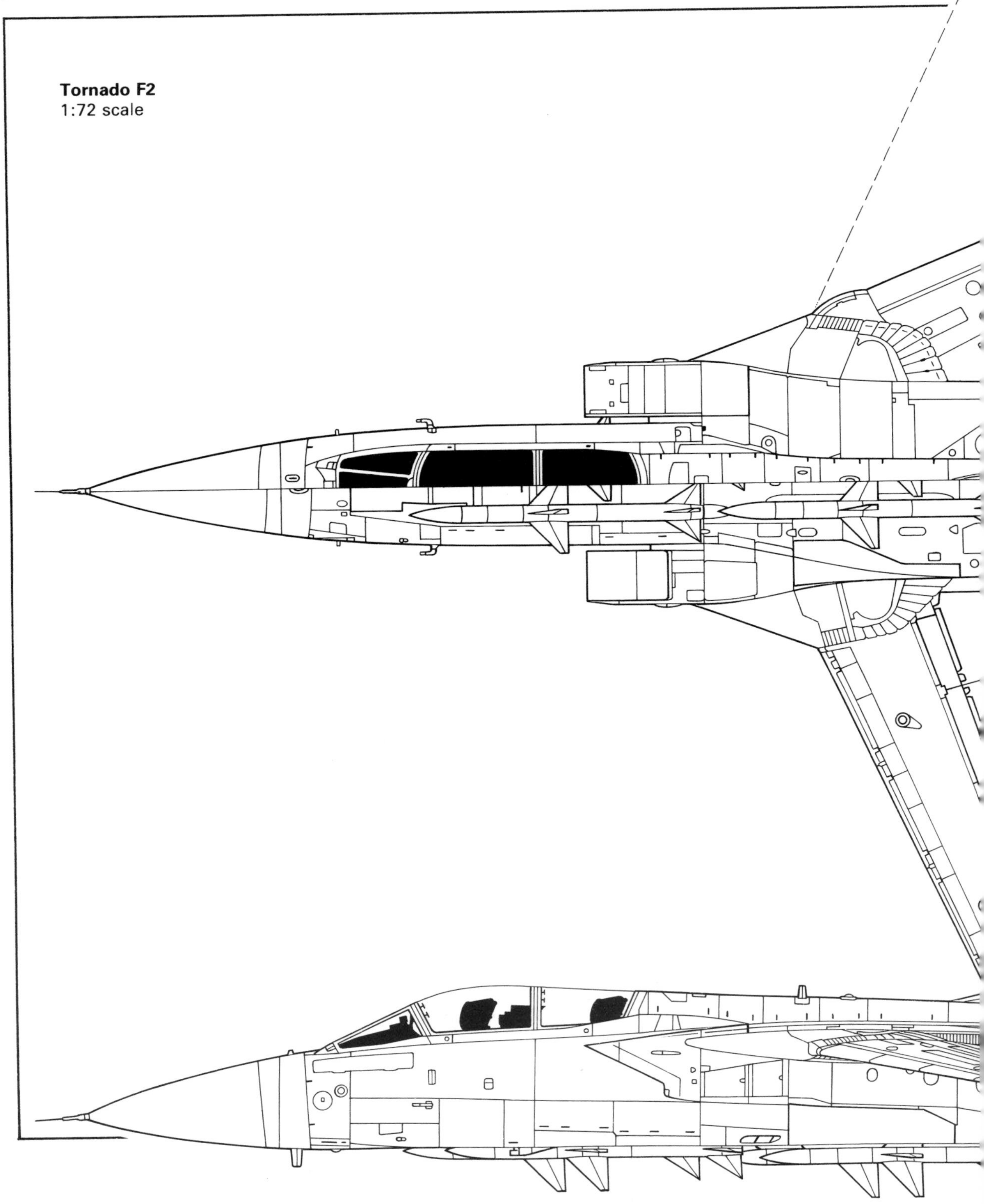
Tornado F2
1:72 scale

Photo montage of a Tornado ADV carrying Alarm anti-radiation missiles. These missiles have been selected as the main anti-radar weapons to be carried by RAF aircraft and should be in service in the late 1980s.

conditions and in all weathers. To cap all this it can operate from battle-damaged or otherwise shortened runways.

The airframe of the Tornado F 2 and 3 has 80 per cent commonality with the Tornado GR 1 but it is longer overall as the nose has been extended to accommodate the Foxhunter multi-mode radar. Four Sky Flash missiles can be carried under the fuselage in recesses and wing stations can carry more weapons or stores. The fuselage of the Tornado F 3 is packed with avionics of all description, not only relating to such items as digital fuel control but to data interface and transmission systems that allow each Tornado F 3 to act as an early warning aircraft for ground-based defences when required. A head-up display is provided for the pilot while the navigator in the back seat handles the various attack electronics in addition to his normal navigating duties. He is mainly responsible for the overall fire control system with all its various ramifications, not the least of which is that it can detect targets up to 185 kilometres away.

The only built-in armament for the Tornado F 3 is a single Mauser 27 mm IWKA cannon in the starboard side of the lower front fuselage. It is anticipated that the main interception weapons will be the four Sky Flash missiles, with AIM-9L Sidewinders for close-in defence. More advanced missiles are expected to be carried in the future. To extend mission or loiter time a fully-retractable in-flight refuelling probe is carried on the port side of the nose.

It is expected that most of the production total of 165 Tornado F 2 and F 3s will be based in the United Kingdom. Initial planning anticipates that the Tornados will replace most of the existing Phantoms but they will arrive too late to replace any Lightnings. It is expected that two squadrons will be based at RAF Leuchars, two at RAF Binbrook and three squadrons at RAF Leeming which is being virtually rebuilt to accommodate them. The first squadron to be fully equipped is rumoured to be No 29 Squadron, currently based at RAF Coningsby, home of No 229 OCU which was established during late 1984 to convert aircrew to the Tornado F 3.

Phantom FG Mark 1, FGR Mark 2 and **F-4J** (UK)
(Data for FGR Mark 2).
Crew 2; **Span** 11.77 m; **Length** 17.55 m; **Height** 5.02 m; **Max take-off weight** 26,308 kg; **Max speed** 1,464 km/h; **Armament** AIM-7 Sparrow, AIM-9 Sidewinder, 20 mm M61A1 Gatling Gun; **Engines** 2 × Rolls-Royce Spey 202 turbojets.

A political decision taken during the mid-1960s dictated that the Phantom aircraft ordered from McDonnell Douglas in the United States were to use Rolls-Royce Spey engines. The subsequent conversions to the airframe and the trials programme involved meant that not only was the unit cost per example much higher than if an existing model had been purchased 'off the shelf', but that a separate logistic supply line had to be established specifically for the British Phantoms. This had led to criticism that the Spey-engined Phantom is a lesser vehicle than the American originals, but is far from the truth for the 'British' Phantoms have performed well over many years. The years have to be mentioned for it was back in 1967 that the first Spey Phantoms commenced their flight and trials programmes.

The first 'British' Phantom was the Phantom FG 1 for the Fleet Air Arm. The second type was the Phantom FGR 2 for the Royal Air Force, which differed in several ways, in both detail and equipment, from the naval version. The Phantom FGR 2 took over many of the interceptor roles previously carried out by the Lightning and completely assumed the interceptor role in RAF Germany where Nos 19 and 92 Squadrons still fly from RAF Wildenrath. The United Kingdom-based Phantoms were augmented by Phantom FG 1s as they left Fleet Air Arm service but these ex-naval aircraft had to undergo a modification programme to bring them to somewhere near Royal Air Force standards, especially in the armament, for they had to be fitted with the 20 mm M61A1 Vulcan rotary cannon which operates along the same lines as the Gatling Gun of the last century. Today all the ex-Fleet Air Arm Phantom FG 1s are based at one location at RAF Leuchars with Nos 43 and 111 Squadrons.

Above *A little piece of RAF history is made as a FGR 2 of No 23 Squadron touches down at RAF Stanley after the long flight from the United Kingdom. The new low visibility grey colour scheme makes the small pastel-shade roundels almost invisible.*

Left *56 Squadron FGR 2 in its Quick Readiness Alert hangar at RAF Wattisham.*

Far left *Phantom FGR 2 with a full load of Sparrow missiles.*

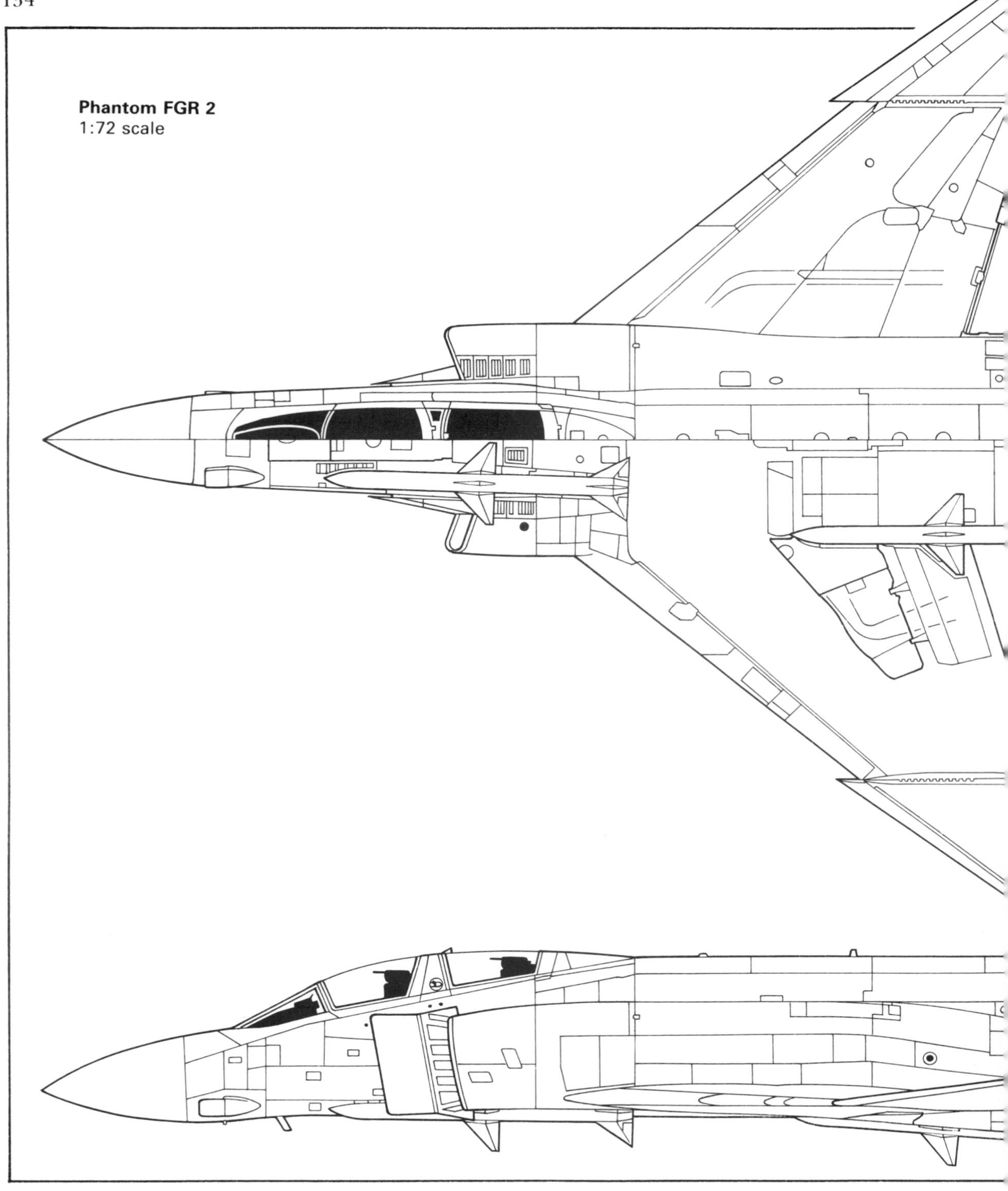
Phantom FGR 2
1:72 scale

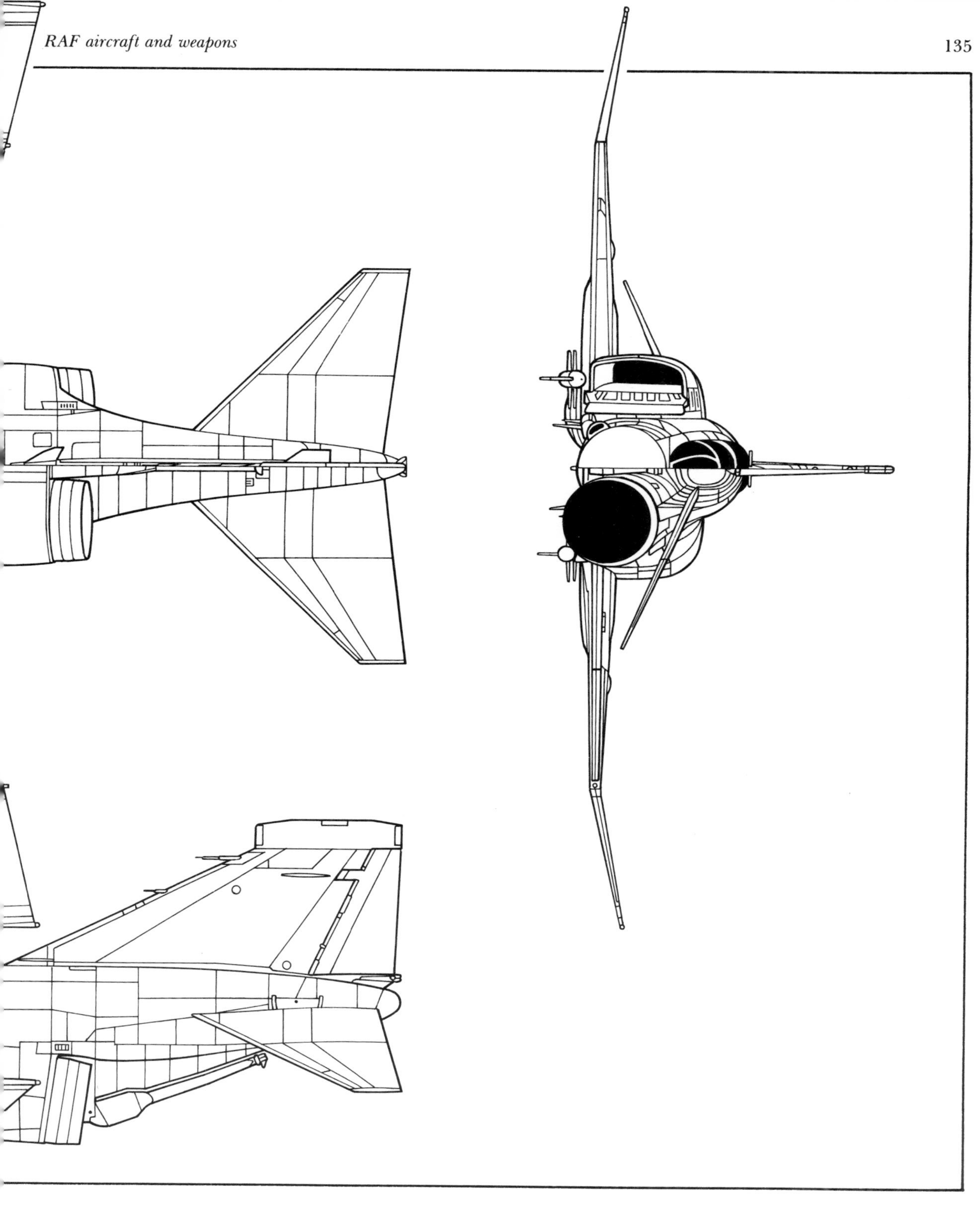

Phantom FG 1 of 111 Squadron at RAF Leuchars.

At the time of writing the Phantom FGR 2s involved in the defence of the United Kingdom are operated by No 56 Squadron at RAF Wattisham and No 29 Squadron at RAF Coningsby. RAF Coningsby is also the base for No 228 OCU which includes No 64 Squadron as a 'shadow' squadron for employment in an emergency. No 23 Squadron used to be based as part of the defence of the United Kingdom but is now far away to the south at RAF Mount Pleasant in the Falkland Islands. At one time No 29 Squadron supplied a detachment to stand guard over Wideawake airfield in the Ascension Islands, and no doubt it would re-assume this task if necessary, but the absence of so many Phantoms from the United Kingdom left the home defences over-stretched. The RAF Germany squadrons are committed to NATO and cannot be drawn upon so in the end the only answer was to order more aircraft direct from the United States. This order was made during late 1982 and the new aircraft were delivered direct off the shelf with as few modifications from the usual US Navy standard as possible—there was neither the money nor the time to allow another re-run of fitting out with British equipment and engines as had been carried out in the mid-1960s. The Phantoms involved were of the F-4J model with General Electric J79 engines and other items unique to the type. These aircraft are known to the RAF as the Phantom F-4J(UK) and understandably they are used by only one squadron (the original order was described as being for 'at least' 12, but is actually 15), No 74 Squadron at RAF Wattisham. This allows all unique equipment and spares holdings etc to be concentrated on one station only.

The new aircraft will be a useful reinforcement for the air defence of the United Kingdom, for the Phantoms have now been in service so long that normal attrition rates and other accidents have reduced the original purchase of 170 (51 FG 1s; 118 FGR 2s) to only about 110. In the foreseeable future many of the Phantoms will be replaced by the Tornado F 3 although there are no current plans to re-equip the two RAF Germany squadrons with this type. So, the Phantom will be around for some time to come and despite its design age it remains a potent and effective interceptor. It can also undertake other roles, including ground attack, and little alteration other than hanging on a few pods would enable it to carry out the reconnaissance role. As an interceptor its radar and missile armament combined with its possible range and speed makes it a formidable opponent. For long range interception of supersonic targets the

Phantoms can carry four American AIM-7 Sparrow radar-guided air-to-air missiles in recessed positions under the fuselage. These missiles can tackle all manner of targets flying at altitudes from sea level to the stratosphere. For close-in combat the Phantoms can carry the AIM-9 Sidewinder on four wing pylons. The 20 mm rotary cannon with its very high rate of fire (a maximum of 6,600 rpm) is also a very potent weapon in air-to-air combat.

The Lightnings

Crew 1; **Span** 10.61 m; **Length overall** 16.84 m; **Height** 5.97 m; **Normal take-off weight** 18,144 kg; **Max speed** 2,110 km/h; **Armament (F 6)** 2 × Red Top missiles, 2 × 30 mm Aden guns in ventral pack; **Engines** 2 × Rolls-Royce Avon 301s.

The Lightning interceptor aircraft entered Royal Air Force service in 1960 and has been around ever since as a local interceptor aircraft, usually as part of the air defence of the United Kingdom. It has a stupendous climb rate and a high maximum speed but throughout its Service life it has generally suffered from a lack of operational range mainly caused by the high fuel consumption of the vertically-stacked Rolls-Royce Avon turbojets and their thirsty afterburners. Thus, when more efficient aircraft in the shape of the Phantoms came along, the Lightnings were gradually phased out. That process began in 1971 but the type is still in use as a short-range interceptor.

Inside one of the RAF Binbrook Aircraft Servicing Flight (ASF) hangars with, nearest to the camera, two No 11 Squadron aircraft.

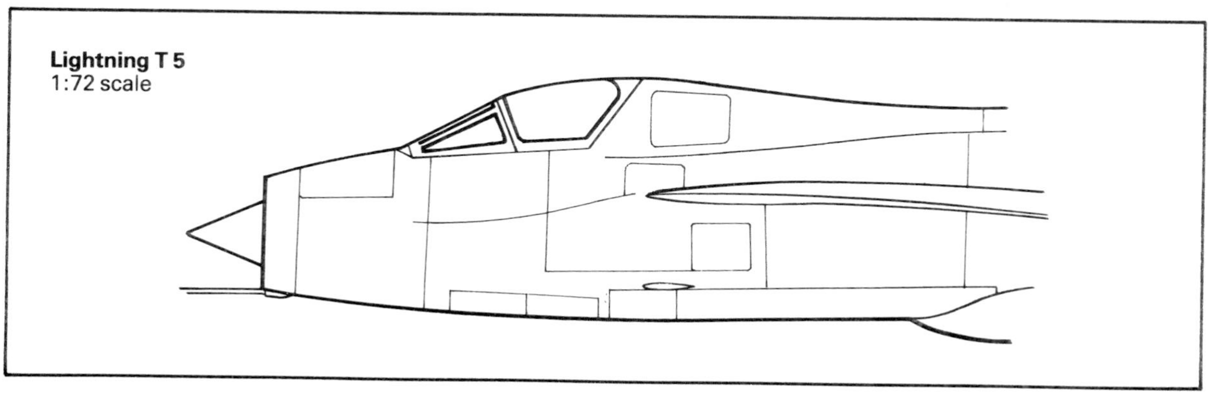

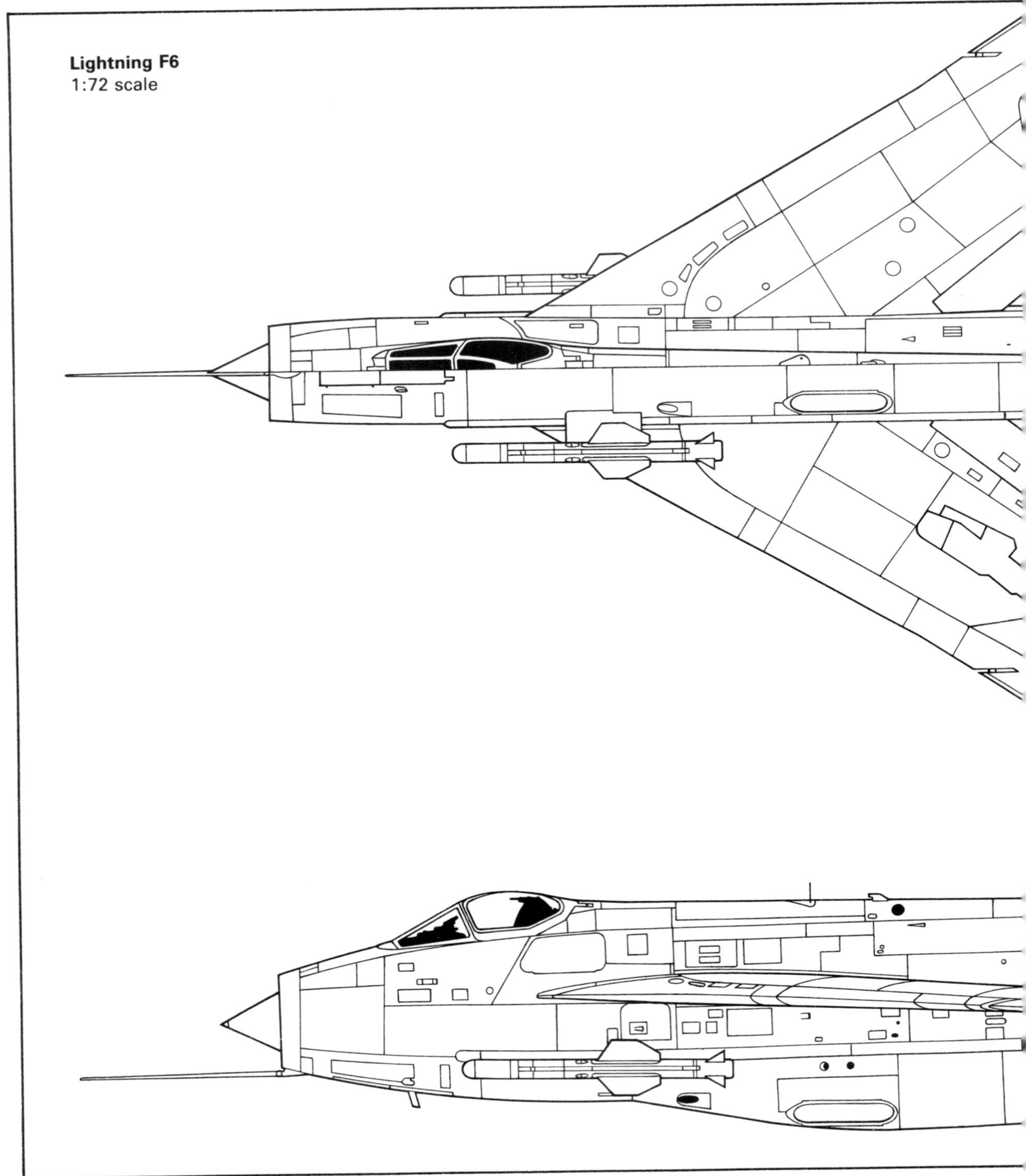
Lightning F6
1:72 scale

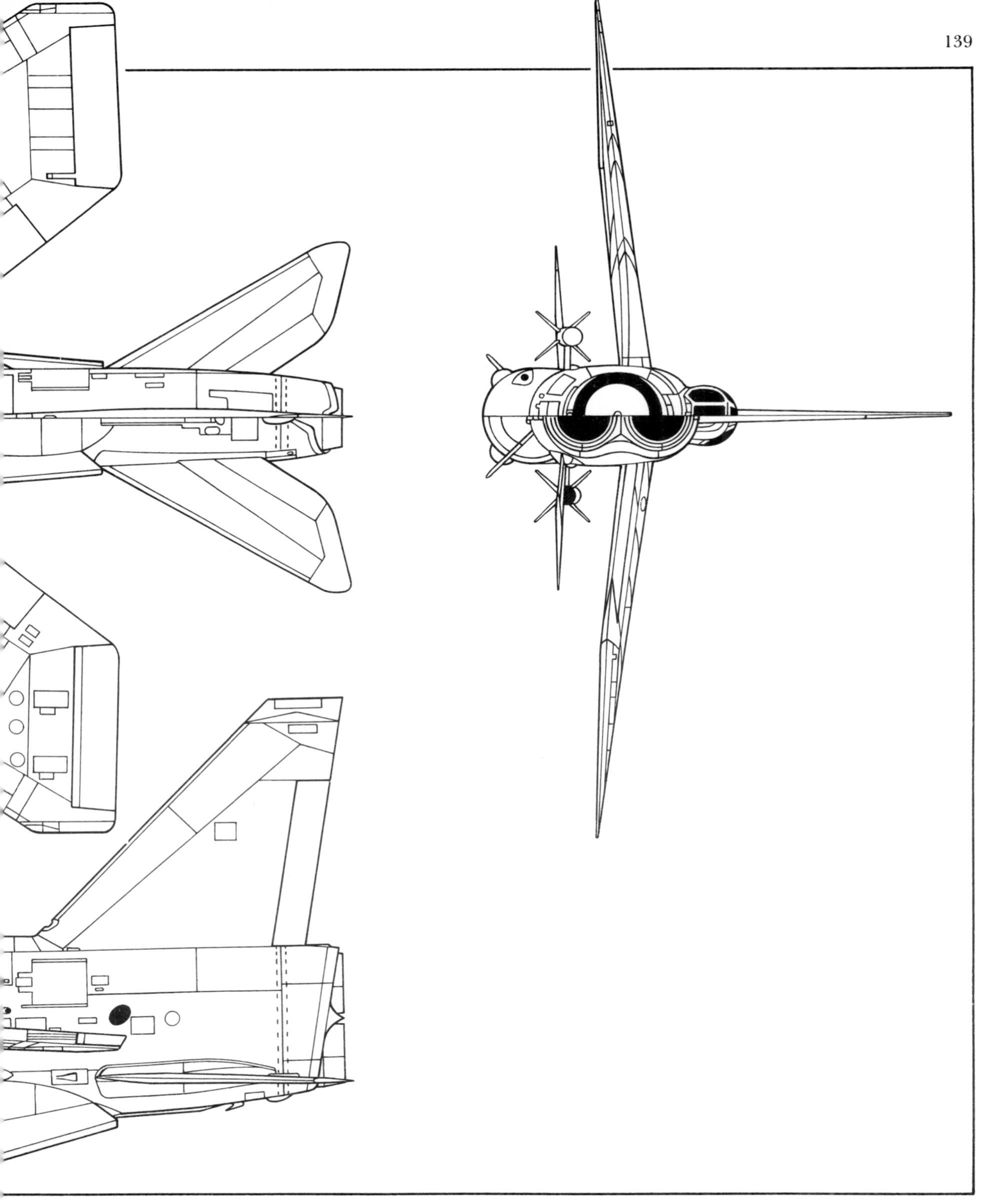

Above *RAF Binbrook Lightning F6.*

Above right *Hunter T 7 showing the single 'Sabrina' for the 30mm Aden Gun carried.*

Today only two Lightning squadrons remain and it seems very likely that by the time these words are published at least one of those will have been disbanded. The two squadrons are Nos 5 and 11, both of them based on the only remaining Lightning station, RAF Binbrook. All the RAF's remaining Lightning servicing and other facilities are concentrated at RAF Binbrook, including the Lightning Aircraft Servicing Flight which valiantly manages to keep the venerable Lightnings airworthy. There is also the Lightning Engineering and Support Flight that is tasked with holding and maintaining reserve aircraft for exercises and other purposes. The Lightning Training Flight (LTF) has already been disbanded.

The Lightning marks still in use are the F 3, F 6 and two-seater T 5. Most of the RAF Binbrook Lightnings are F 6s armed with Red Top or Firestreak missiles and with provision for over-wing ferry tanks. These tanks are used when the squadrons carry out their annual Armament Practice Camps, usually air-to-air firing, at sunny RAF Akrotiri in Cyprus.

The Lightning F 6 can also carry a ventral fuel tank that houses two 30 mm Aden cannon and their ammunition. The Lightning T 5 is a two-seat version of the F 3 with two pilots seated side-by-side. Although intended for conversion and advanced training, the Lightning T 5 can have a full operational role in which case one crew member can concentrate on the flying while the other manages the radar and weapon systems.

It now seems very likely that the last Lightnings will be retired just before the first Tornado F 3 squadrons become fully operational. Exactly what will happen to the Lightnings has yet to be announced. Some will no doubt find their way to museums while others will carry on flying as high speed or other types of hack at various aircraft establishments. Some might make their last flights as unmanned drone targets on missile ranges. That seems rather unlikely in view of the conversion costs involved so it is more possible that others might end up in the same undignified manner as numbers of the earlier marks of Lightning once they were retired. They can still be seen on some RAF Germany and United Kingdom airfields staked out in the open to act as decoy targets in the case of an air attack.

RAF Binbrook is to become one of the bases for the Tornado F 3 squadrons.

The Hunters

Crew 1 or 2; **Span** 10.26 m; **Length, single seat** 13.98 m; **Length, two seat** 14.9 m; **Height** 4.26 m; **Weight (FGA 9, max take-off)** 10,885 kg; **Max speed (FGA 9)** 1,144 km/h; **Armament** 2 or 4 × 30 mm Aden guns, bombs/rockets; **Engine** 1 × Rolls-Royce Avon 203 or 207.

The Hunter has had a long and distinguished service life with the Royal Air Force since the mid-1950s but very soon that service life will end and the last link with a former era will be broken. In its time the Hunter has been used as a fighter, ground attack fighter, photo reconnaissance aircraft, research platform and trainer. All its former combat duties have now terminated and today only a few are managing to remain in the Service by acting as training and check-out aircraft for the Buccaneer

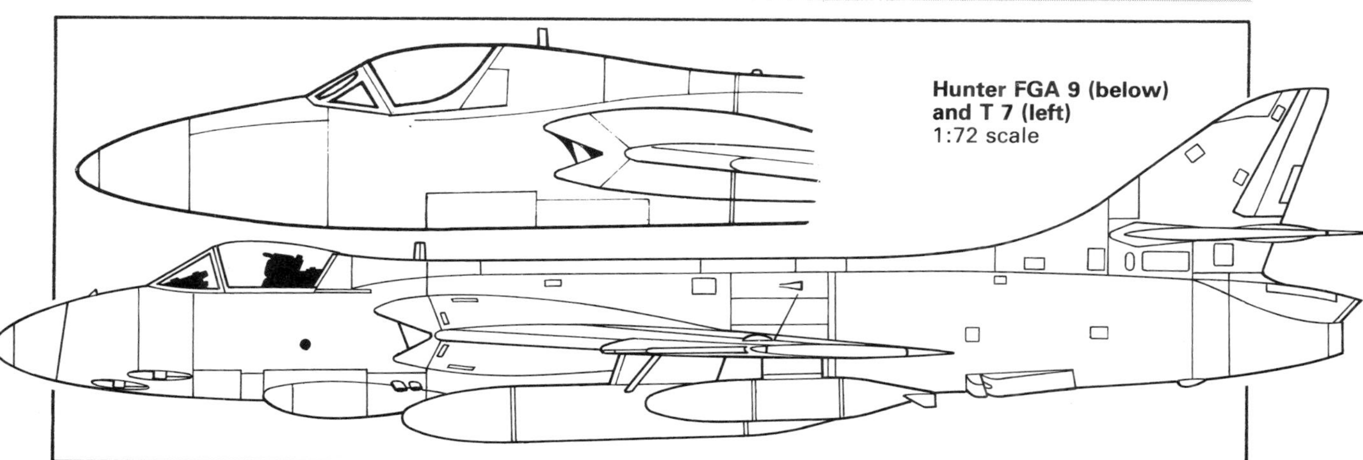

Hunter FGA 9 (below) and T 7 (left)
1:72 scale

OCU (No 237) at RAF Lossiemouth. These aircraft, a mix of T 7B, T 8B and T 8C (the latter being ex-Fleet Air Arm aircraft), are two-seaters fitted with cockpit instrument layouts and controls similar to those of the Buccaneer S 2. This allows them to be flown for training and check-out purposes at a lower cost than the larger Buccaneers, thereby saving money for the taxpayer. A few Hunters manage to remain flying with various aircraft establishments but their numbers are dwindling and the day when Service Hunters are no more appears to be in sight.

When that day comes it will be a sad one for the Hunter was not only a highly successful aircraft in its day but also a highly attractive one and perhaps one of the most photogenic flying machines ever to take to the sky. Many airmen and ex-airmen will miss the Hunter.

Nimrod MR Mark 1, MR Mark 2, MR Mark 2P and R Mark 2

Crew 3 + 9; **Span** 35 m; **Length** 38.63 m; **Height** 9.08 m; **Max take-off weight** 80,150 kg (MR 1); **Max speed** 926 km/h; **Typical ferry range** 8,340–9,265 km; **Normal endurance** 12 hours; **Armament** Sidewinder, Harpoon missiles, up to 9 torpedoes, bombs, sonobuoys and markers; **Engines** 4 × Rolls-Royce RB 168-20 Spey Mark 250 Turbofans.

The design work for the aircraft that was to replace the Shackleton in the maritime reconnaissance role began in mid-1964 and Government authorization to proceed was given the following year. Hawker Siddeley were the prime contractors although their name has now been submerged into the British Aerospace conglomerate. The Hawker Siddeley design was their HS 801 based on the

Nimrod MR 2
1:168 scale

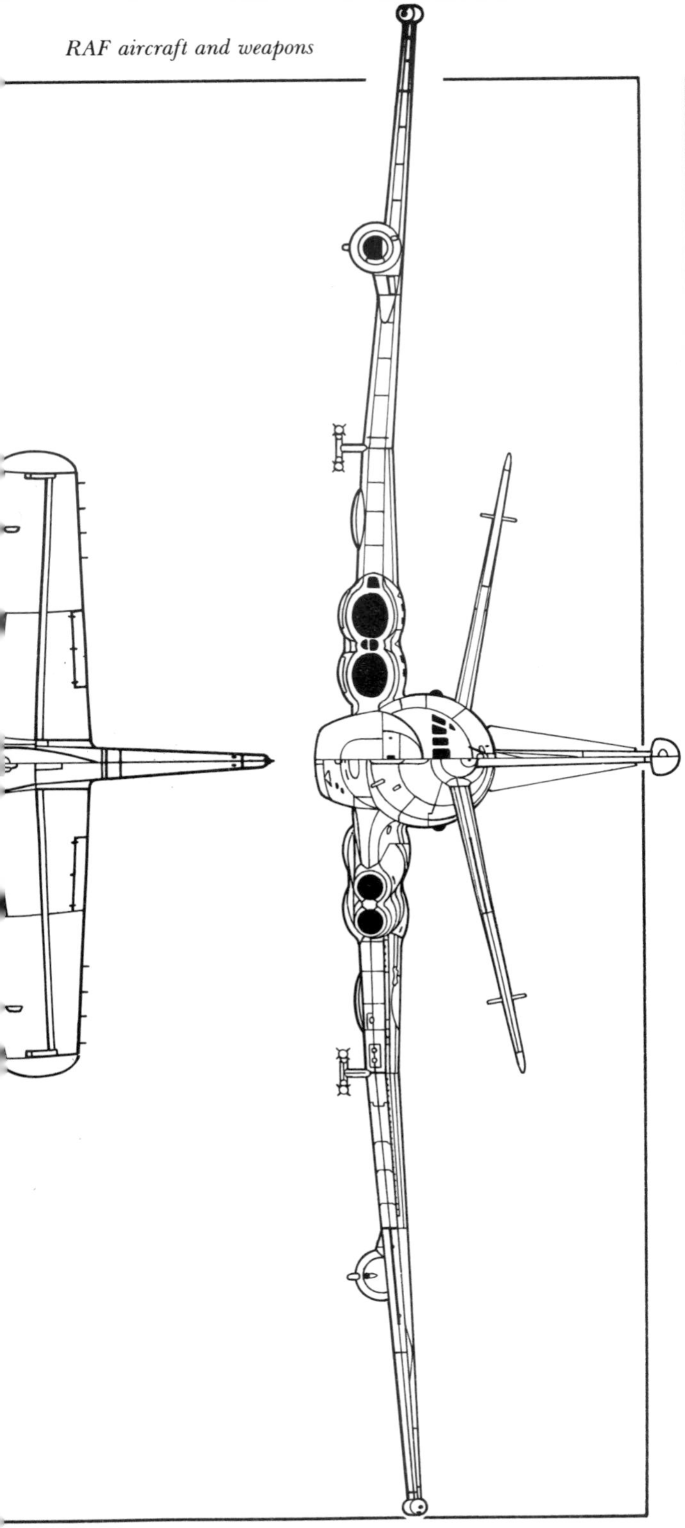

The routine navigation station on board a Nimrod.

Comet 4C airframe. In fact the first two prototypes were flown using converted Comet 4C airframes, the first flying on May 23 1967. The first production version flew during June 1968, by which time the aircraft designation had become Nimrod MR 1. The initial order was for 46 aircraft, of which 43 were scheduled to be delivered as Nimrod MR 1s. In fact this early clear-cut plan did not materialize for the 46 aircraft began to be used as the basis for revised plans. Three of the original aircraft were converted to act as development aircraft for the Nimrod AEW 3 programme and a further eight airframes were earmarked for the same project. Almost as soon as they were delivered a conversion programme to bring the Nimrod MR 1s up to a new Nimrod MR 2 standard was initiated. 31 aircraft were scheduled to be brought up to MR 2 standard and by the time these words are published that programme may well have been completed. To complicate matters still further numbers of Nimrod MR 2s have been further updated to accommodate AIM-9L Sidewinders on underwing pylons, an in-flight refuelling probe has been added over the cockpit and Loral electronic packs have been added to the wing tips. These modifications have meant that the tailplane has now been fitted with extra directional strakes and has resulted in yet another designation, this time Nimrod MR 2P.

Nimrod MR 1; most MR 1s have now been converted to MR 2 standards.

The Nimrod has been described as the most complex airborne system to enter service with the Royal Air Force. In this context the word 'system' is well chosen for the Nimrod is really a flying weapons platform devoted to maritime reconnaissance and anti-submarine warfare rather than an airframe. The airframe itself can readily be seen to have Comet antecedents as the main fuselage has been adapted from the commercial original. From the cockpit rearwards the main pressurised fuselage has been retained, but slung underneath it is a long unpressurised pannier that contains the main weapons bay and equipment storage space, while the glass fibre radome is slung forward under the nose. At the extreme rear is the magnetic anomaly detector (MAD) boom. The wings are of obvious Comet parentage with the leading-edge pods retained and the tail unit is visually adapted from that of the Comet but with the addition of a glass fibre pod on the top to contain electronic surveillance measures (ESM) equipment. The engine arrangements have been enlarged to accommodate the four Rolls-Royce Speys in place of the Comet's Avons and the result is an aesthetically attractive military aircraft that belies its operational capabilities.

The Nimrod's fuselage is packed with all manner of electronic equipment. Forward, its cockpit appears conventional enough for an aircraft of its size and accommodates the pilot, co-pilot and the flight engineer. Behind the cockpit is the main tactical compartment and here are housed the routine navigator, the tactical navigator, the radio operator, the radar operator, two sonic systems operators, the ESM/MAD operator and two observers who also act as stores loaders. At the heart of the Nimrod avionics is a large tactical display screen controlled from a central digital computer. On this display can be presented all manner of information, including aircraft position and tracks, sonobuoy positions and range circles, ESM bearings, MAD information, radar bearings and visual information. Using the computer, flight information can be presented to the pilot in the front cockpit, but if required the computer can directly feed the aircraft's autopilot to allow the tactical navigator to direct the aircraft to a predicted

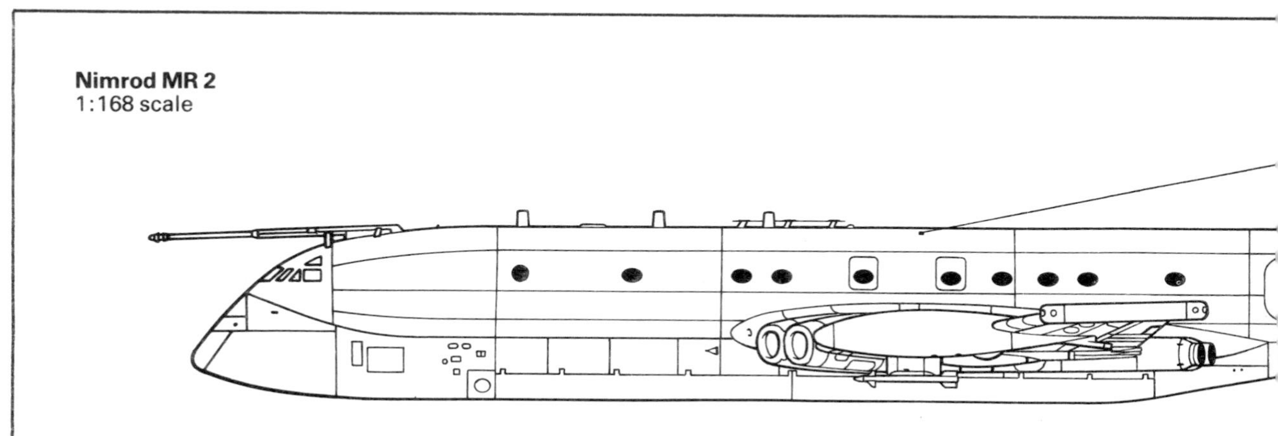

target interception or a weapon release point. This tactical display is coupled to virtually all the other sensors mounted in the Nimrod; on the MR 2 the most obvious of these sensors is the nose-mounted Thorn EMI Searchwater radar which has its own data processing sub-system. Searchwater is resistant to counter-measures and can provide a much improved range and overall performance than the equivalent in the MR 1.

Another improvement in the MR 2 is the acoustics processing and display system which can be used with a wide array of sonobuoy types, both active and passive. It must be stressed that all these sensors are integrated by the central computer and display system in such a manner that they become part of a weapon system. While the sensors combine to discover and analyse targets and their position, track, etc, those targets still have to be eliminated and here the massive weapon bay of the Nimrod comes into play. The bay in the under-slung pannier can accommodate up to six lateral rows of weapons. A separate bay in the rear of the fuselage is used for the sonobuoys and markers. Under each wing are hardpoints for the carriage of missiles, rockets or cannon pods. These weapon pods were used during the Falkland Islands campaign when Nimrods operating from the base on Ascension Island were equipped with Sidewinder and Harpoon missiles. Another Falkland campaign addition was the provision of an in-flight refuelling boom over the cockpit area which enabled flight endurances of up to 19 hours to be carried out (the normal endurance with in-flight refuelling is about 12 hours).

In times of peace Nimrods are used for all manner of maritime surveillance other than anti-submarine activities, although training exercises are constantly being carried out. Nimrods are used for general coastal patrol, keeping an eye on the North Sea oil installations and also for fishery patrol. In the latter role the Nimrod crews often employ special Agiflite hand-held cameras to record the presence of suspicious small craft that might be transgressing the various fishing laws (including the seemingly ever-present 'trawlers' from Warsaw Pact fleets). These cameras are used from the large vision 'bubbles' on each side of the fuselage and have the facility of not only recording the image of the craft involved but also of recording the position, time, etc, of the target, which is fed into the camera from the aircraft's central navigation system.

The Electronics Surveillance Measures Operator on a Nimrod.

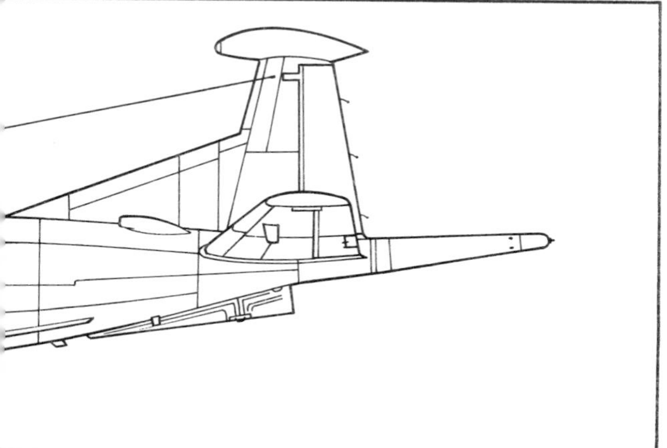

Another electronic gadget that can be called into play in the Nimrod system is a crew training device known as the ACT-1 (Airborne Crew Trainer Mark 1). Most anti-submarine exercises are carried out at considerable ranges from the land and using expensive sonobuoys. The ACT-1 is a form of electronic computer-controlled device that can feed in simulated information under the control of a crew member. Displayed on the central tactical display, this can be used to test drills and reactions without the expenditure of stores, and at times when the crews have nothing else to do.

The squadrons using the Nimrod MR 2 are No

A Nimrod MR 2 of No 206 Squadron, RAF Kinloss, sporting the new 'hemp' colour scheme and flying over one of the many North Sea oil rigs on its 'beat'.

42 Squadron at St Mawgan in Cornwall and Nos 120, 201 and 206 Squadrons, all at RAF Kinloss in Scotland. Aircraft from these squadrons are currently operating from Ascension Island, and may at times operate from such outlying bases as RAF Gibraltar. The OCU is No 236 at RAF St Mawgan.

At this point mention must be made of three Nimrods that are among the Royal Air Force's least-known aircraft. These are the three Nimrod R 2s belonging to No 51 Squadron of Strike Command and based at RAF Wyton in Huntingdonshire. Delivered in 1972, these Nimrods are over and above the initial order for 46 and differ from the maritime Nimrods by having no MAD boom behind the tail, while the forward sections of their wing pods house electronic aerial fairings. All three of these Nimrod R 2s are used for the gathering of electronic intelligence (elint) from all manner of sources and have been discovered by the Royal Swedish Air Force operating over the Baltic Sea.

The Nimrod will provide the Royal Air Force with its main maritime reconnaissance component until well into the 1990s and maybe beyond then. It is a large and expensive piece of equipment but it is a lethal weapon system for use against submarines and other vessels. The complex electronics also provide the Royal Air Force with a sound basis in advanced systems of their type and here the Service is well provided to carry forward the technology that will be required for the future.

AWACS

(Data provisional)
Crew up to 20; **Span** 44.42 m; **Length** 46.61 m; **Height** 12.73 m; **Radome diameter** 9.14 m; **Max take-off weight** 147,417kg; **Max speed** 853 km/h; **Armament** nil; **Engines** 4 × CFM International F108-CF-100 (CFM56-2A-2)

It is now part of aviation history that the RAF was supposed to procure the Nimrod AEW 3 for the airborne early warning aircraft role but that did not happen. The Nimrod AEW 3, a derivative of the Nimrod MR 2 but with nothing in common with that aircraft apart from the basic airframe, had been under development for nine years by late 1986 and its planned in-service date of 1984 had slipped by. The main reasons were the expensive GEC radar and electronic systems which proved to be either not up to specification, too unreliable or still under development. Despite constant promises that more time would put things right the AEW 3's system simply would not offer any immediate prospect that they would ever work properly and in the end the RAF was forced to ask for the Boeing AWACS system, something which the RAF had really wanted way back in 1977 when the whole programme was initiated and which is already in NATO and US Air Force service. (The already-completed Nimrod AEW 3 airframes will not be wasted. In time they will be used for various electronic warfare development, training and target purposes).

In 1986 the AWACS decision was announced to a mixed reception for the RAF is to (initially) get only six, with another two on option, and the first of them will not arrive until 1991. The cost will be £860 million for the first six fully-equipped aircraft but a great proportion of these costs will be off-set by the production of many system and other components in the United Kingdom.

The Boeing AWACS (Airborne Warning and Control System) version for the RAF will probably be delivered with its systems installed up to the US Air Force E-3C Sentry standard, complete with the fuel-efficient CFM56 turbofan engines in place of the earlier Pratt & Whitney engines. If normal RAF designation procedures are followed the aircraft will probably be known as the Sentry AEW 1 and it seems likely that No. 8 Squadron will eventually operate them from RAF Waddington.

Based on the airframe of the Boeing 707 airliner,

the first AWACS development commenced in 1970 and after a complicated evolution the last of a batch of 35 for the US Air Force was delivered in 1984. A composite NATO force received a further 18 systems (which differ somewhat from the American version) and Saudi Arabia ordered a fleet of eight with a somewhat simpler data handling system.

The E-3C Sentry is immediately recognisable by the large circular radome carried over the fuselage and which rotates at an operational speed of six revolutions per minute. The radome contains the aerial for the core AN/APY-1 surveillance radar, the heart of the AWACS system but this radar is but one of many sensor systems that enable the aircraft to detect targets up to 370 kilometres away and track them to transmit target data to ground stations or to other aircraft. On-board computers process all the data obtained and make the data handling and display processes virtually automatic. The US Air Force and NATO use their AWACS systems for airborne command and control stations as well as target detection and it seems very likely that the RAF will take up this capability even if the full system does take up to 17 personnel to operate or supervise in addition to the basic flight crew of three or four. For long periods on station relief crews may have to be carried.

The main operational advantage of the Boeing AWACS system is that it is operational *now* and has been repeatedly demonstrated to be thoroughly efficient and reliable. Both the US Air Force and NATO have been using the system for some years and more experience has been accumulated by Saudi Arabia so by the time the RAF gets its aircraft all the various systems will have been thoroughly checked out and brought up to the very latest operational standards.

As the RAF will be getting only six AWACS aircraft this is not enough to maintain constant surveillance over all the possible approaches to the United Kingdom and it seems very likely that time on station will have to be extended by in-flight refuelling — the extra two aircraft will have to be obtained eventually if a constant on-watch capability is to be maintained.

In the meantime the remaining Shackleton AEW 2s will have to carry on as best they can until well past their expected retirement time.

A US Air Force E-3A Sentry. The E-3C standard aircraft for the RAF will be similar in appearance but will have CFM56 turbofans that are chubbier than the Pratt & Whitney engines shown here.

AWACS
1:300 scale

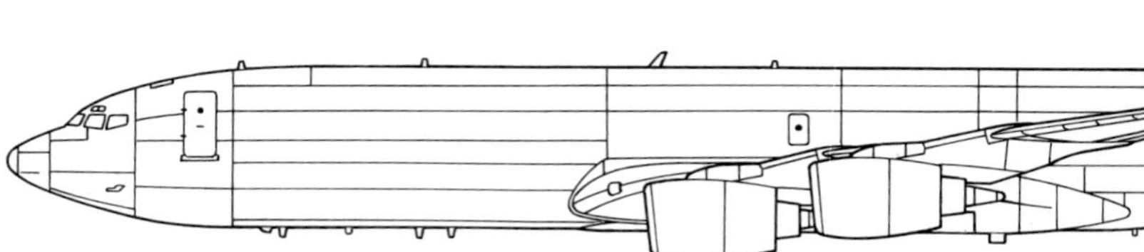

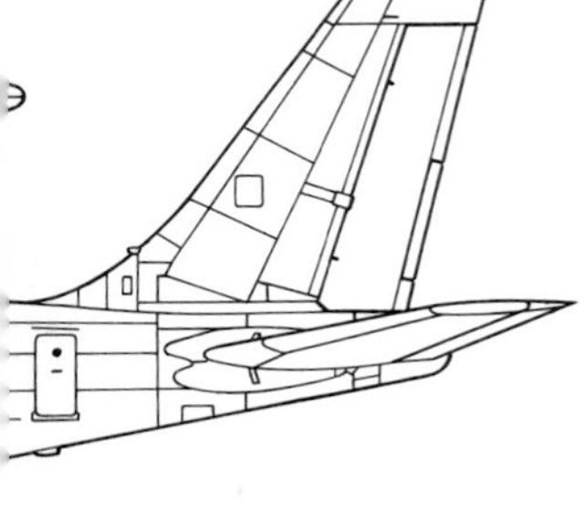

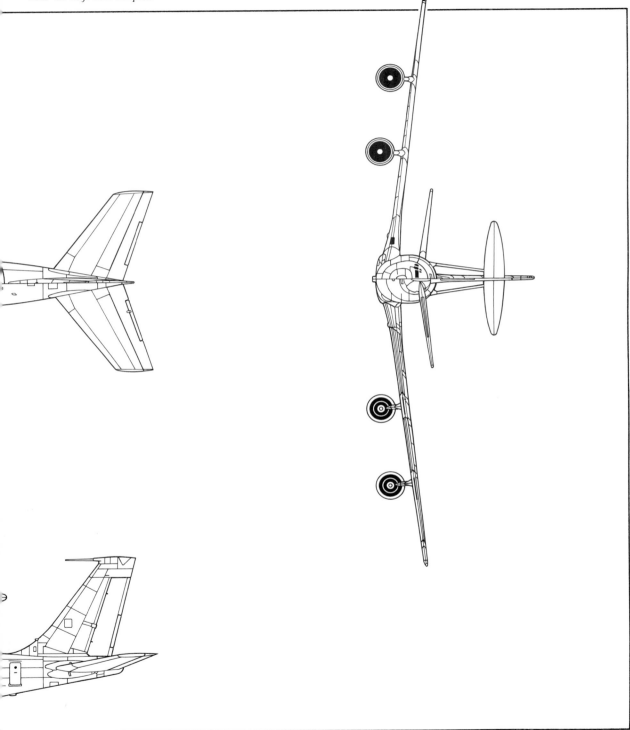

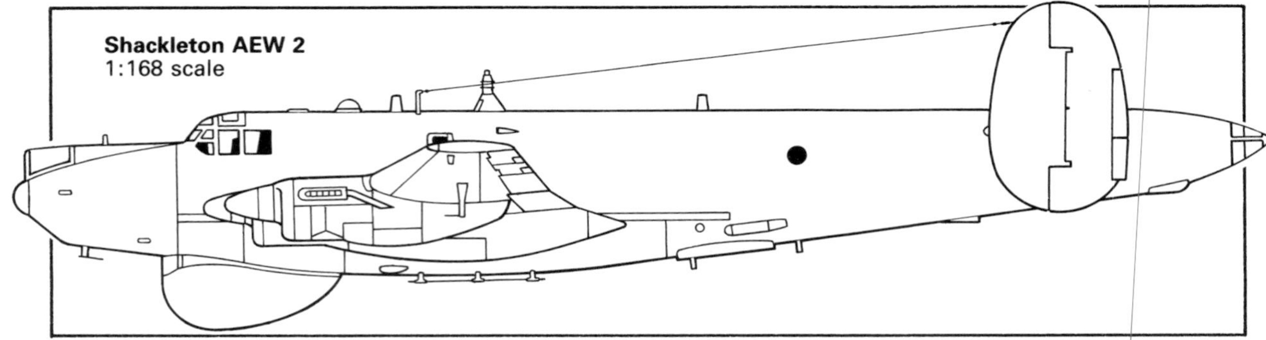

Shackleton AEW 2 of No 8 Squadron, RAF Lossiemouth.

Shackleton AEW Mark 2

Crew 4 + 6–8; **Span** 36.52 m; **Length** 26.62 m; **Height** 5.1 m; **Weight** 44,450 kg; **Max speed** 439 km/h; **Max range** 4,665 km; **Armament** nil; **Engines** 4 × Rolls-Royce Griffon 57As.

When the last Shackleton leaves the Royal Air Force the Service will have lost a link that can be traced back to the Avro Manchester of 1939. From the abortive Manchester came the immortal Lancaster and from that came the Lincoln. The first Shackleton, which flew in March 1949, was an advanced development of the Lincoln, and ever since the Shackleton MR 1 entered service during 1951 the type has been giving sterling service all over the world. From the Shackleton MR 1 came the MR 2 which was the type in service in largest numbers. The Shackleton MR 3 was a considerable advance on the MR 2 but, when it was decided to improve the overall high speed performance of the tricycle-undercarriage MR 3 by the addition of two Viper turbojets, it spelt the demise of the mark for the resultant stresses produced severely curtailed the airframe life. They were replaced as soon as possible by the Nimrod MR 1 and the Nimrod also took over from the remaining Shackleton MR 2s.

The MR 2s now found a new role in airborne early warning, at first mainly for the Royal Navy but increasingly for the overall air defence of the United Kingdom. Twelve Shackleton MR 2s were coverted to the AEW 2 mark, mainly by the addition of a AN/APS-20 search radar mounted under the cockpit area and a revision of the internal layout to suit the new equipment involved. These aircraft were delivered during 1971 and ever since have been used by No 8 Squadron, currently based at RAF Lossiemouth, Morayshire. The original 12 aircraft have now been reduced to six by a combination of airframe fatigue and defence spending cutbacks, and these will eventually be replaced by AWACS.

Despite the age and discomfort of the 'Shack', it has been around so long that it has virtually become a fixture in the Royal Air Force. There will be few involved who will actually mourn its passing for it is a noisy aircraft in which to work and fly and the internal fixtures belong to a past generation when aircrew comfort was little regarded. Despite this, the Shackleton in all its forms has survived for over 30 years in the most punishing of all aviation environments, namely flying at low altitudes in all weathers across the wide expanses of ocean and their salt-laden skies. Over the years numerous ground crew have done their bit to 'keep them flying' and a measure of their long-term success can be seen in the fact that the surviving Shackletons still have forecast airframe lives reaching into the next century.

The crew of the Shackleton AEW 2 comprises the pilot, co-pilot, navigator and a flight engineer along with a variable number of personnel to operate the AEW equipment. These include a tactical co-ordinator (TACO), an AEW controller, a radio and radar operator, and three or more AEW operators. They combine to form a team that can detect enemy aircraft over the sea and transmit their track and other such data to a ground station to alert interceptor aircraft and then guide them to their targets. Most of the No 8 Squadron task is carried out over the North Sea but the squadron also has a responsibility for the AEW role to naval vessels in the eastern Atlantic (EASTLANT). The squadron has a search and rescue (SAR) function as well, for which role the aircraft carry Lindholme rescue gear and smoke and marker floats.

The crews of the Shackleton AEW 2s do their best to make life bearable during the long patrols that can last 12 hours or more—the maximum is about 15 hours and there is no in-flight refuelling capability. Throughout that time the noise produced by the Griffon engines and their contra-rotating propellers can become a trifle wearisome so, food, using the aircraft galley for preparation, becomes an important distraction on any mission agenda. On exercises one crew member is usually detailed off as 'chef' and by all accounts the menu is worthy of consideration. No doubt this 'ex Coastal' attribute will be carried over to AWACS.

VC 10 C Mark 1

Crew 4 + 150 passengers; **Span** 44.55 m; **Length** 48.36 m; **Height** 12.04 m; **Max take-off weight** 146,510 kg; **Max speed** 914 km/h; **Armament** nil; **Engines** 4 × Rolls-Royce Conway 301s.

The civil VC10 was one of those British aviation industry's projects that seemed to offer so much at the time they were mooted but subsequently failed to make much commercial impression. Designed to operate from 'hot and high' short runways in remote locations, by the time it was ready for use the forecast runways had been replaced by modern equivalents and the economics of the type failed to make their mark on an increasingly crowded market. This did not deter the Royal Air Force from obtaining no less than 14 as VC 10 C 1s, which are combinations of the standard airframe combined with the uprated engines and fuel capacity of the Super VC 10. Other changes from the commercial versions include a large side-loading freight door and an interior altered to suit the variable requirements of the Service.

Today, 13 VC 10 C 1s are still in service on the strength of No 10 Squadron, based at RAF Brize Norton, where they form the main component of the transport unit known to the other armed forces as 'Crab Air' ('Eat Army, Sail Navy, Fly Sideways'). These aircraft still range the airways of the world, connecting the various far-flung outposts where

VC 10 C 1 of No 10 Squadron loading up at RAF Brize Norton.

VC 10 C Mark 1
1:192 scale

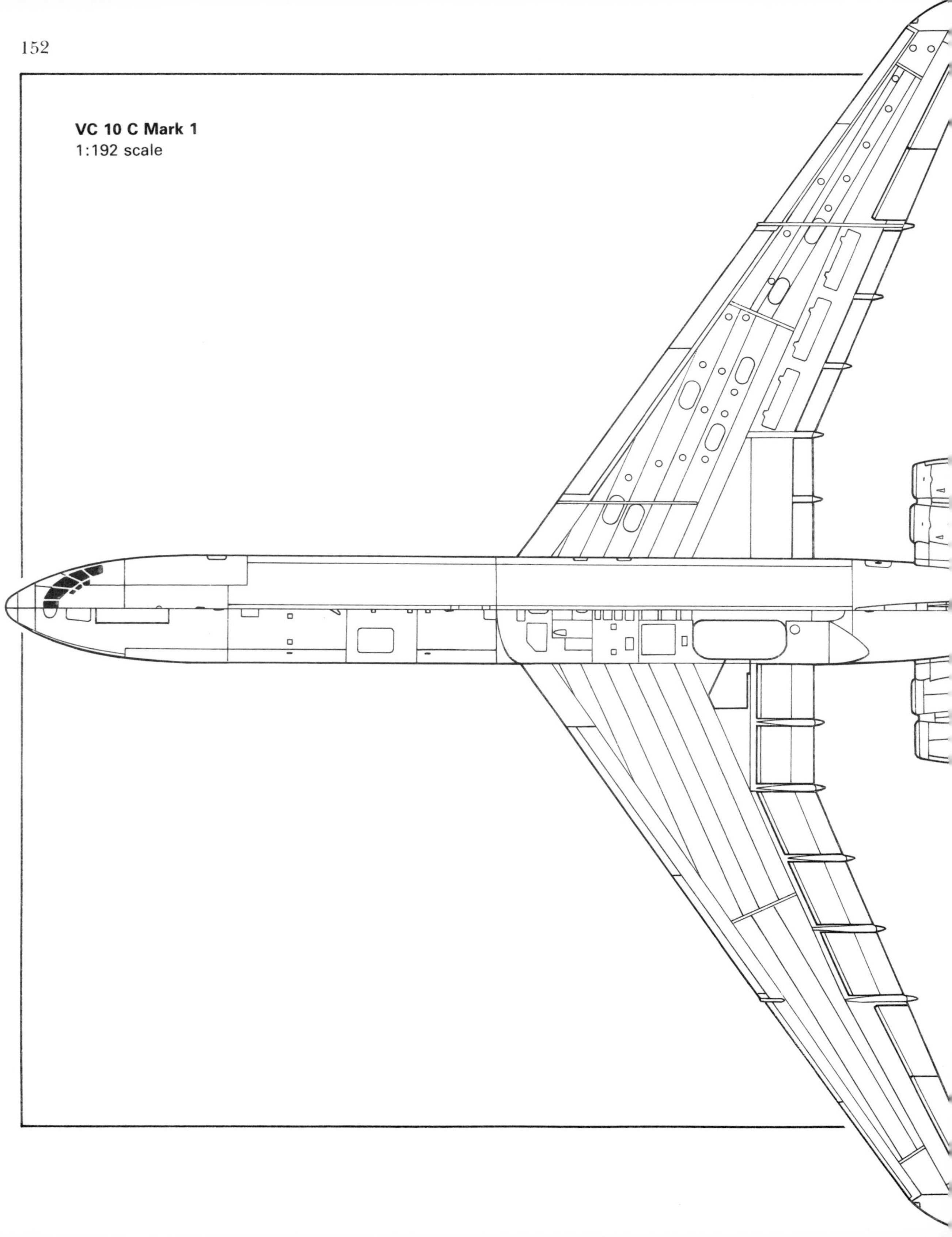

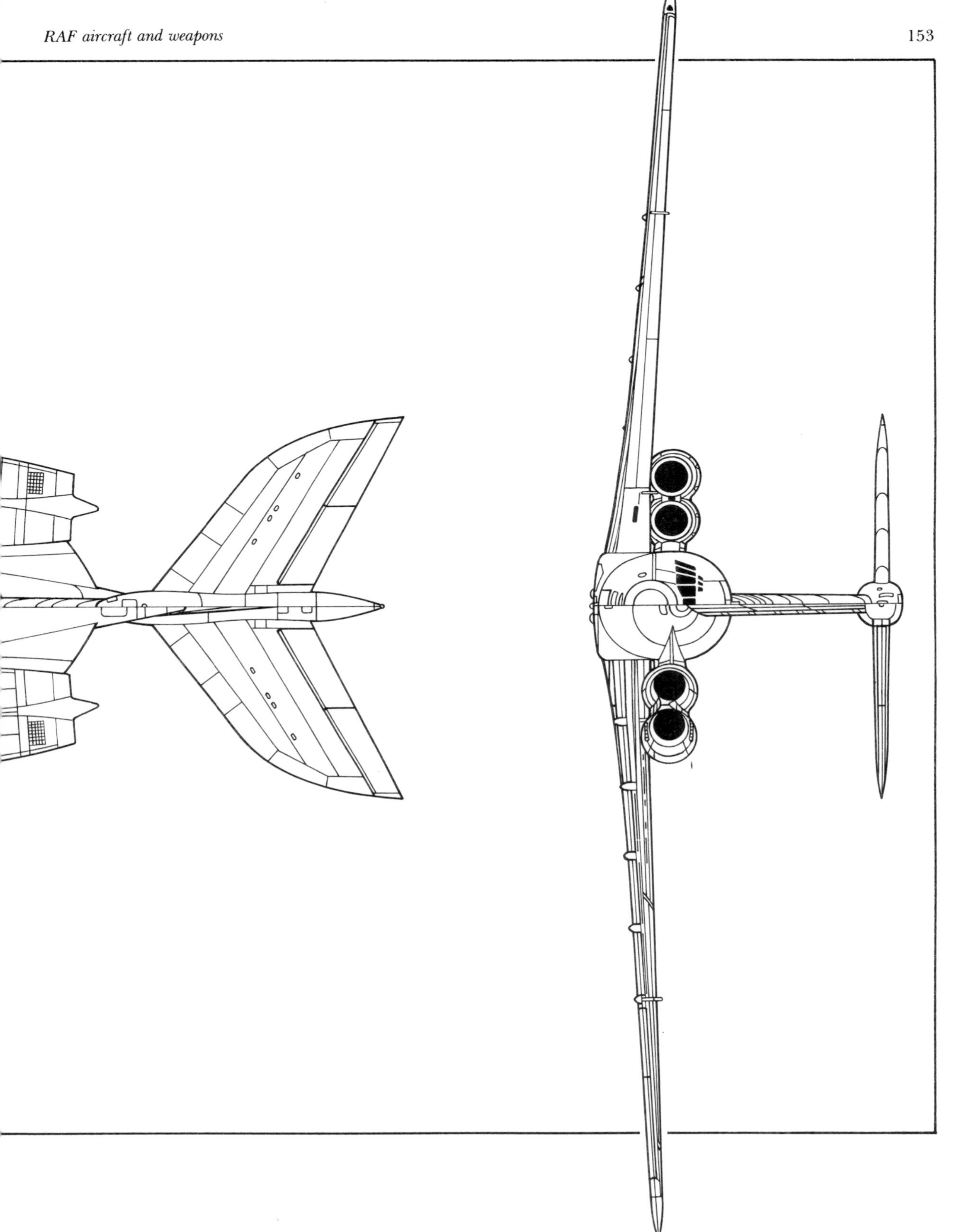

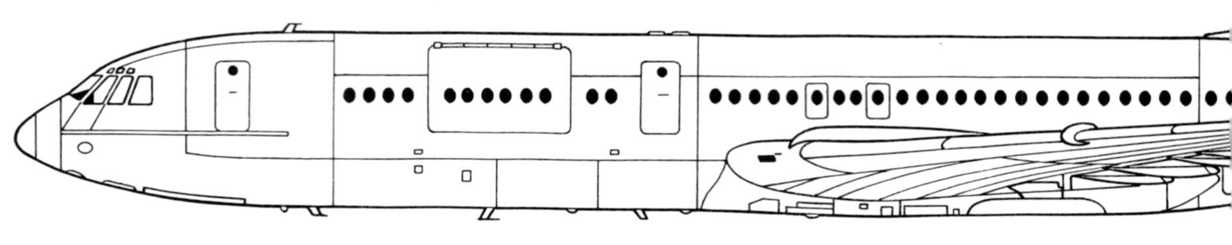
VC10 C Mark 1
1:192 scale

Hercules C 1 getting rather close to the photographer. This Lyneham-based machine was photographed on a murky day in 1980.

British influence still reigns, from Washington, DC, to Hong Kong. Most of these flights are on a scheduled basis but from time to time special medical or ambulance flights have to be carried out, often taking much-needed emergency equipment to the scene of some natural or man-made disaster. Much of the scheduled flying is used by Royal Air Force personnel and their families, but the same priority is given to other armed forces personnel and associated officials. The interiors of the VC 10s are altered to suit their particular mission so freight and passengers are often mixed on the one flight. In the all-passenger mode up to 150 passengers can be carried, all on the rearward-facing seats which civil airlines persist in rejecting for 'commercial' reasons despite their proven additional safety factor in an emergency. On such flights the full cabin in-flight food and refreshments routine can be applied; these are at least as good, if not better than, their civil equivalents, with the exception that no alcohol will be served.

The full flight crew of a VC 10 comprises pilot, co-pilot, navigator and flight engineer, plus whatever cabin staff are required. On medical flights, special medical attendants are carried.

With the increase in in-flight capacity that the Royal Air Force of the future will require, some existing VC 10 C 1s may well be converted to the full tanker role. In the meantime, some aircraft are to be converted to assume the tanker role in an emergency.

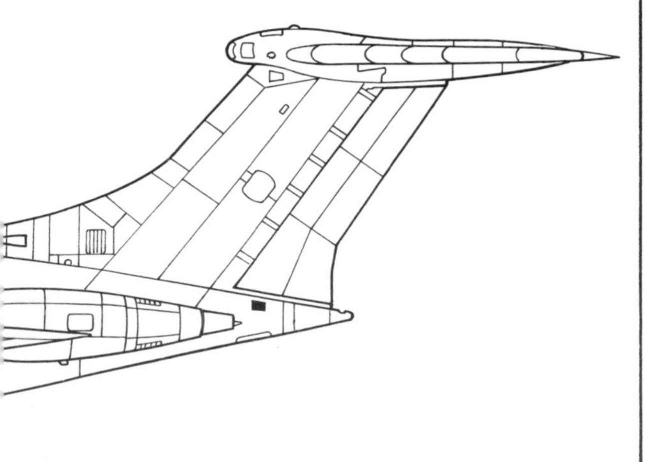

Hercules C Mark 1, C Mark 1 (K), W Mark 2 and C Mark 3

Crew (basic) 4; **Span** 40.41 m; **Length (C 1)** 29.79 m; **Length (C 3)** 34.37 m; **Height** 11.66 m; **Max take-off weight (C 1)** 79,380 kg; **Max speed (C 1)** 621 km/h; **Armament** nil; **Engines** 4 × Allison T56-A-15 turboprops.

The Lockheed C-130 has in many ways taken over the mantle of the dear old C-47 Dakota in the postwar transport aircraft scene, for in numbers and ubiquity it must now rival the Douglas veteran. But for all that, back in the 1960s when it was announced that a special version, the C-130K, was to be ordered for the Royal Air Force, it came as rather a surprise. This was due to the fact that the Service was expecting to receive an aircraft known as the Hawker Siddeley HS 681, a four-engined jet aircraft intended for roughly the same tactical role as the C-130. This was, however, sufficiently advanced in design concept for the development costs to frighten off the Treasury who acted to enforce the cancellation of the project. Thus the HS 681 became the latest in a long line of cancelled projects and the Royal Air Force prepared for the Hercules.

The first C-130K flew during 1966 and became the Hercules C 1. It differed from other C-130 marks by having an all-British avionics and instruments fit but was otherwise similar to the US Air Force C-130H. Once in service it soon became the workhorse of the four (originally six) main Hercules squadrons, namely Nos 24, 30, 47 and 70 Squadrons who pool their aircraft at RAF Lyneham. Lyneham is also the home of No 242 OCU and in all there are 61 Hercules based on the field as part of the 'Lyneham Wing'. From there the Hercules have gradually spread their wings over most of the Western world, and sometimes beyond. Although the aircraft are 'pooled' for maintenance and other purposes, the squadrons do tend to specialise. Nos 47 and 70 Squadrons largely concentrate on the purely transport role in direct support of the Army, while Nos 24 and 30 Squadrons tend to stick to route flying (and, as will be related, to the refuelling role). These specialisations are not rigid and the squadrons frequently swop roles, even at times assuming a search and rescue service when called upon. The route flying involves scheduled flights to such locations as Gibraltar, Cyprus, Belize, Sardinia and, more recently, the Falkland Islands (of which more below). The Hercules do carry out a small in-Service deployment role but the bulk of their efforts is normally devoted to support of the Army in the field.

It was the improvement of this Army support role that led to the most drastic aircraft modification taken on any in-Service transport aircraft for some time. This was the conversion of some Hercules C 1s (the final total was 30) to Hercules C 3 standard.

One Hercules from another.

Hercules C3
1:192 scale

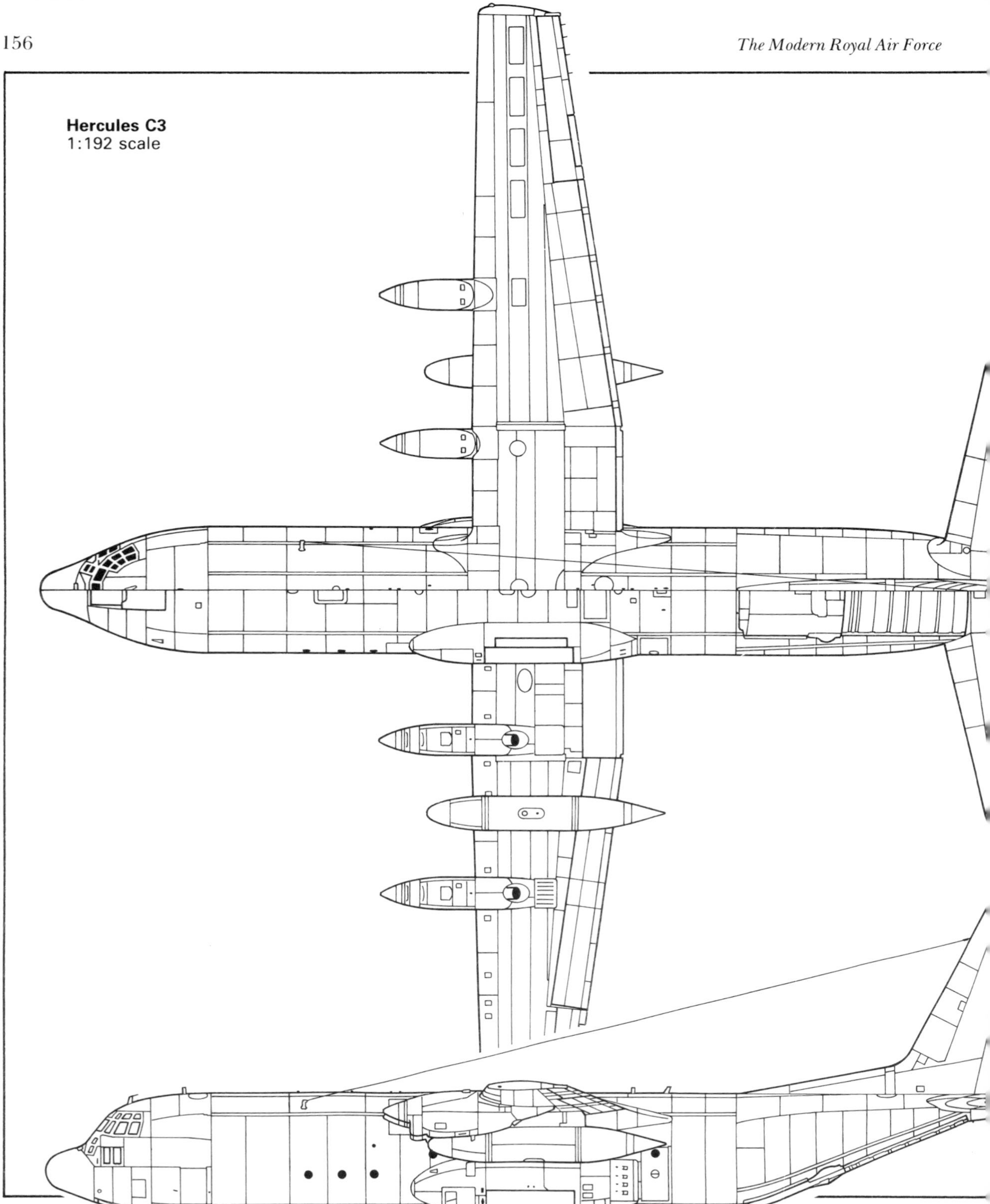

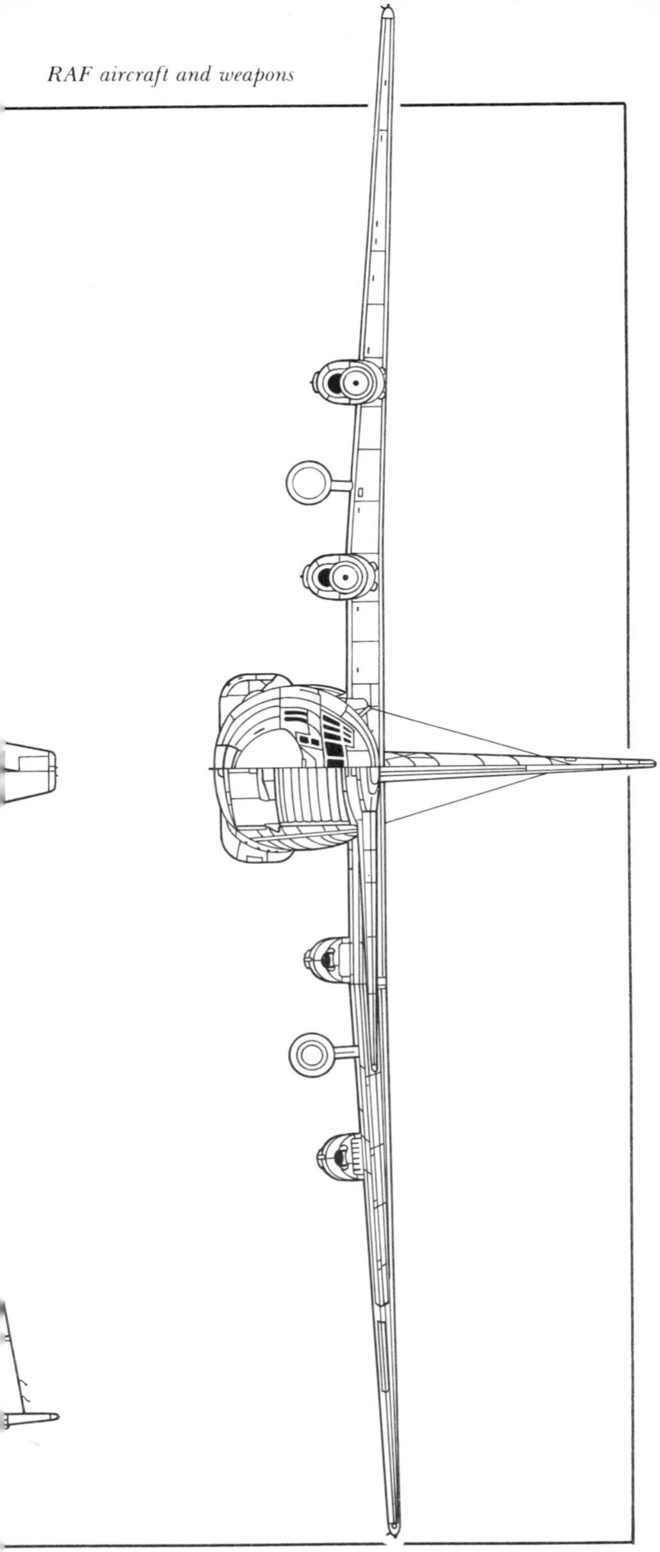

Hercules C 1s in close formation for para-dropping. Now that the Hercules (mainly the C 3s) will once more have a large-scale para-dropping role to play in support of the Army's 5 Airborne Brigade, such scenes will be more common than they have been for years past.

This involves the lengthening of the fuselage by the insertion of two new fuselage 'plugs', one in front of the wing and one behind. The resultant increase in fuselage length raises the cargo hold internal volume from 127.4 cubic metres to 171.5 cubic metres; to put these figures into perspective, this means an increase in a possible typical load from three Land Rovers and two trailers to four Land Rovers and three trailers. Another example would be the increase from five to seven pallet loads. These conversions were carried out by Marshall's of Cambridge and the resultant increase in carrying ability for No 1 Group has been most marked.

Of course, this has not been the only Hercules conversion for, as is now well known, the Falklands campaign gave rise to the use of the Hercules in the in-flight refuelling role. The first of these conversions was the fitting of in-flight probes above the Hercules C 1 cockpit and the fitting of extra internal fuel tanks. In all, 16 aircraft were so equipped and known as PLR2s (probe, two long range tanks). These were the Hercules that made the long weary flights from Ascension Island down to the Falklands and back so many times.

The Hercules tankers have now been withdrawn

Left *In the foreground can be seen the two fuselage plugs that turn a Hercules C 1 into a C 3—the aircraft in the background shows where one of the plugs will be placed.*

Below *The finished result as the insertion of two fuselage plugs at Marshall's of Cambridge results in a Hercules C 3.*

Bottom *The sole Hercules W 2 of the Meteorological Research Flight, Farnborough.*

from the Falklands routine in-flight refuelling role but the formal tanker conversions have not been withdrawn. These 'formal' conversions were to six Hercules C 1s and included the fitting of a topping-up in-flight refuelling probe over the cockpit, four internal long-range fuel tanks and a hose and drogue unit at the rear. These conversions have been referred to as the Hercules C 1(K) or even Hercules K 1. They have been seen with wing-tip containers that no doubt contain some form of electronics. Exactly what these conversions

are now used for is uncertain but they will certainly provide the RAF with a useful alternative in-flight refuelling capability. They may also have the ability to use their capacious holds to carry all manner of electronic warfare and 'snooping'.

In the transport role the Hercules normally carry two pilots, a navigator, a signals and avionics operator and a Loadmaster. This crew may be increased at times, especially on the South Atlantic runs. On the Hercules C 1, up to 92 fully equipped troops can be carried. In the para-drop role, up to 62 paratroops can jump from the side doors or 40 over the open rear ramp. All manner of supplies can be carried and low-level para-drops are regularly carried out using special load platforms. The crews have to operate to very high standards as their tasks are extremely demanding and varied; their training is carried out by No 242 OCU.

It cannot be said that travelling in the stark interior of a Hercules is a pleasing experience, for only rudimentary seating is provided and noise is at a deafening level. For all this the Hercules is a real workhorse, carrying out all manner of missions from the Falklands flights to short-range supply dropping. It can even be used as an air ambulance.

There is one more Hercules type to be mentioned. This is the Hercules W 2, another Marshall's of Cambridge conversion but this time to the weather research role. This version looks like no other Hercules. It is crammed full with all manner of research equipment and is covered with aerials of all kinds, including a brightly painted nose boom. Only one Hercules W 2 exists and this is operated from the Royal Aircraft Establishment at Farnborough by the Royal Air Force Meteorological Research Flight.

BAe 146 CC 2 of the Queen's flight.

BAe 146 CC Mark 2

Crew 2 + 19; **Span** 26.34 m; **Length** 26.19 m; **Height** 8.61 m; **Max take-off weight** 38,102 kg; **Max operating speed** 555 km/h; **Armament** nil; **Engines** 4 × Avco Lycoming ALF 502R-5 turbofans.

The replacement of the Andover CC 2s of the Queen's Flight had been mooted for some before it was announced during 1983 that two British Aerospace BAe 146 Series 100 transports had been ordered for evaluation purposes as possible replacement aircraft. The BAe 146 was thought to be a good choice as it was designed to be a quiet-operating aircraft that could operate from short runways when required. It has also turned out to be a considerable commercial success after a rather shaky start caused by a political withdrawal of development funds at a time of national economic crisis. Once development recommenced the orders soon began to flow and the prospect of an order for the Queen's Flight was a considerable boost for potential sales.

The two initial aircraft were used for evaluation purposes only and never became part of the Queen's Flight. They were operated by a unit known as 146 Evaluation Flight, an off-shoot of No 241 OCU, and after the two-year evaluation period was over the Flight was disbanded and the two aircraft involved were sold to Dan-Air. This sale was soon followed by an order for two more BAe 146 Series 100s and these are now in service as the BAe 146 CC 2 (the CC 1s were the two evaluation aircraft).

The BAe 146 CC 2s have a special VIP interior fit which seats up to 19 people—the usual Series 100 can seat up to 71. Few details of the internal arrangements have been released but the exterior sports tastefully–arranged high vision panels and the usual glossy and well-maintained finish. A larger than usual communications and navigation electronics package is carried to cater with the wide range of beacons and airfield radios the CC 2s will encounter in their travels. As before, the aircraft are based at RAF Benson but fly to wherever they are wanted.

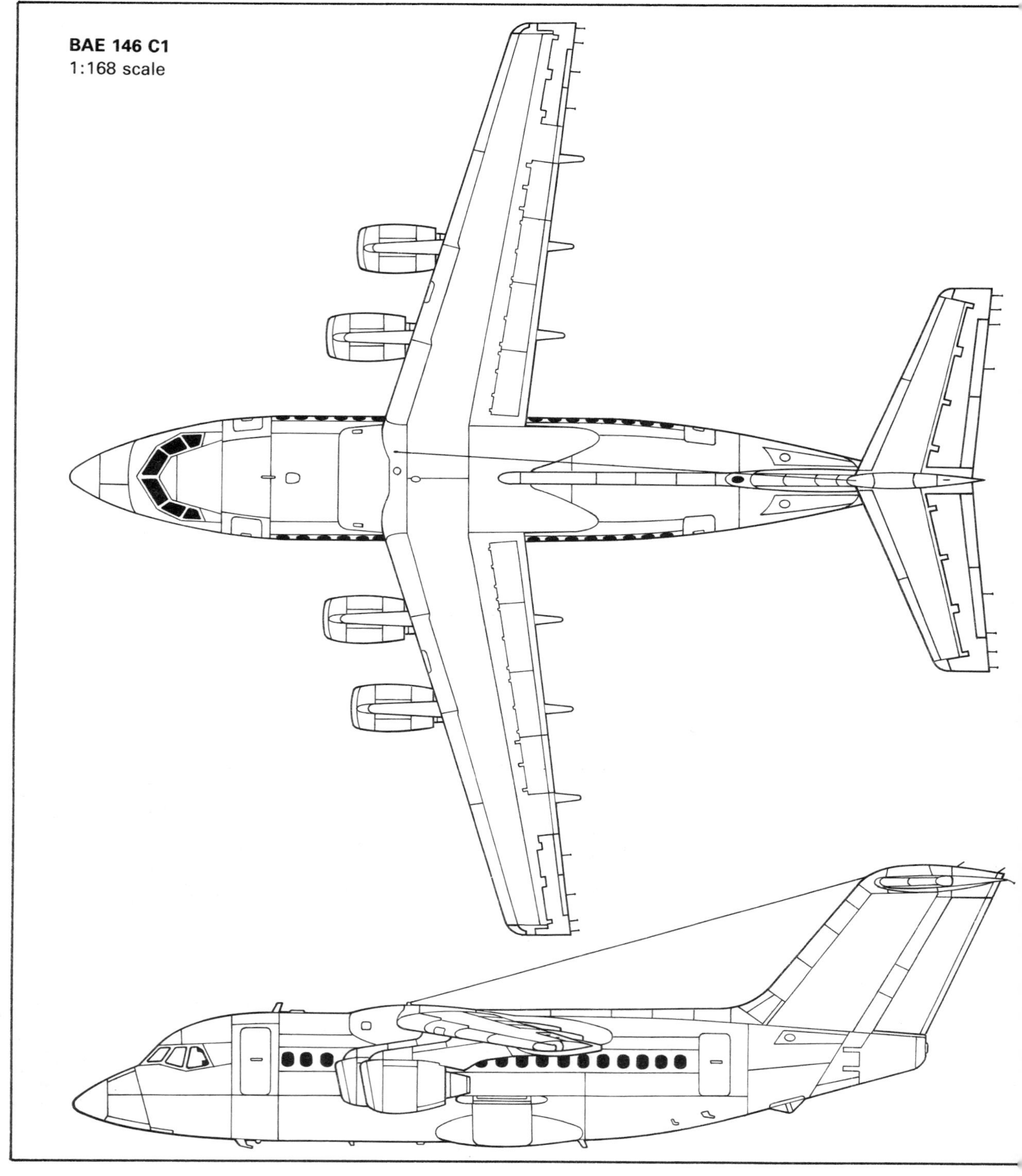
BAE 146 C1
1:168 scale

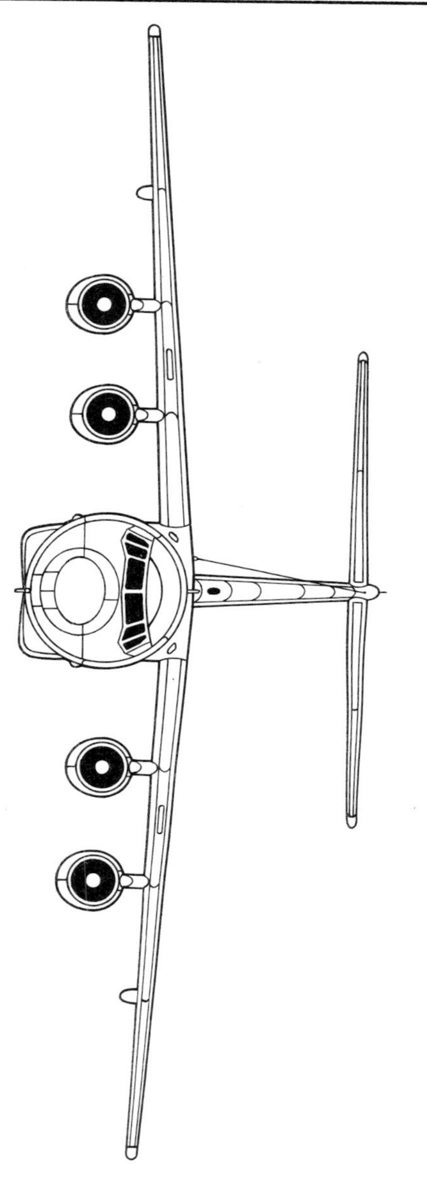

HS 125 CC Marks 1, 2 and 3

Crew 2 + 8; **Span** 14.33 m; **Length** 15.46 m; **Height** 5.36 m; **Max take-off weight** 11,566 kg; **Max speed** 592 km/h; **Armament** nil; **Engines (CC 3)** 2 × Garrett TFE731-3-1RH turbofans.

The civil HS 125 executive jet first flew in 1962 and, as a follow-on from the purchase of their 20 Dominie T 1s, the Ministry of Defence purchased a total of seven 'standard' HS 125s in their executive configuration. Five of these were Series 400s and became the HS 125 CC 1; two were Series 600s which became the HS 125 CC 2. In March 1983 it was announced that a further four HS 125 Series 700 aircraft were to be ordered for the Royal Air Force and six of the existing aircraft already in service were to be re-engined to the full Series 700 standard, ie, with Garrett turbofans. These aircraft will then be known as the HS 125 CC 3.

The HS 125s are operated by one unit, No 32 Squadron based at RAF Northolt. Of the six aircraft on the squadron, two are operated by Royal Navy crews and the others by Royal Air Force personnel. They are used to carry Government ministers and senior officials, officers and VIPs throughout the United Kingdom and to locations in Europe. They provide a fair degree of comfort and are able to avoid airport congestion, delays and the ever-present security problems that beset modern political life.

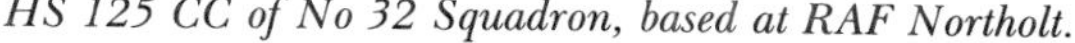

HS 125 CC of No 32 Squadron, based at RAF Northolt.

Andover C 1 of No 32 Squadron, RAF Northolt

Andover C Mark 1, CC Mark 2 and E Mark 3

Crew 2 or 3 + 58; **Span** 30.02 m; **Length (C 1, E 3)** 23.77 m; **Height (C 1, E 3)** 9.15 m); **Normal operating weight (C 1)** 22,860 kg; **Max speed** 452 km/h; **Armament** nil; **Engines** 2 × Rolls-Royce Dart 201 turboprops.

The Andover is a military version of the highly successful Hawker-Siddeley (now British Aerospace) 748 civil airliner, an aircraft that first flew in 1960 and a design that is still subject to updating and 'stretching'. The military Andover differed mainly from the civil HS 748 in having a longer fuselage and a swept-up tail to accommodate a rear-loading ramp and door. Unfortunately, the Andover turned out to be a 'political' aeroplane for the old Hawker Siddeley company placed a great deal of money, effort and development potential into its military conversion, only to discover that the Royal Air Force merely wanted 31. As a result (although the Andover was not the only reason involved), the respected Hawker Siddeley became part of the British Aerospace conglomerate.

The Andover C 1 was for many years the RAF's standard short-range transport but, by 1975, the withdrawal from the Middle East removed the main reason for the type remaining in service. The last 'full' Andover transport squadron was No 46 at RAF Thorney Island, on the south coast. In 1975 the type was retired as a transport and many were sold off to the Royal New Zealand Air Force where they still serve well. Not all were sold, however, as it is now used within the United Kingdom as a general communications aircraft, while one is based at Oslo for the use of the CinC AFNORTH. Some Andover C 1s are on the strength of No 115 Squadron at RAF Benson and a single example is used by the Andover Training Flight (ATF) at the same airfield. A single C 1, much modified, is used by the Electronic Warfare Avionics Unit (EWAU) at RAF Wyton. No 115 Squadron is also equipped with the Andover E 3, a modified version of the C 1 but internally much changed to accommodate all the various electronics and other black boxes involved in the checking of the various landing aids and navigation equipment used by Royal Air Force airfields. The Andover E 3 can be recognised by the Milligan Lamp under the nose which is used in conjunction with ground-based survey instruments to check airfield and runway approach angles and flight paths.

In contrast the Andover CC 2 is a militarized version of the standard civil HS 748 (now the BAe 748) and does not have the upswept tail of the Andover C 1. The Andover CC 2s are now operated by one squadron only, No 32 Squadron based at RAF Northolt, just to the north of London where it is close to most of their government and military VIP customers. Three of the aircraft used by the squadron, a multi-type unit, are the three ex-Queen's Flight Andover CC 2s, now replaced by the BAe 146 CC 2. The squadron also operates a single Andover C 1. All of these aircraft have comfortable interiors that can be altered to suit the task in hand.

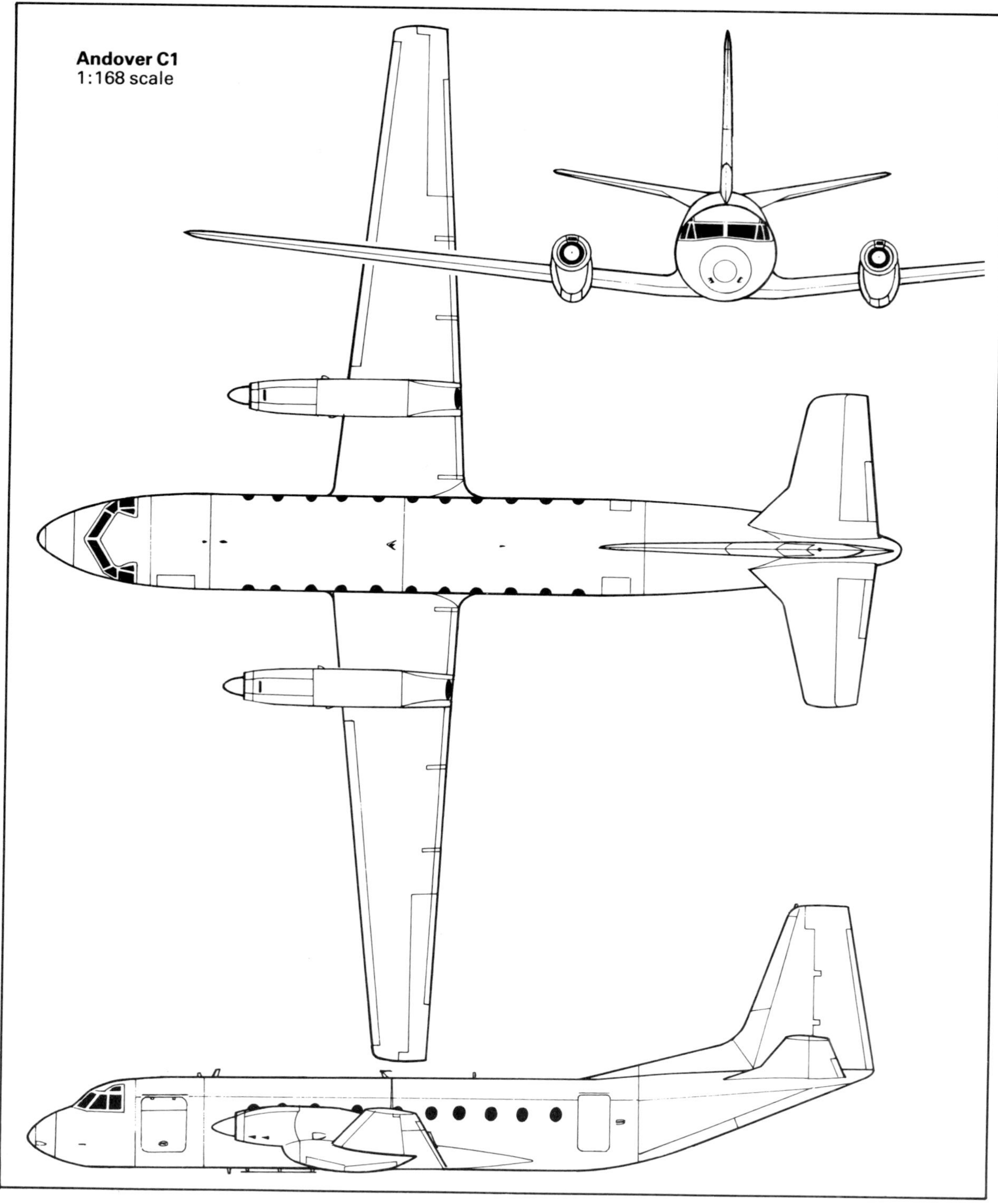
Andover C1
1:168 scale

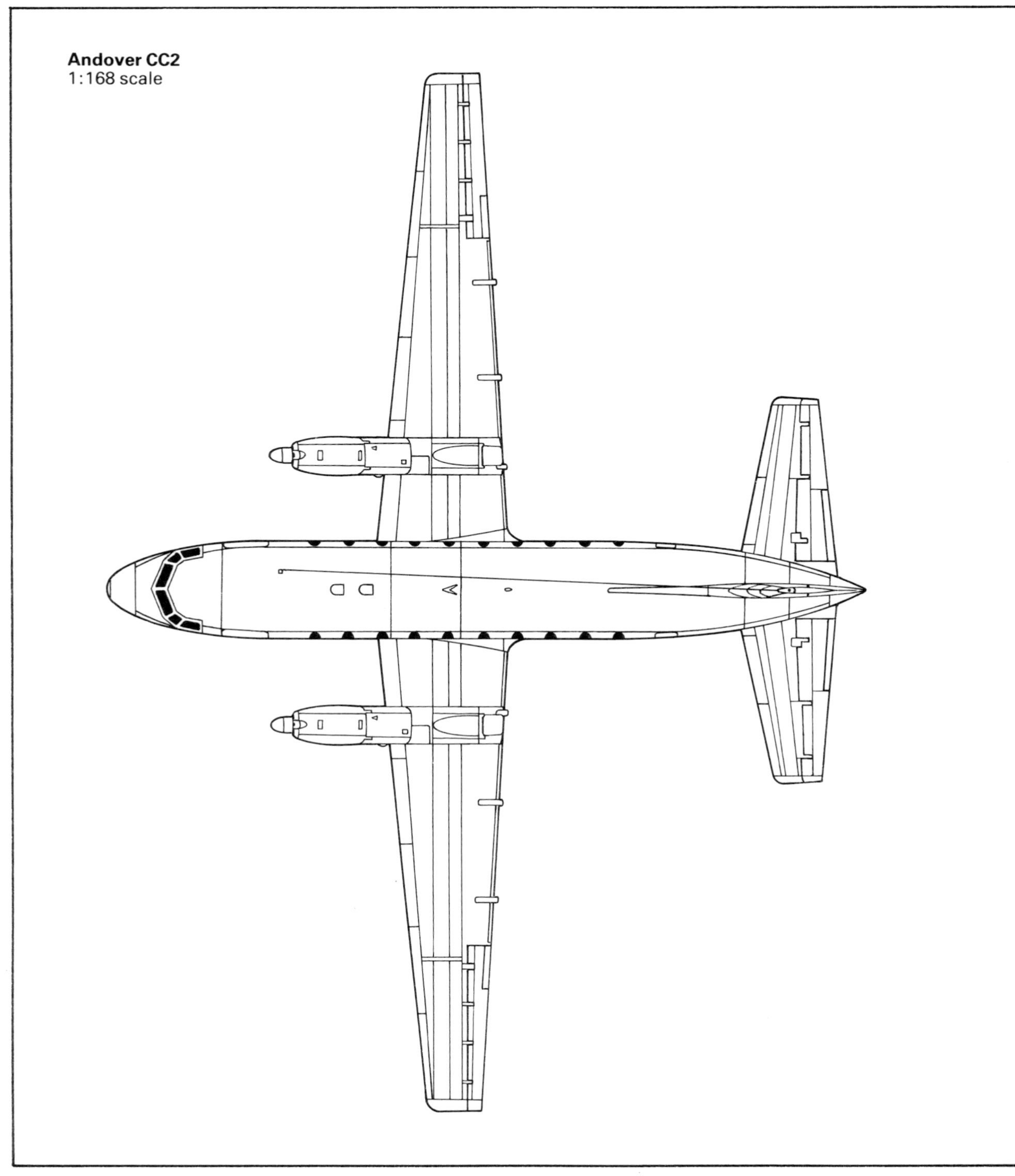
Andover CC2
1:168 scale

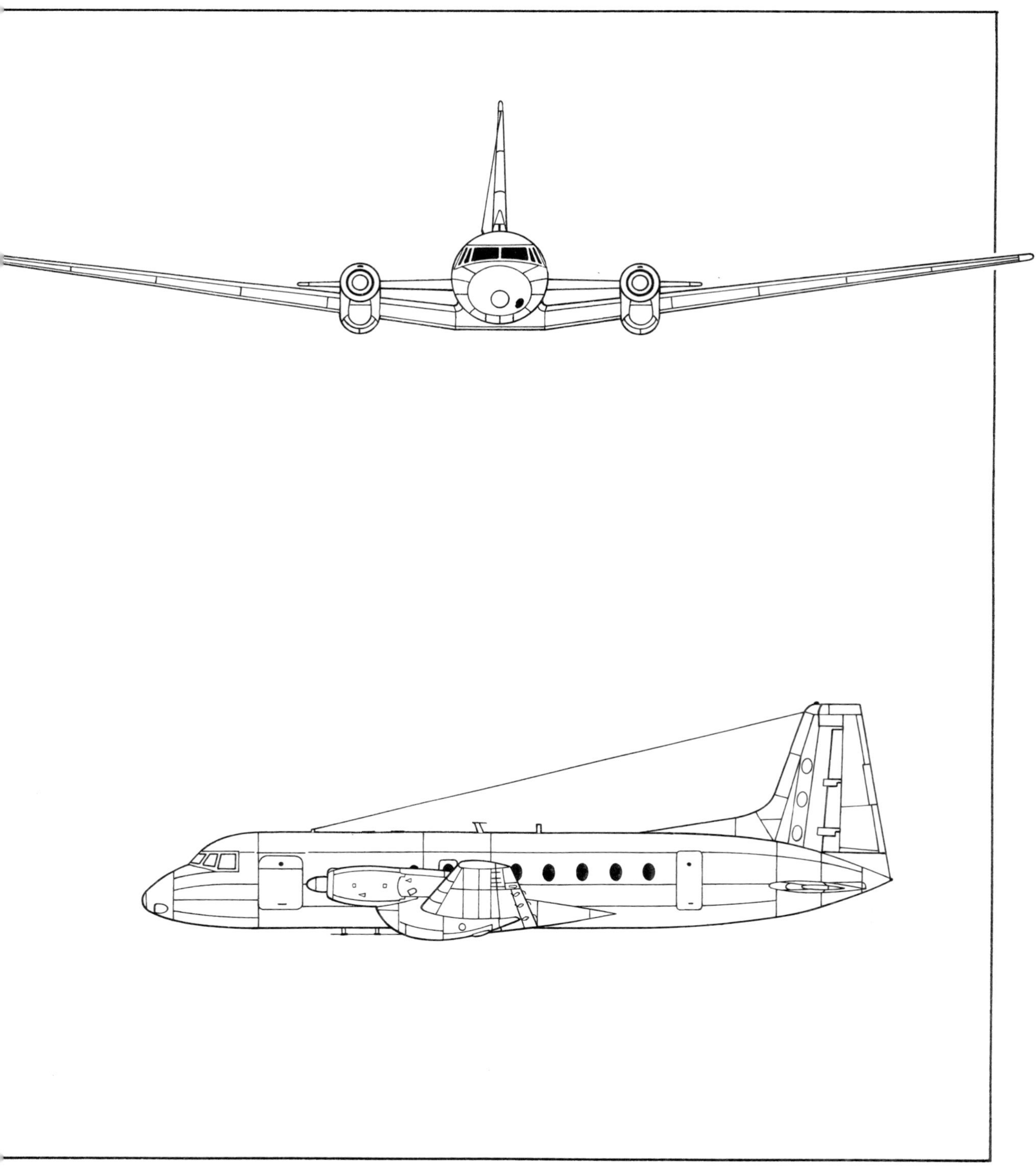

Pembroke C Mark 1

Crew 2 + 10; **Span** 19.6 m; **Length** 14 m; **Height** 4.9 m; **Max take-off weight** 6,125 kg; **Max speed** 360 km/h; **Armament** nil; **Engines** 2 × 540 hp Alvis Leonides piston radials.

The Pembroke has been around a long time as the first examples were ordered in 1951. Originally a product of the old Percival company, later part of the Hunting Group, it was a fully militarised version of the Percival Prince civil feeder-liner with an increased wingspan and increased operating weights for the military role. The full production total for the Royal Air Force was 52; six of these were equipped for a photographic role as the Pembroke C (PR) 1, but none of these now survive. Pembrokes were used for all manner of general communication and light utility tasks and the few that remain are still used for these purposes.

By the late 1960s the Pembroke became an obvious candidate for replacement but funds for light utility aircraft were not forthcoming. It had been planned to replace the Pembroke with a Jetstream or a Beech King Air version, but this was not to be. Instead, starting in 1969, a wing spar modification programme commenced to prolong the in-Service life of the remaining aircraft, which will be around for some time to come.

The Pembroke can carry up to ten passengers in relative comfort on rearward-facing seats but the aircraft can also be converted to a flying ambulance when it can carry six stretchers and a medical attendant. A pilot and co-pilot complete the crew.

Pembrokes can still be spotted pottering around the skies of the United Kingdom but only one complete squadron uses the type; this is No 60, based at RAF Wildenrath in West Germany, which is used as a general communications unit.

Current plans call for the phasing out from service of the Pembroke by 1987.

VC 10 K Mark 2 and K Mark 3

Crew (K2) 4 + 18 passengers; **Crew (K3)** 4 + 17 passengers; **Span** 44.55 m; **Length (K2)** 48.36 m; **Length (K3)** 52.32 m; **Height** 12.04 m; **Max take-off weight (approx)** 146,510 kg; **Max speed** 914 km/h; **Armament** nil; **Engines** 4 × Rolls-Royce Conway 301s.

By 1978 the future in-flight refuelling requirements of the Royal Air Force were so forecast that more capacity would obviously be required. At one point consideration was given to procuring readily-available American equipment, but the costs involved ruled this out. Instead, the attractions of converting civil VC 10 aircraft to the tanker role were such that not only would commonality with an existing in-service type be achieved but the overall costs involved much reduced. Accordingly, British Aerospace were awarded a design and conversion contract, carried out at the old Concorde facility at Filton, near Bristol. The aircraft converted to the tanker role included five standard VC 10s once operated by British Airways

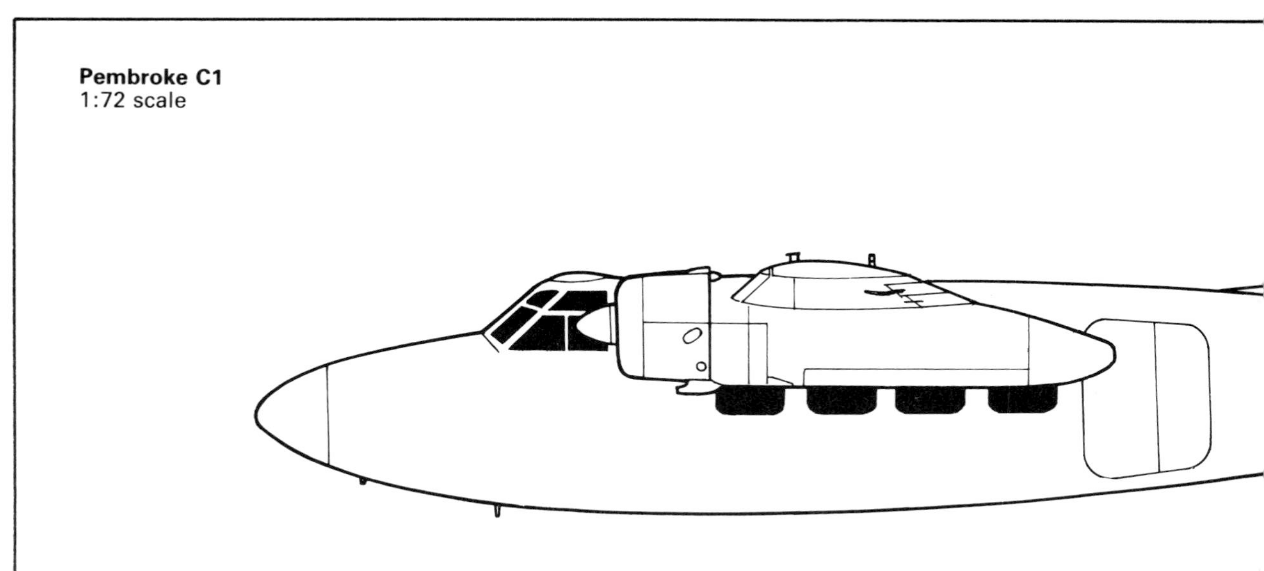

Pembroke C1
1:72 scale

Pembroke C 1 of No 60 Squadron, based at RAF Wildenrath.

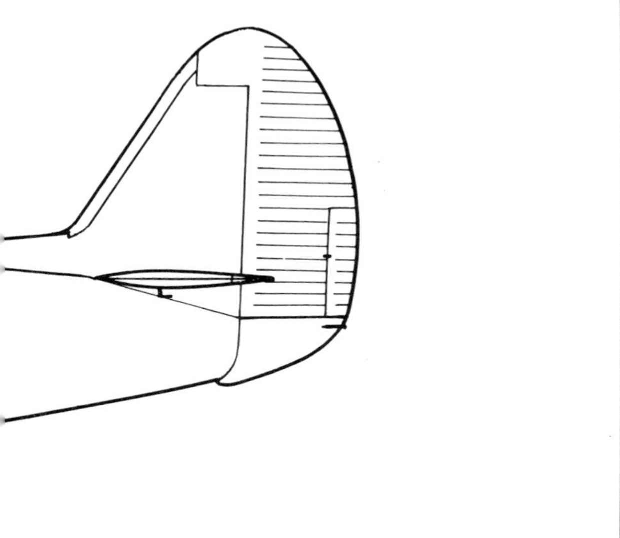

which became VC 10 K 2s plus four Super VC 10s from East African Airways which became VC 10 K 3s. Additionally, the last 14 Super VC 10s used by British Airways were purchased for the Royal Air Force in 1981. Three of these were broken up to provide 'Christmas tree' spares for the conversion programme while the remaining 11 are stored awaiting some future tanker or transport requirement.

The first VC 10 K 2 conversion flew on June 22 1982. This incorporated the full conversion to be applied to future aircraft which consists mainly of internal tankage to supply a fuselage-mounted hose and drogue unit under the rear fuselage plus two wing-mounted pods, also mounting hose and drogue units. Each of these wing units can transfer up to 1,270 kg of fuel every minute. A refuelling probe is mounted on the nose. Other refuelling equipment includes a tail-mounted video camera to monitor approaching aircraft, and floodlighting

VC 10 K 2 with its central refuelling hose deployed (P. Guiver).

sources in the tail and wing fairings to illuminate the underside of the aircraft for night operations. The engines to be used are the same as those for the VC 10 C 1. Internally, five double-skinned cylindrical tanks are interconnected with the aircraft's own fuel system. Compartments are provided to carry a small number of passengers or ground crew. Much of the general avionics 'fit' will be comparable to that of the VC 10 C 1.

It is expected that the current commercial conversions will be completed by the end of 1984. More conversions may be carried out on the stored aircraft and the in-Service VC 10 C 1s when funds and/or operational requirements permit.

The first VC 10 K 2 was handed over to the Royal Air Force on July 25, 1983. The first of the VC 10 K 3s followed during 1985. They are now operated by No 101 Squadron from RAF Brize Norton. It is possible that once the Victors have been retired more of the stockpiled ex-British Airways Super VC 10s will be converted to the tanker role.

Tristar K Mark 1, KC Mark 1 and K Mark 2

(No figures for the tanker version have yet been released—the following data refers to the British Airways version only).

Crew (basic) 3 or 4; **Span** 47.34 m; **Length** 50.04 m; **Height** 16.87 m; **Max take-off weight** 224,982 kg; **Max speed** 978 km/h; **Armament** nil; **Engines** 3 × Rolls-Royce RB.211-524B turbofans.

There is an old saying that 'it's an ill wind that blows nobody any good', and for the Royal Air Force this has recently once more come true. In the aftermath of the 1982 Falkland Islands campaign one of the lessons that stood out sharply from the mass of operational data sifting was a glaring need for more in-flight refuelling capacity. As ever, money for new equipment of this nature was scarce and a quick glance at the price tag for the obvious existing product, the American McDonnell-Douglas KC-10A Extender (already in service with the US Air Force), soon ruled out any prospect of a direct purchase of that expensive aircraft.

Fortunately for the Royal Air Force, an alternative was in the offing. British Airways found itself with excess aircraft capacity, especially in Lockheed Tristars, due to the world recession and down-turn

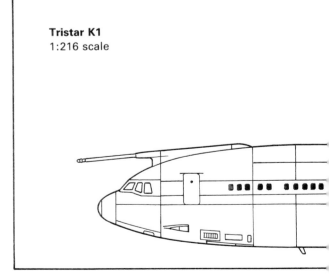

Tristar K1
1:216 scale

A Tristar K 1 refuelling a Hercules C 1 during trials.

in air travel that came in the early 1980s. There was little prospect of any Tristars being unloaded onto a sated second-hand aircraft market but the ill wind syndrome arose for the type was immediately siezed upon by the Ministry of Defence as a way out of their in-flight refuelling problem.

At the end of 1982 it was decided that six ex-British Airways Lockheed L1011-500 Tristars were to be purchased and converted to the tanker role. The hand-over was made within months and for a while British Airways personnel operated the first of the Tristars involved on trooping flights to Canada and elsewhere, with RAF personnel watching and learning. Then the first aircraft were moved to Cambridge where Marshall of Cambridge (Engineering) Limited began the conversions proper.

The conversion involves the stripping of most of

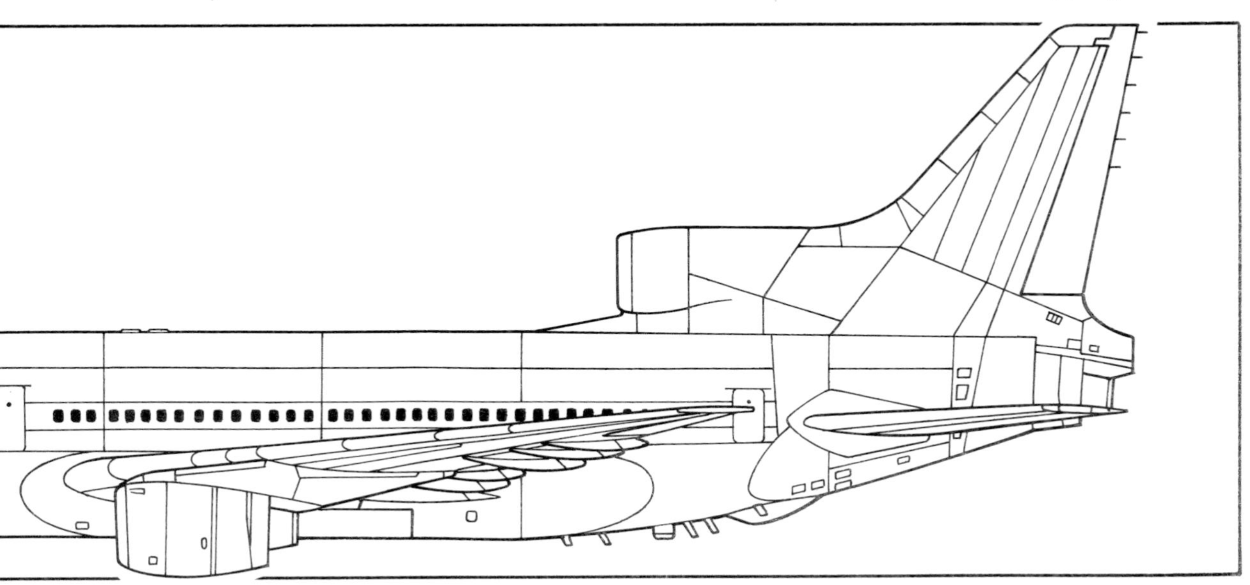

the seating and baggage compartments and the installation of fuel tanks and in-flight refuelling hose drum units. A probe is fitted over the cockpit and a fuel system management unit is fitted at the flight engineer's position. Provision is made for the accommodation of a spare aircrew in a special rest area and more seating is provided for travelling ground crew members.

The first two Tristars were modified for use as tankers only and are known as Tristar K 1s. The next four conversions also had a cargo door measuring 2.64 × 3.56 metres inserted into the port side forward of the wing. A cargo handling system was fitted and the cabin floor strengthened to allow the aircraft to carry cargo and passengers as well as fuel. This version is the Tristar KC 1, and eventually (by 1988) the two Tristar K 1s will be modified to Tristar KC 1 standards.

The first conversions have been carried out with few troubles other than one aircraft being badly damaged in a heavy landing during training. In fact more conversions are planned. Three Pan-Am Tristars were placed on the market at an advantageous price and were promptly snapped up by the Ministry of Defence. The go-ahead to the conversion of these aircraft into tankers has been given and as there are sufficient differences between the ex-Pan Am and ex-British Airways Tristars to prevent full inter-operability, even after conversion, so the 'Pan Am' Tristars will be known as the Tristar K 2. Eventually they too will be provided with cargo doors.

The Tristar tankers are operated by No 216 Squadron from RAF Brize Norton. They provide the Royal Air Force with what is described as 'a significant force multiplier', but there is no hiding the fact that many in the Service would have preferred a conversion based on the McDonnell-Douglas DC-10 to maintain at least a degree of commonality with the US Air Force's KC-10A Extenders. It is rumoured that contingency plans have been made to hastily convert civil DC-10s to the tanker role in an emergency (along with Boeing 737s) rather than Tristars, but in the meantime the Royal Air Force has acquired the much-needed increase in its in-flight refuelling capacity.

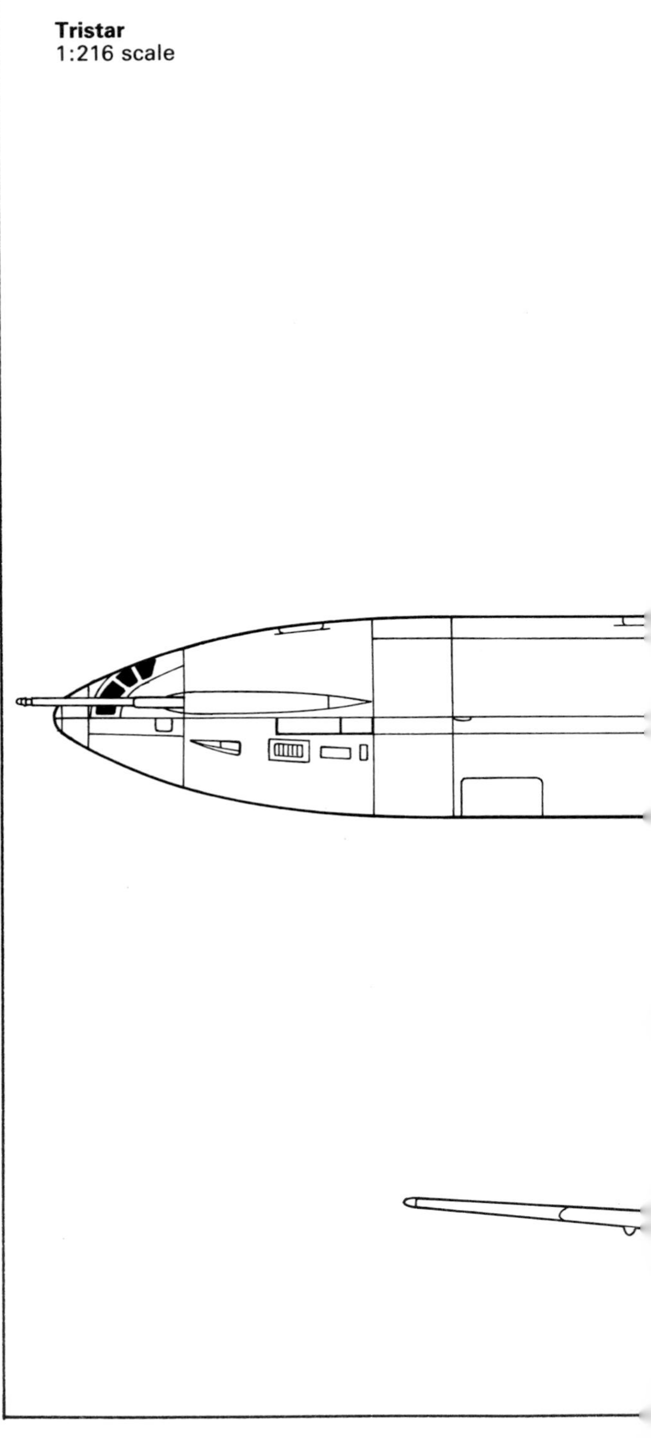

Victor K Mark 2

Crew 5; **Span** 35.69 m; **Length** 35.02 m; **Height** 9.18 m; **Max take-off weight** 101,150 kg; **Max speed** 966 km/h plus; **Armament** nil; **Engines** 4 × Rolls-Royce Conway 201 turbojets.

The first Victor flew as a bomber in 1952. It was one of the three famous 'V' bombers and carried out its nuclear-orientated tasks for many years

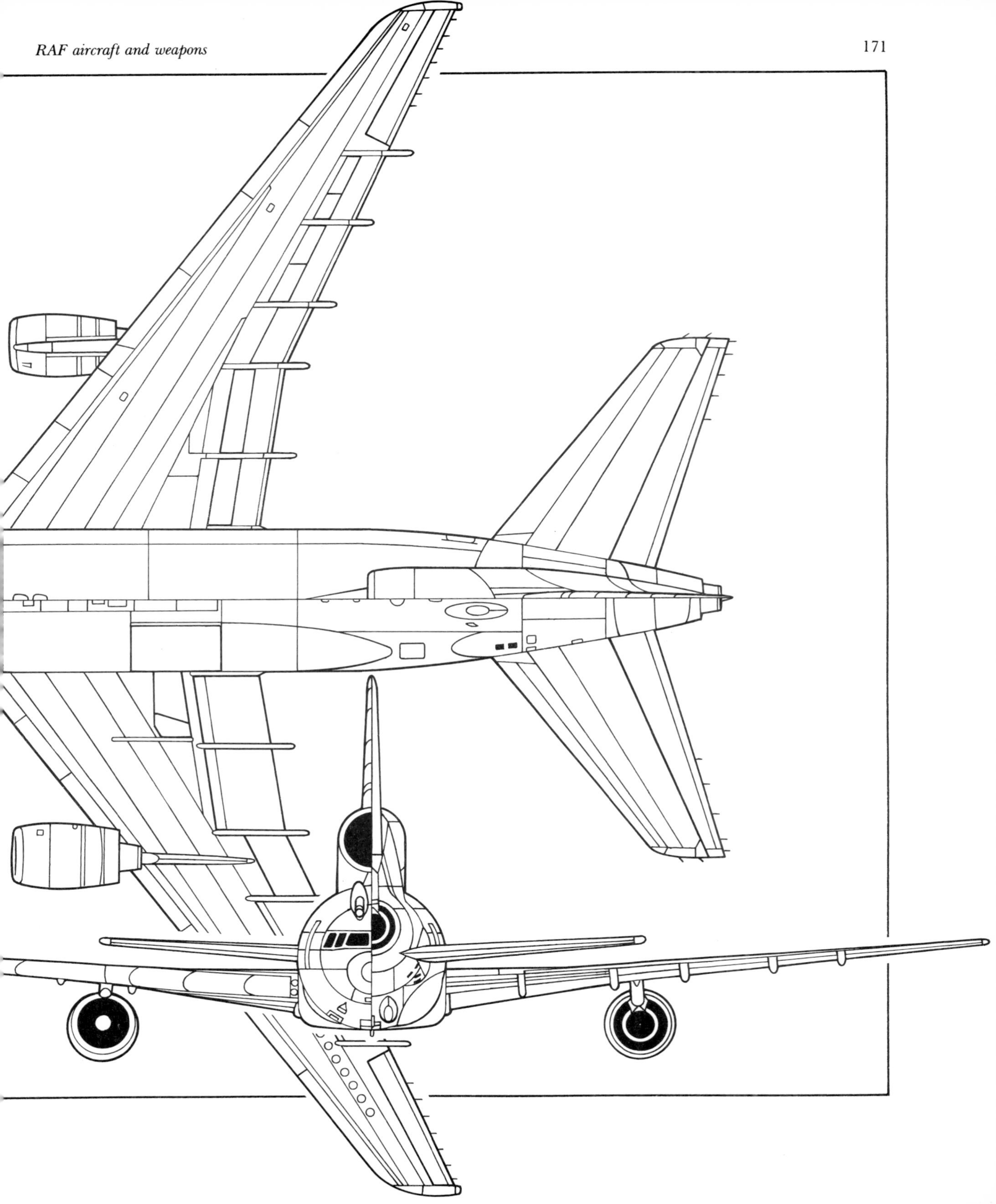

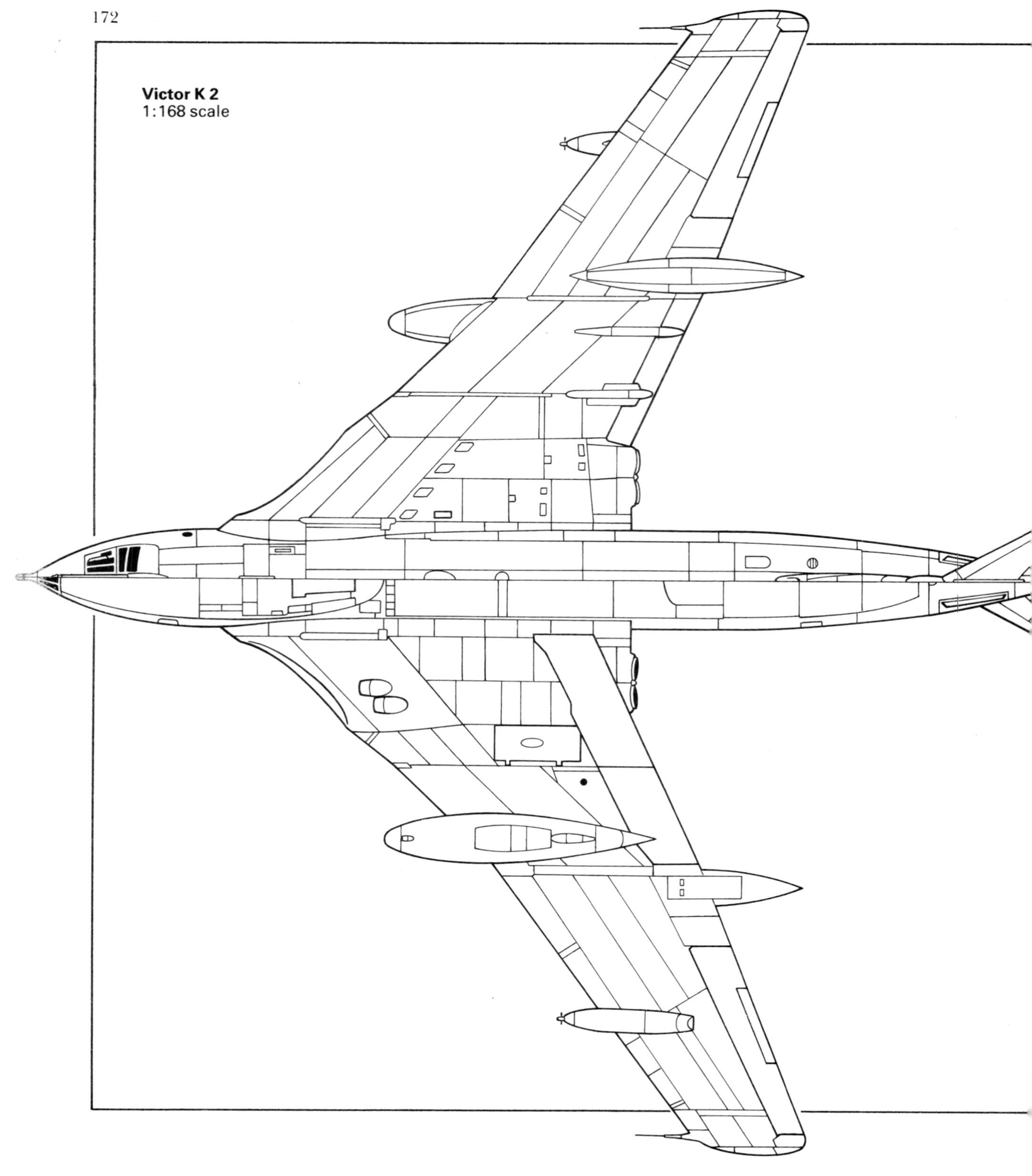
Victor K 2
1:168 scale

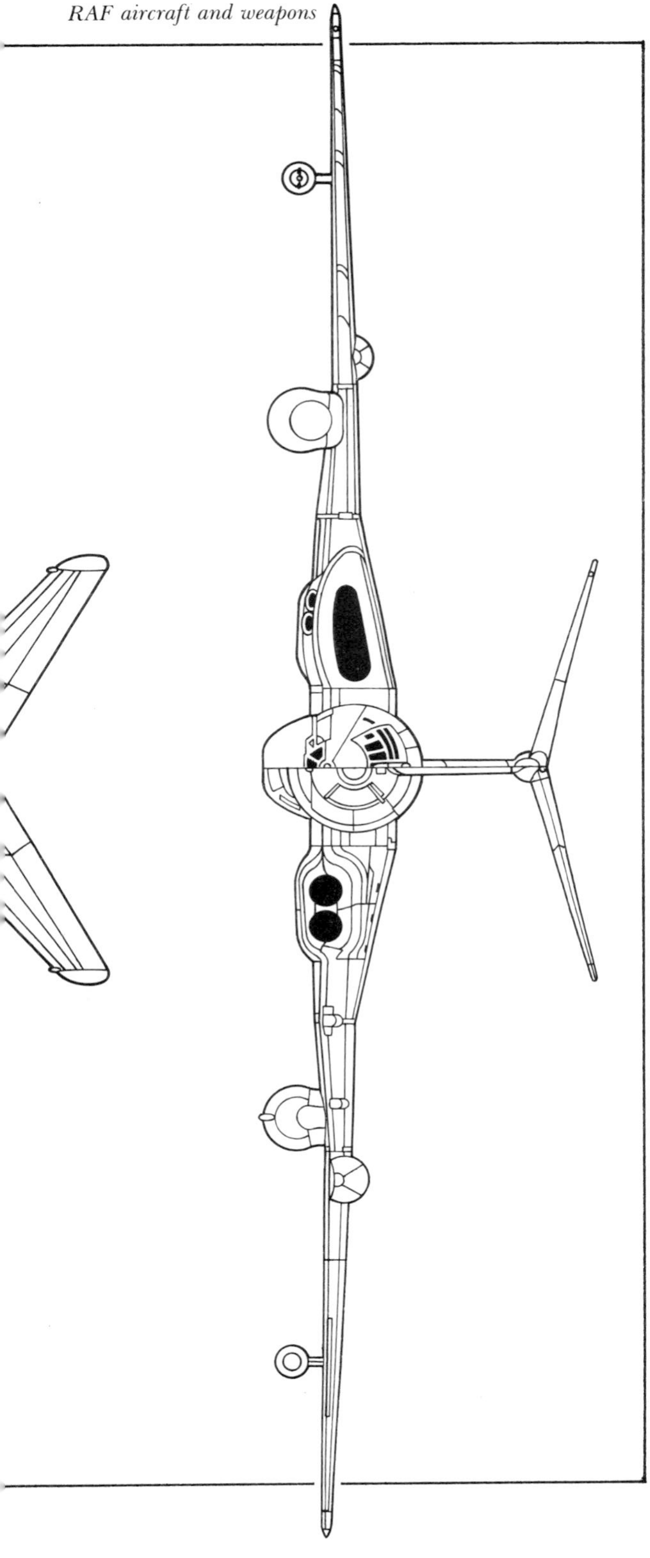

One of the in-flight refuelling drogues from a Victor K 2.

before its subsonic bomber role was phased out and it assumed new duties. By the time it was phased out, the marks in Service were the B 2 with Rolls-Royce Conway engines and the Victor SR 2 reconnaissance version. The original Victor B 1s had by then been converted to the tanker role so, when the Victor B 2 commenced its run-down, it was an obvious candidate for the same role. By 1977 the Victor K 1s were phased out in favour of the newly-converted K 2s. The conversion programme had not gone smoothly because Handley Page went out of the aircraft business in its middle, and there was a pause before Hawker Siddeley at Woodford assumed the task.

The conversion involved the fitting of all necessary internal tankage plus the provision of no less than three hose and drogue units, one in the redundant bomb bay and the other two from new pods, one under each wing. In all, 24 aircraft were converted to the role and one source states that 19 of these are still operational. Their crews of five include two pilots, two navigators and an air electronics officer.

The Victor tankers are now being phased out as they are reaching the end of their useful Service lives. Already No 232 OCU has been disbanded and so has No 57 Squadron. That leaves only No 55 Squadron still operating the Victor K 2 from RAF Marham. The type has even been withdrawn from its tanker role supplying the long supply flights to the Falkland Islands.

The period immediately following 'Operation Corporate' proved to be the most active of the Victors' entire career. They were kept very busy topping up the succession of aircraft, usually probe-equipped Hercules, that had to make the

long flights across the South Atlantic to and from Ascension Island. For months Victor K 2s were an everyday sight on Wideawake field and the same base was engraved into the memories of Victor ground crews as they struggled to keep the aircraft flying while the flight crews did their best to get some sleep between long refuelling missions.

Those missions did nothing to improve the airframe fatigue lives of the Victors and now their end is in sight—it may even have arrived by the time these words are read. When they are withdrawn they will be the last of the 'V' bombers to do so and the last reminders of an era when the Royal Air Force was the nation's main nuclear force will have gone.

Above *A Victor K 2 of the old 57 Squadron refuelling a Tornado GR 1.*

Above right *Recipient's eye view of a Victor K 2.*

Victor K 2
1:168 scale

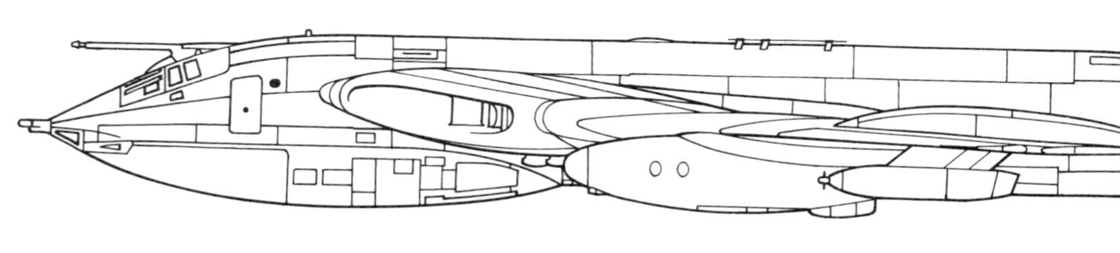

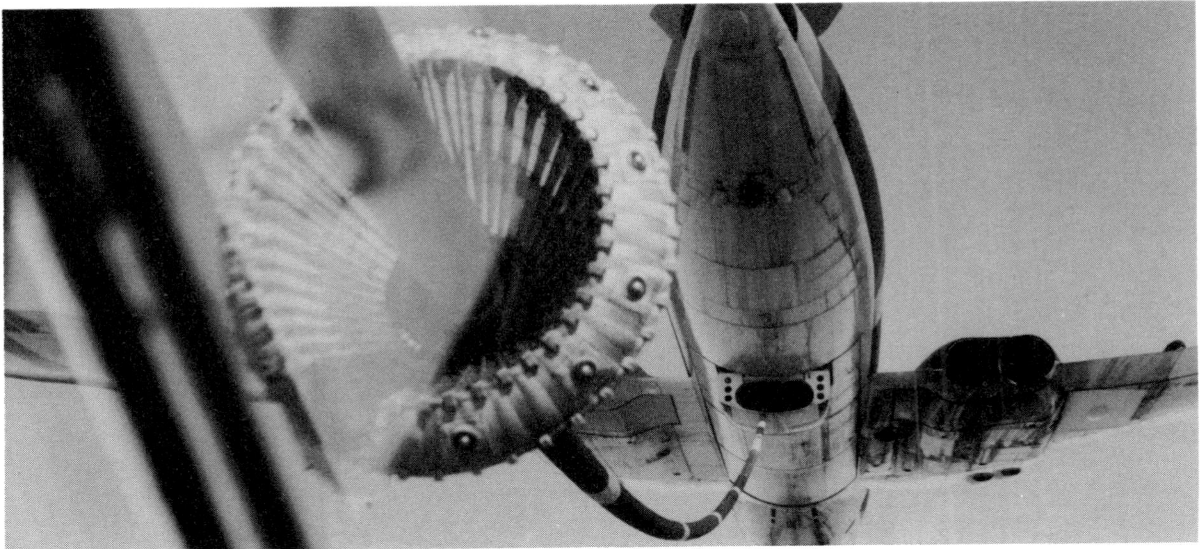

Hawk T Mark 1 and T Mark 1A

Crew 2; **Span** 9.39 m; **Length** 11.17 m; **Height** 3.99 m; **Max take-off weight** 7,750 kg; **Max speed** 1,038 km/h; **Armament** 1 × 30 mm Aden, 4 × practice bombs, 2 × 2.75-in rocket pods, (2 × Sidewinder missiles); **Engine** 1 × Rolls-Royce Turbomeca Adour Mk 151 (Mk 861).

The Hawk T 1 started life as the Hawker Siddeley HS 1182 as the result of a Ministry of Defence decision announced in October 1971. The first of these aircraft flew on March 2 1972, by which time the aircraft had been given the service designation of Hawk. Hawker Siddeley later became part of British Aerospace (1977), so the aircraft is now the BAe Hawk. In all 175 Hawks were delivered to the Royal Air Force and the type has gone on to become a useful export revenue producer.

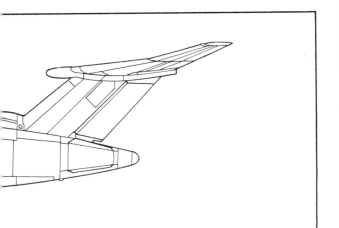

The first full production Hawks were delivered during 1976 and since then have become highly successful advanced flying and weapons trainers. Having a useful performance and excellent flying characteristics, the Hawk has proved so useful that some early forecasts of how long flying training programmes would have to last have been drastically curtailed, to the extent that whole familiarisation chunks of flying training programmes have been eliminated with much-needed cost savings.

The Hawk T 1 uses tandem seating for the student pilot and instructor and the instrumentation comprises standard instruments and control lay-outs. Ejection seats are provided for both occupants and the cockpit is pressurised. The wing is a one-piece item with 26 degrees of sweep-back on the leading edge, much of its internal volume being used for fuel. There are four weapon attachment points under the wings although these are not usually used for the advanced flying training role, only for tactical training.

Hawks are used for advanced flying training at No 4 Flying Training School at RAF Valley. They are also used at No 1 Tactical Weapons Unit at RAF Brawdy in South Wales and No 2 Tactical Weapons Unit at RAF Chivenor, Devon. Aircraft based at these two units can be provided with full camouflage and carry training weapon loads. Each of the underwing weapon points can carry a nominal 454 kg of stores but a typical

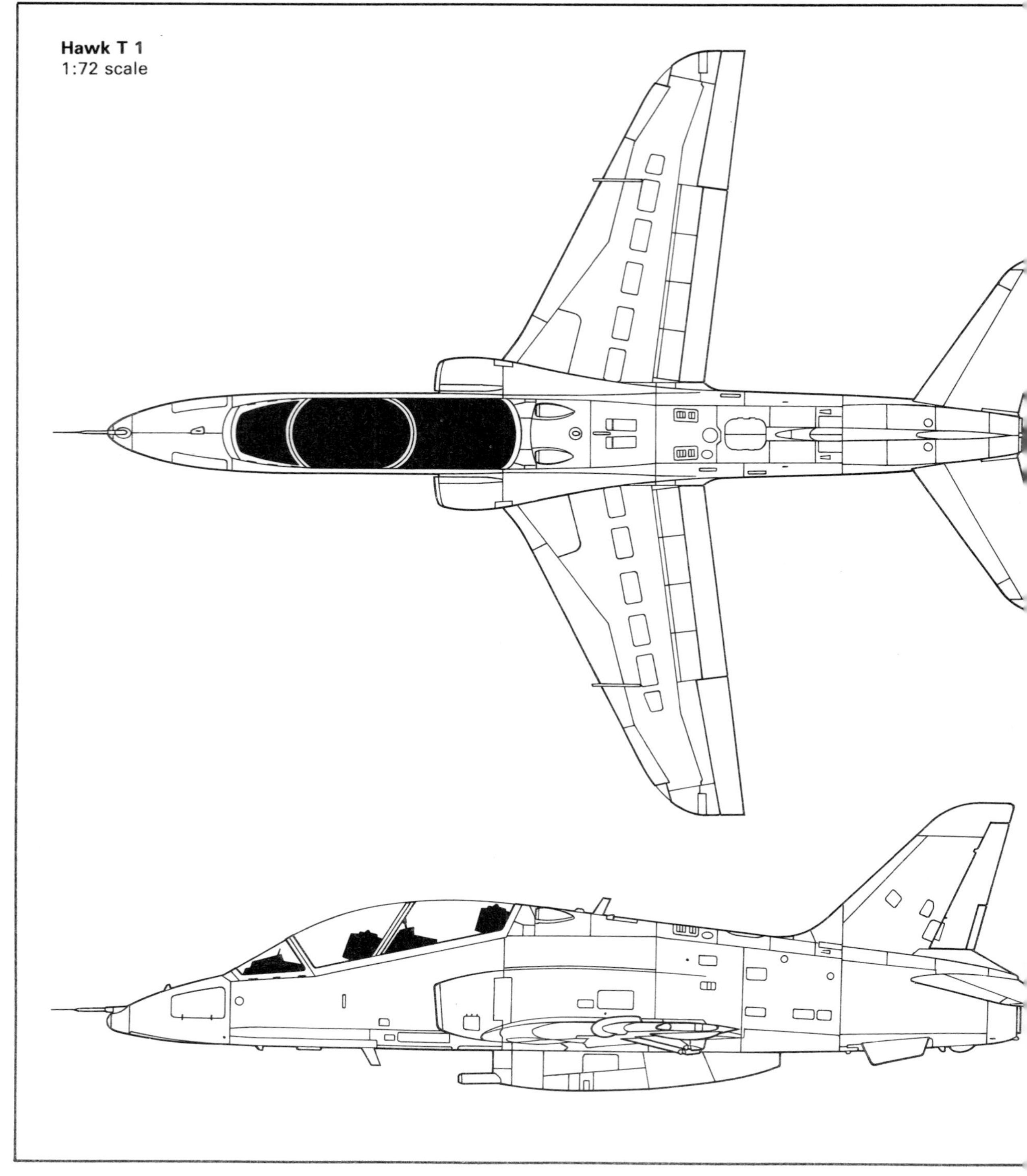
Hawk T 1
1:72 scale

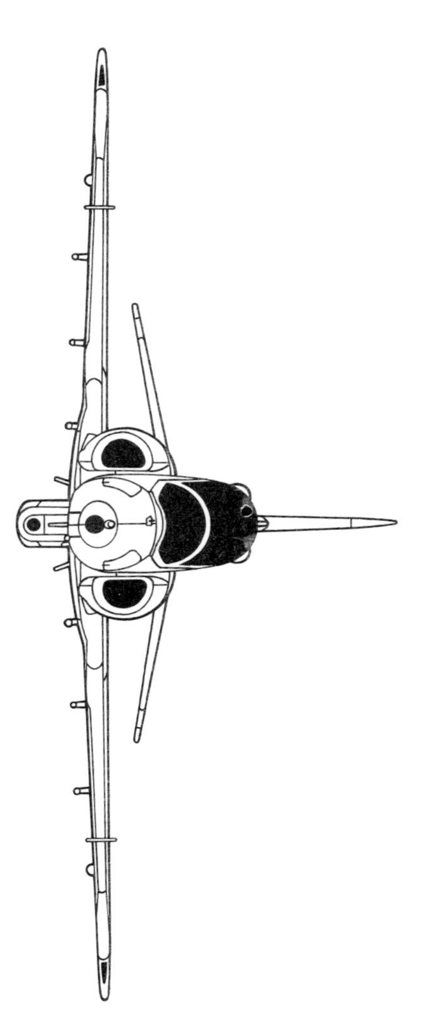

Above *Hawk T 1 of No 4 Flying Training School at RAF Valley.*

Below *A pair of RAF Brawdy Hawk T 1s over the Pembrokeshire coast.*

training load would consist of two 2.75-in rocket pods, each with 18 rockets, or two clusters of four practice bombs along with the single 30 mm Aden gun and ammunition pack. Some Hawk export models can carry much more than this but the Royal Air Force uses the Hawk in one fully operational role only and that is as a 'last ditch' interceptor carrying two AIM-9L Sidewinder missiles and piloted by training school instructors. Hawks equipped for this interception role are known as Hawk T 1As. They can carry a Sidewinder under each wing with a large pod containing a 30 mm Aden cannon and its ammunition under the fuselage centre line. The Hawk T 1As have no target-finding radar for the interception role and will have to rely on the pilot's ability to acquire targets visually but there are plans for some form of radar-carrying aircraft, such as a Phantom, to 'mother' groups of Hawk T 1As towards potential targets. 72 Hawks have been converted to the T 1A standard, including the mounts of the Red Arrows.

For the lay public the Hawk is primarily known as the aerobatic mount for the Royal Air Force aerobatic team, the Red Arrows. These specially-painted Hawk T 1As, based at RAF Scampton, are specially equipped with smoke-producing equipment to enhance their displays.

In service the Hawk has produced few problems and has proved to be easy to service and maintain, the latter being enhanced considerably by the use of the same engine as that of the Jaguar, although the Hawk version does not have re-heat. It seems very likely that the Adour Mk 151 engine will be replaced in service by its Mk 861 version in order to improve all-round performance at no great increase in costs.

Jet Provost T Mark 3A, T Mark 4 and T Mark 5A and 5B

Crew 2; **Span (over tanks)** 11.25 m; **Length** 10.27 m; **Height** 3.1 m; **Normal take-off weight** 3,460 kg; **Max speed** 525 km/h; **Armament** nil; **Engine** (T 3A) Rolls-Royce Viper Mk 102 (T 4/T 5A) Rolls-Royce Viper Mk 202.

The Jet Provost, or 'JP' as it is often known (among other things!), has been around for an alarmingly long time. The prototype first flew in 1954 and even then the design was basically a conversion of a radial piston-engined trainer aircraft to take a jet engine, and *that* design first flew in 1950. The first Jet Provost T 1 with its gawky long undercarriage entered service in 1955. Progressive improvements led to the T 3 (now the T 3A), the T 4 with a more powerful engine and, ultimately, the T 5 (now the T 5A) with a pressurised cockpit of distinctive appearance. The first Jet Provost T 5 flew during 1967 and a refit programme carried out during the mid-1970s led to the T 3A and T 5A designations being applied.

The Jet Provost is still what is has always been, a primary jet trainer. Generations of Royal Air Force pilots have been trained on it and it seems fair to say that every pilot serving today has at some time or another been at the controls of a JP. It is still a forgiving, docile aircraft with a surprising ability to perform all manner of aerobatics, and

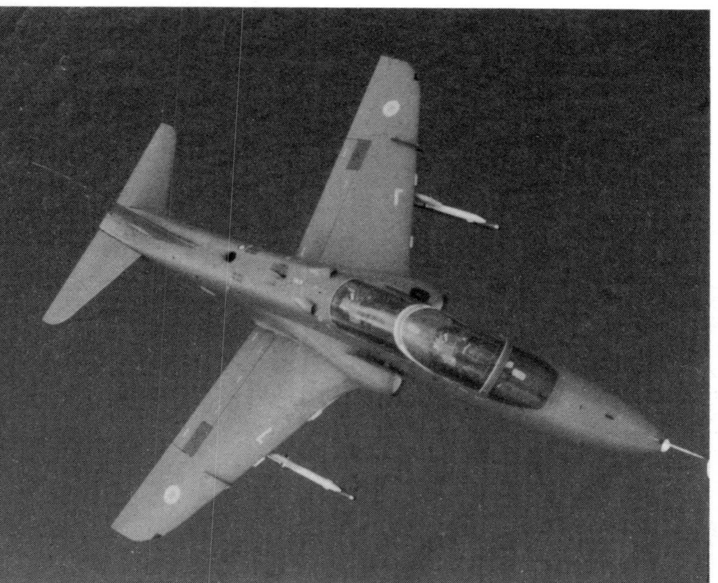

Left *One of the Hawk T 1As sporting its new grey camouflage.*

Below *One of the camouflaged Hawk T 1s used at the Tactical Weapons Unit, RAF Brawdy.*

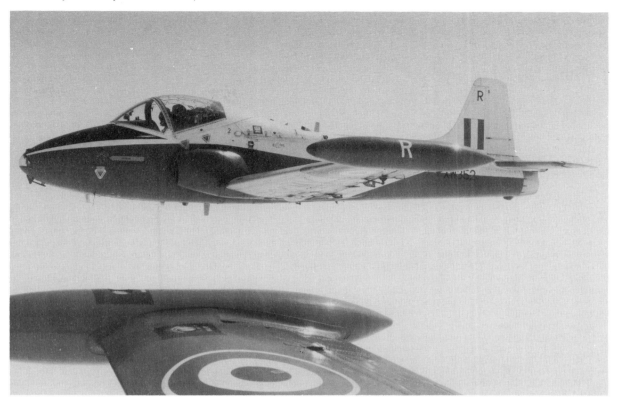

Above *Jet Provost T 5A used for navigation training at No 6 FTS, RAF Finningley.* **Below** *A Jet Provost T 5A about to touch down.*

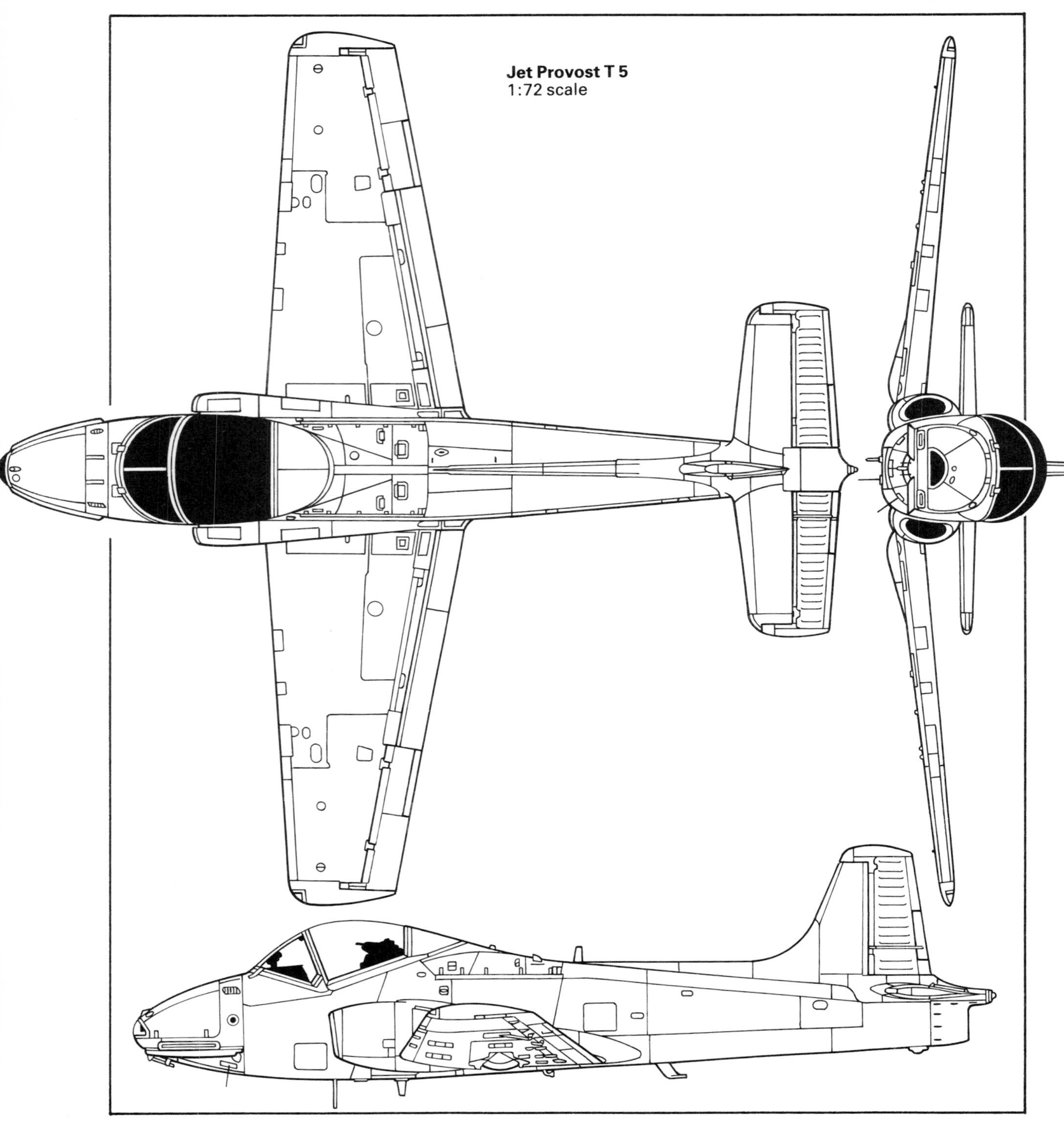
Jet Provost T 5
1:72 scale

Jet Provost T 3s and T 5s at RAF Linton-on-Ouse.

one possessing a surprisingly robust airframe and a reliable engine. It has a side-by-side cockpit arrangement with the instructor normally seated on the right. Martin-Baker ejection seats are fitted as standard. There is really nothing else to say about the aircraft for it is one of the most well-known of all Royal Air Force types.

Jet Provosts are flown by the Central Flying School at RAF Cranwell and the Royal Air Force College at the same location (both T 5A). No 1 FTS flies T 3As and T 5As from RAF Linton-on-Ouse. 6 FTS flies the Jet Provost T 5B from RAF Finningley while 7 FTS at RAF Church Fenton flies both the T 3A and the T 5B. The Jet Provost T4 is used by the Central Air Traffic Control School (CATCS) at RAF Shawbury.

Tucano T Mark 1

Crew 2; **Span** 11.28 m; **Length** 9.86 m; **Height** 3.4 m; **Max take-off weight (aerobatic)** 2,650 kg; **Max speed** approx 448 km/h; **Armament** nil (see text); **Engine** 1 × Garrett TPE331-12B turboprop.

Even aircraft as sturdy as the Jet Provost cannot last for ever, so several years back the Ministry of Defence issued Air Staff Target 412 outlining the requirements for a replacement. For a while the exact definition of the type of aircraft called for was hazy. At first a follow-on jet design seemed likely but the costs involved then seemed to favour a turboprop design. In the end the lower operating costs of the turboprop won through and several designs were put forward. In the end only two designs remained in the serious running, the Swiss Pilatus PC-9 and the Brazilian EMBRAER EMB-312 Tucano.

The selection process took place over a period of two years and in March 1985 it was announced that the Tucano had been chosen to be the Royal Air Force's new primary trainer. By then EMBRAER had teamed with Short Brothers of Belfast to build the aircraft in the United Kingdom—130 Tucanos were ordered.

The RAF ordered some changes from the Brazilian original. A new and more powerful Garrett turboprop was ordered to be fitted to boost low-altitude performance and the wings have been strengthened to allow higher loadings and to increase fatigue life. The undercarriage has also been strengthened. Other alterations involve a ventral air brake and the cockpit has been much changed to resemble the layout of a Hawk T 1. British equipment has been fitted wherever possible.

The Tucano is a good-looking aircraft with a

A Tucano test-flying its new Garrett turboprop and clearly showing off its large bubble cockpit cover.

tandem cockpit layout, the instructor seated to the rear. Lightweight ejection seats are fitted. Both cockpit occupants have an excellent all-round view through the large bubble canopy, essential in crowded training base circuits, while on the ground the tricycle undercarriage is similar to that of more advanced jets. The controls have a very similar response to those of a jet aircraft and the performance is nippy.

For basic training the Tucano T 1 will not carry armament but it may be possible to carry some forms of underwing light weapon load to provide the aircraft with some small measure of strike potential.

Tucano T 1s will be delivered to the Royal Air Force over the next few years—it is anticipated that all 130 will be delivered by the end of 1988.

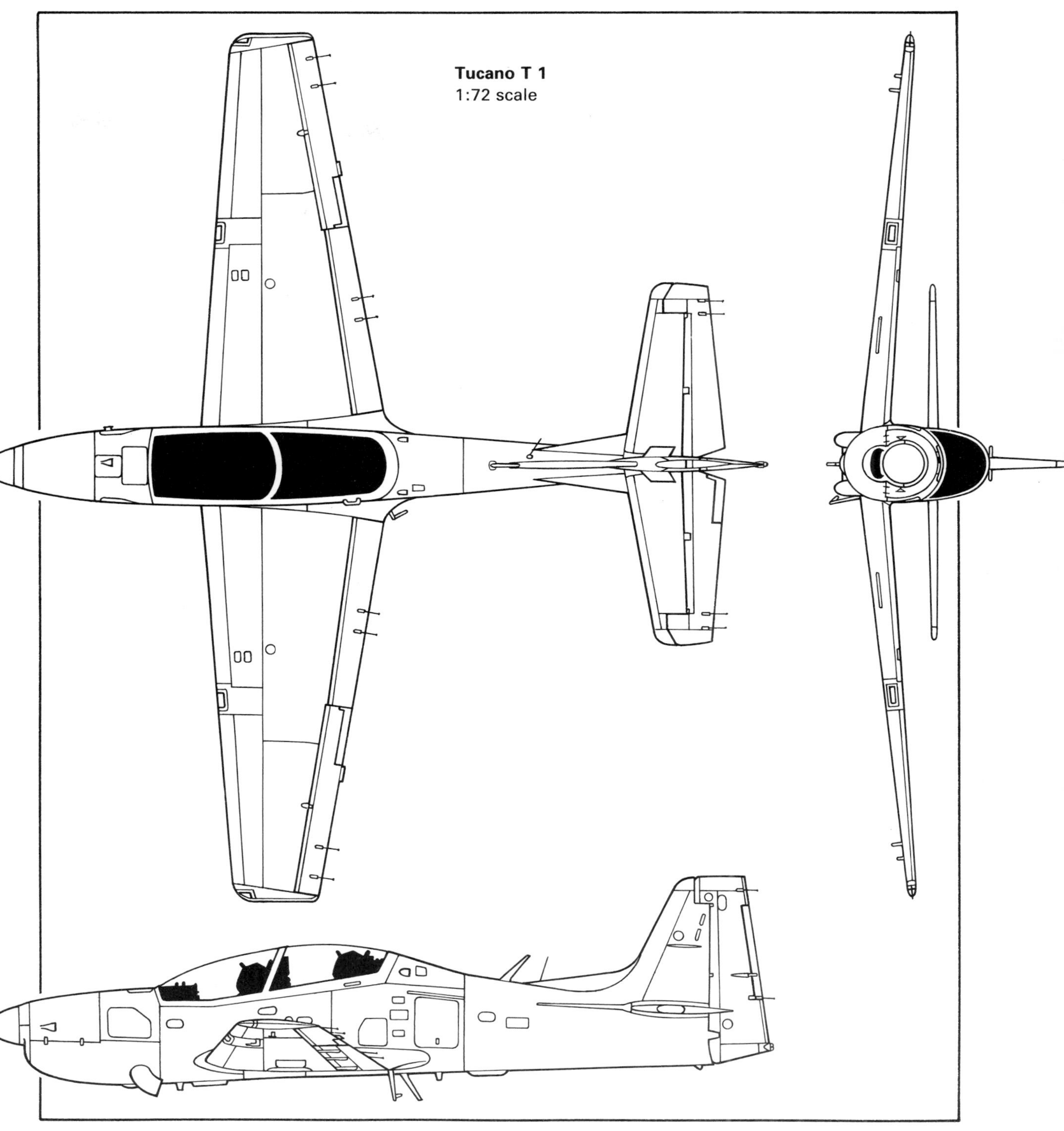
Tucano T 1
1:72 scale

Jetstream T 1
1:72 scale

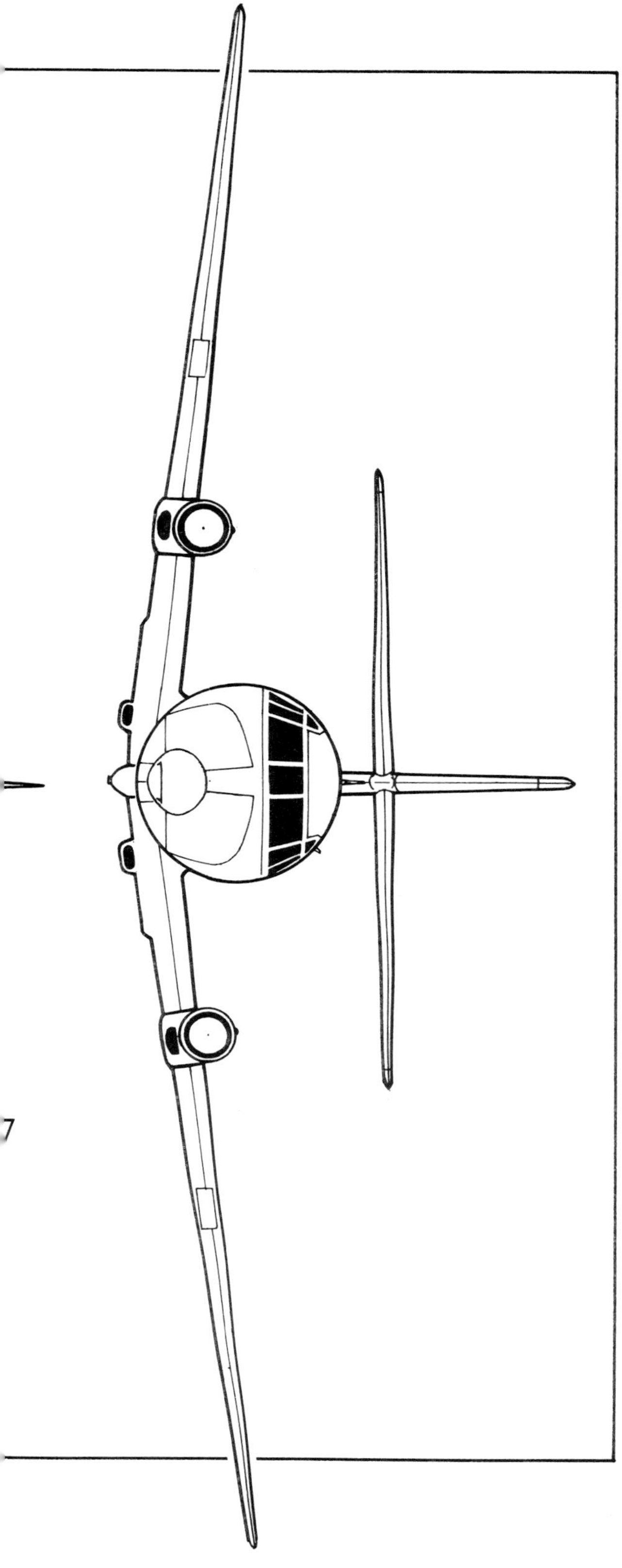

Jetstream T Mark 1

Crew 2 + 3 or 4; **Span** 15.58 m; **Length** 14.37 m; **Height** 5.32 m; **Max take-off weight** 5,670 kg; **Max speed** 454 km/h; **Armament** nil; **Engines** 2 × Turbomeca Astazou XV1 Ds.

The Jetstream is now used for the training of Group 2 trainee pilots (those streamed for multi-engine types) and for training Air Engineers and Air Electronics Officers to a lesser degree Navigators also spend some time in Jetstreams so the type is rather an important one for the Royal Air Force, even if it is almost entirely centred at one airfield, namely RAF Finningley, home of No 6 Flying Training School.

The Jetstream has had rather a varied life both in and out of the service. The type was originally a Handley Page design built to suit a civil market as the HP 137 Jetstream Series 100 during the late 1960s. From this evolved the Series 200, a military version which was ordered for the Royal Air Force as the Jetstream T 1. The first of these flew in early 1973 and 26 were delivered to No 5 Flying Training School starting in 1974. But en route to this delivery Handley Page encountered financial problems and the Jetstream production run was assumed by Scottish Aviation who completed the order, some from Handley Page components. Even in service the Jetstream had its problems for cut-backs in spending on the Services severely curtailed the training of multi-engine pilots for the Royal Air Force. Thus the Jetstream T 1 was effectively removed from Service and stored, although 16 were converted to a T 2 standard for the Royal Navy.

During 1976 the training climate was such that the stored Jetstreams were once more called upon for further use. In November of that year they re-entered service at RAF Leeming but later moved to RAF Finningley, where they remain.

The Jetstream T 1 has two pilots, a student and an instructor, with a further four seats in the cabin used for trainees. Apart from the multi-engine pilot training, most instruction in the rear compartment is for Air Engineers, Navigators and Air Electronics Operators spending only a limited amount of flying time on the type.

Jetstream T 1 of No 6 FTS, RAF Finningley.

Dominie T 1
1:72 scale

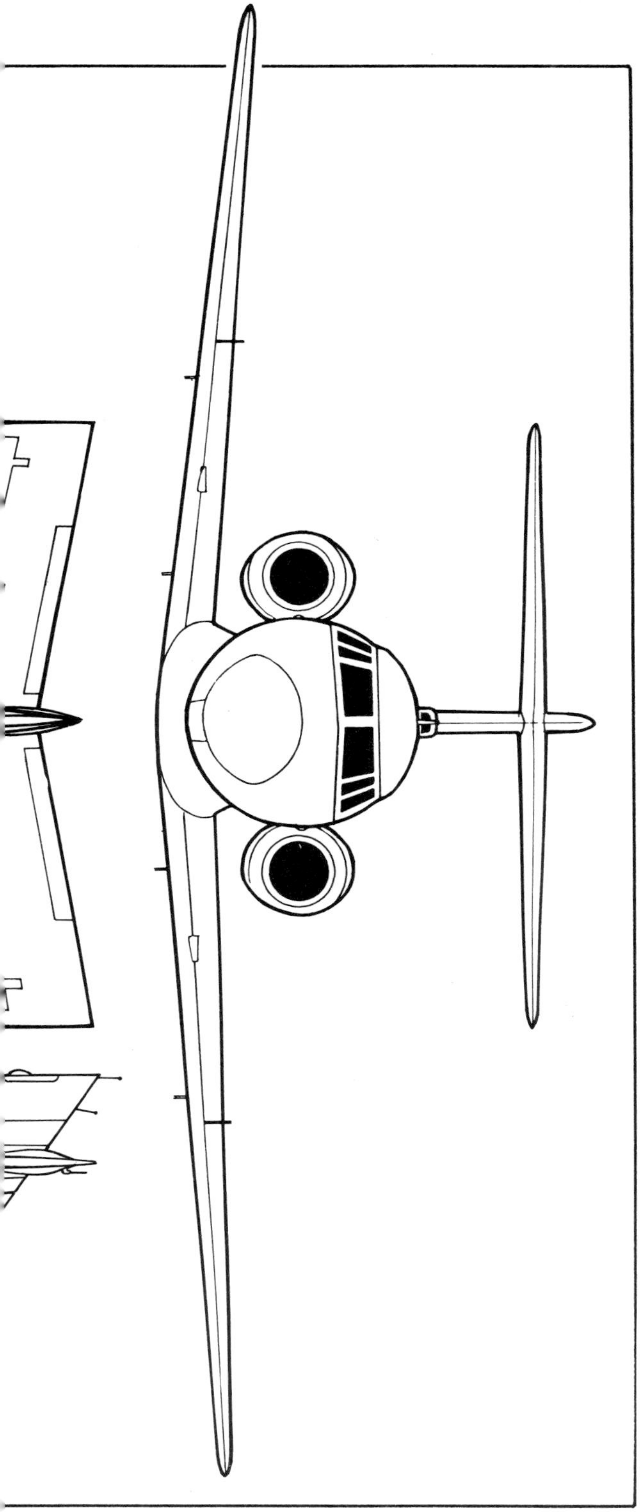

Dominie T 1 coming in to land at RAF Finningley.

Dominie T Mark 1

Crew 2 + 4; **Span** 14.33 m; **Length** 14.45 m; **Height** 5.03 m; **Max take-off weight** 9,615 kg; **Max speed** 805 km/h; **Armament** nil; **Engines** 2 × Rolls-Royce Viper 301 turbojets.

The training variant of the civil HS 125 was chosen by the Royal Air Force as a navigation trainer during the early 1960s and the first example flew on December 1 1964. The last of a batch of 20 was delivered in 1966, ever since when the aircraft, designated the Dominie T 1, has been in service as a long-range and high-speed navigation trainer. Most of the Dominies are based with No 6 Flying Training School at RAF Finningley.

The Dominie T 1 has a front cockpit crew of two, although one pilot only is required on many missions. All controls are duplicated for training if necessary. The main cabin is occupied by two student navigators and an experienced navigator to check their results. An extra position is provided for other instructors or for a ground crew member for servicing on overseas flights. Both students are provided with a full array of navigational instruments and equipment. There is provision for a periscopic sextant and full communications equipment is fitted. The Decca Navigator and Doppler aerials are housed in a wing leading edge extension that leads under the fuselage; a fin strake under the tail is another Dominie recognition feature.

The Finningley Dominies range far and wide on their navigation exercises, sometimes reaching as far as Gibraltar.

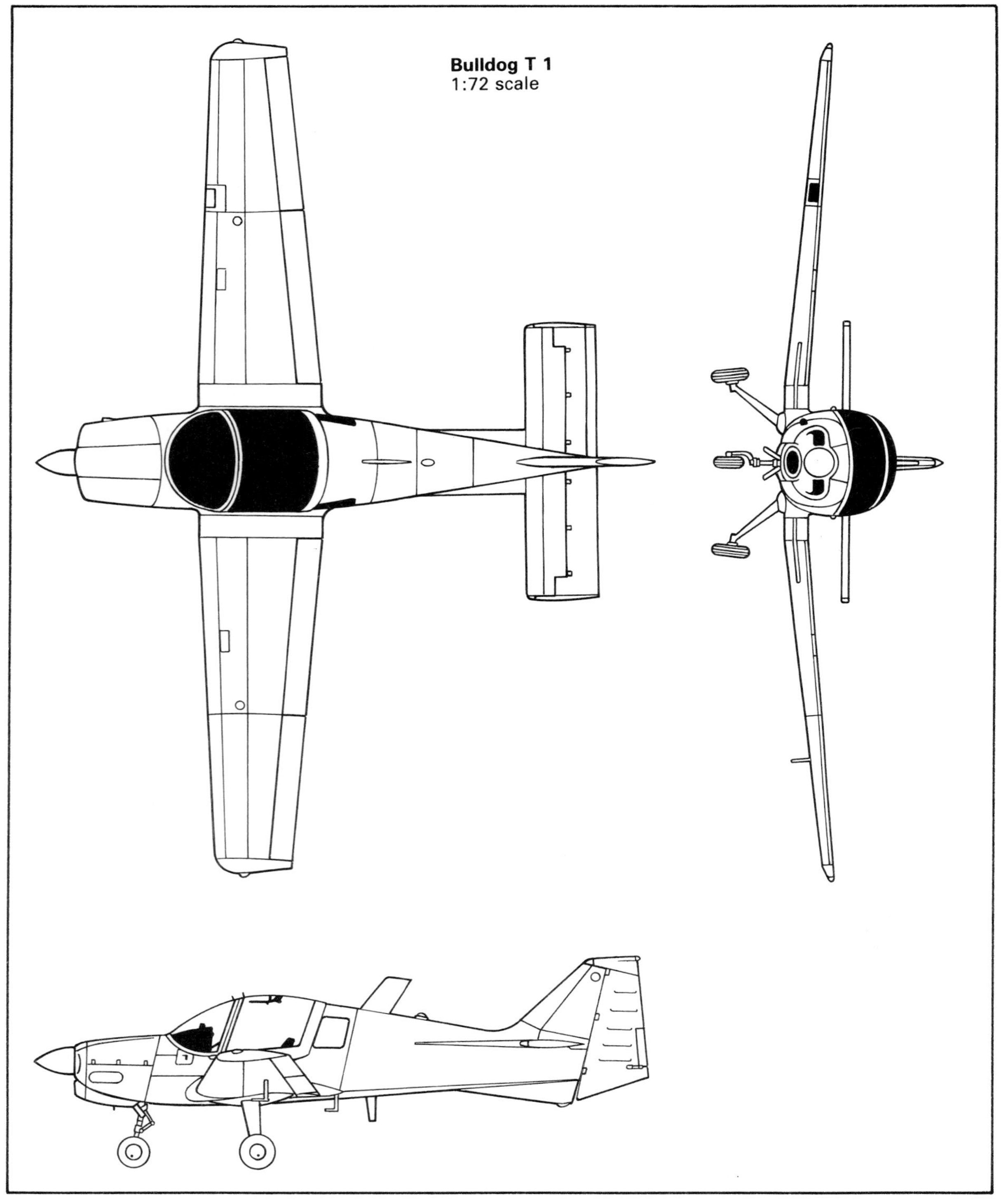
Bulldog T 1
1:72 scale

Bulldog T Mark 1

Crew 2(+ 1); **Span** 10.06 m; **Length** 7.09 m; **Height** 2.28 m; **Max take-off weight** 1,066 kg; **Max speed** 241 km/h; **Armament** nil; **Engine** 1 × 200 hp Avco Lycoming IO-360-A1B6.

The Bulldog was originally a Beagle product, being a militarised version of their civil Pup design with increased wing dimensions and strengthened construction for aerobatics. When the Beagle concern collapsed in a welter of recriminations and problems, construction of Bulldogs was undertaken by Scottish Aviation. In turn, they were eventually taken over by British Aerospace and thus the Bulldog is now a BAe product.

The first Bulldog flew on May 19 1969 and the version used by the Royal Air Force is the Model 121. A total of 130 was delivered to the Royal Air Force and the type now forms the mainstay of the University Air Squadrons and is also used as the basic trainer for helicopter pilots and other such training tasks. The Bulldog cockpit has side-by-side seating for the student pilot and an instructor, with space for a third seat behind them. No armament is carried. The Bulldog is a delight to fly and has few vices, one of them being an inability to get out of a spin in a very rarely encountered flight situation, so that this can virtually be disregarded in everyday training. The undercarriage is fixed.

No replacement for the Bulldog T 1 is in prospect.

Above *Bulldog T 1 from East Lowlands UAS.*

Below *The little Bulldog T 1, the trainer used by the University Air Squadrons.*

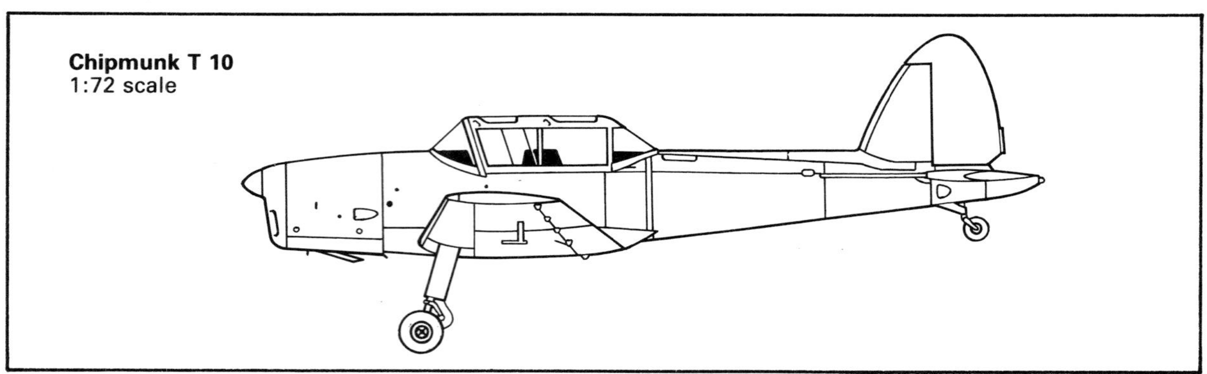

Chipmunk T Mark 10

Crew 2; **Span** 10.46 m; **Length** 7.75 m; **Height** 2.13 m; **Max take-off weight** 953 kg; **Max speed** 222 km/h; **Armament** nil; **Engine** 1 × de Havilland Gypsy Major 8.

The delightful little Chipmunk is one of the Royal Air Force's favourite aircraft as well as one of its longest-serving. The favouritism comes from the fact that many serving airmen and ground crew had their first-ever flight on the type, and many were trained on them. The longest-serving part comes from the fact that the type was first issued to the University Air Squadrons as long ago as 1950. Since then they have been used as *ab initio* trainers, air experience aircraft, glider tugs, internal security aircraft (in Cyprus) and light communications aircraft.

Today, the Chipmunk is still used in the training role as the main equipment of the Flying Selection Squadron (FSS) at RAF Swinderby, near Lincoln. There, the delightful but demanding flying qualities of the aircraft are used to determine whether or not a potential student pilot has the physical co-ordination and aptitude to become a pilot. This is done before the student commences the flying training programme proper, and in this manner expensive training time can be reduced. Some Chipmunks are used from time to time with the University Air Squadrons and more are used on the ATC Air Experience Flights. However, two Chipmunks are used in what might almost be called 'operational' conditions, for these aircraft belong to the Berlin Station Flight at RAF Gatow in Berlin. They are used to exercise the right of the Royal Air Force to fly over the city as part of the 1945 Treaty obligations. If this right was not exercised it could lapse and so the two aircraft regularly fly in their agreed air space in an economic but visible manner.

Chinook HC Mark 1

Crew 3 + 44; **Rotor diameter** 18.29 m each; **Rotor centre spacing** 11.94m; **Length (fuselage)** 15.54 m; **Height (rear rotor head)** 5.68 m; **Max take-off weight** 24,267 kg; **Max speed** 287 km/h (approx); **Armament** nil; **Engines** 2 × Avco-Lycoming T55-L-11E turboshafts (2 × Acvo-Lycoming T55-L-712 turboshafts).

Although development of the basic Boeing-Vertol CH-47 was initiated during 1956, the basic design

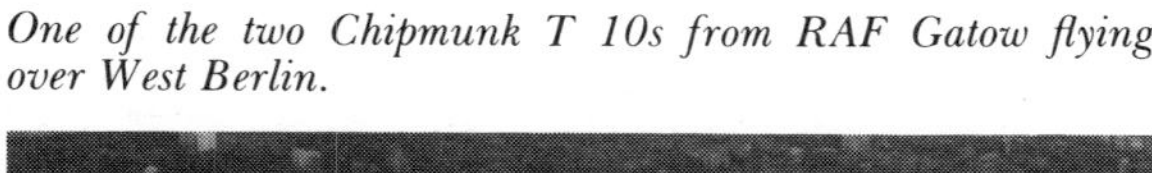
One of the two Chipmunk T 10s from RAF Gatow flying over West Berlin.

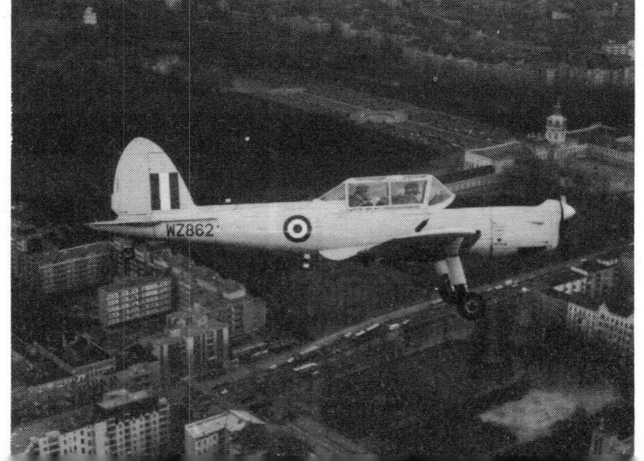

RAF Gatow Chipmunk T 10 flying over one of the Berlin Lakes.

Above *Chinook HC 1 of No 18 Squadron, now of RAF Gutersloh.*
Right *Chinook HC 1 from above clearly showing the bulk of the aircraft.*

and subsequent 'product improvements' have always meant that it has remained among the best designs of its type, and that remains true to this day. The latest American Service version is the CH-47D and the Royal Air Force version is very closely related to this model although it is not identical in all details. Consequently, when the type was ordered during 1978, there was no surprise other than that the order took so long to get through the Treasury funds funnel, since Chinooks had been requested to support the Harriers in the field even before the V/STOL aircraft had entered service.

When the order was finally made in 1978 it was for 33, and the type became the Chinook HC 1. It differed in several ways from the standard US Army Chinook, mainly in the engines and the electronics fit which was based on United Kingdom-produced equipments in the main. The first examples arrived in the United Kingdom in November 1980 and were taken over by No 240 OCU at RAF Odiham, who thus became the OCU for both the Chinook and the Puma. With the arrival of more and more examples, the Royal Air Force started to utilise the considerable increase in carrying capacity of the Chinook to the full. A normal load was two

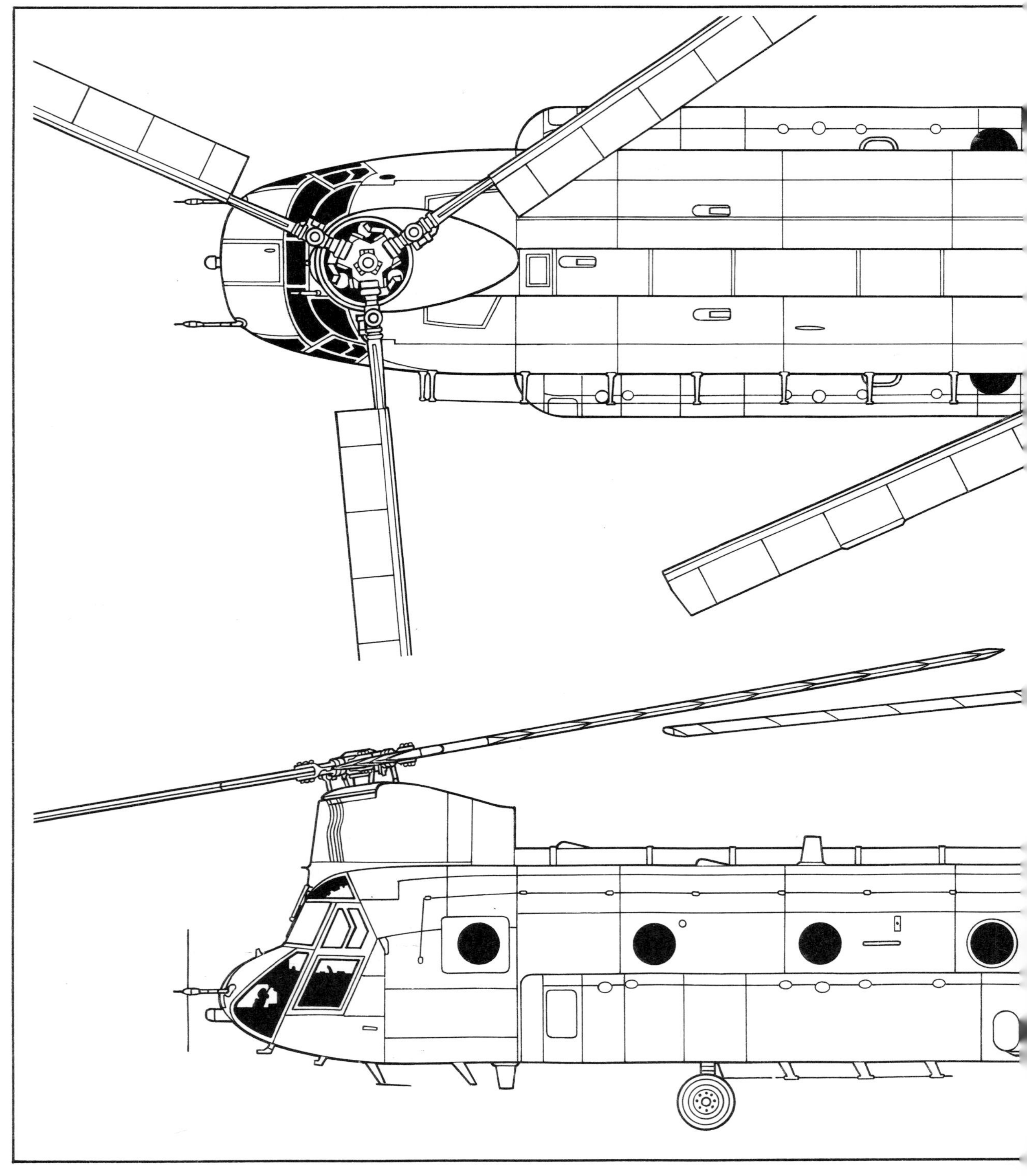

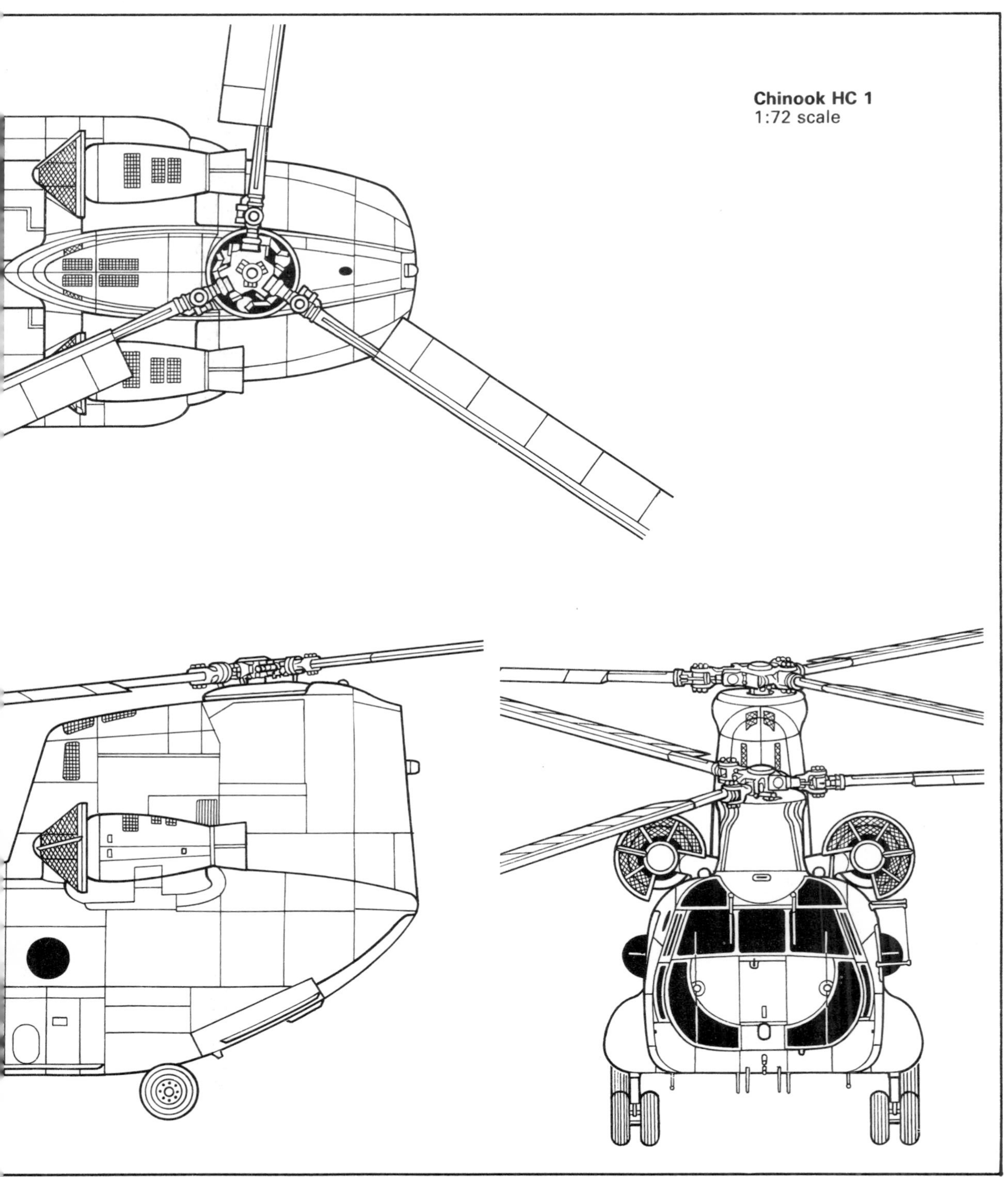
Chinook HC 1
1:72 scale

105 mm Light Guns together with their crews and some ammunition, and whole combat teams were commonplace. Normal peacetime regulations restricted the number of troops carried to 44 but the capacity was there for more and it was soon to be tested.

As everyone now knows, that testing came during the Falkland Islands campaign. Three of the four Chinooks sent on the campaign were lost when the *Atlantic Conveyor* was sunk and the lone survivor (*The Survivor*) was left to assume the heavy load-carrying mantle that should have been shared between four Chinooks. That aircraft deserves to be recorded: it was 'Bravo November', *ZA718*, and did marvellous service carrying fuel and other loads all over the Islands. It is now a matter of legend that on one important mission it carried well over 80 (the exact total is not surprisingly uncertain) fully armed men together with mortars, ammunition and all their other gear. On another date it carried 'about 100' off-duty Gurkhas out to their accommodation ship. Throughout the campaign, 'Bravo November' kept flying and kept working, a remarkable indication of the Chinook's soundness.

When the campaign ended the Royal Air Force had lost three Chinooks but gained another one,

Left *A Chinook HC 1 winching aloft the remains of an Argentinian Pucara.*

Below *Line-up of No 18 Squadron Chinook HC 1s at RAF Gutersloh.*

Chinook HC 1 leaving Boeing plant for rotor de-icing trials to be held at the Canadian Forces Base, Shearwater, Nova Scotia, November 1983.

an Argentinian CH-47C. This aircraft was brought back to the United Kingdom and sent for refurbishing at the Royal Naval Aircraft Yard at Fleetlands, near Gosport. The same base was involved in the updating of the first 14 Chinook HC 1s to be delivered, and Fleetlands retrofitted them with glass fibre rotor blades and a single-point refuelling system, among other more minor changes. These alterations brought the full Chinook fleet to the same standard but are still not yet complete. To replace the three lost Chinooks, an order was placed for three more and then for another five. These will be to US Army CH-47D standards and will have Avco-Lycoming T55-L-712 engines; in time the entire fleet of Royal Air Force Chinooks will be fitted with this engine type.

The first Chinook HC 1 squadron was No 18, initially formed at RAF Odiham and subsequently involved with their single Chinook in the Falklands. They moved to RAF Gutersloh to become part of RAF Germany in May 1983, and there they remain in support of the two RAF Germany Harrier squadrons and 1 (BR) Corps. The second squadron to be formed was No 7, which remains in the United Kingdom at RAF Odiham. No 78 Squadron is a composite Chinook and Sea King squadron based at RAF Mount Pleasant in the Falkland Islands.

Apart from the already-mentioned engine and other improvements to be made, the Royal Air Force Chinook HC 1s have many innovations in the pipeline, including the fitting of night-vision equipment. The aircraft already have a triple external load-carrying point capability and this, coupled with a new Cruise Guide Indicator, enables the aircraft to virtually automatically select its own flight trim settings, even for internal loads. The external load may be as high as 11,300 kg. Passive radar warning and other warning equipments are other innovations.

Thus the Chinook has rapidly established itself as an integral and important item of Royal Air Force equipment. It will be around for years to come and has a great deal of operational life ahead.

Puma HC Mark 1

Crew 2 or 3 + 16; **Rotor diameter** 15 m; **Length (fuselage)** 14.06 m; **Height** 5.14 m; **Max take-off weight** 7,400 kg; **Max speed** 263 km/h; **Armament** nil (RAF version); **Engines** 2 × Turbomeca Turmo 111C4 turboshafts.

Although the Puma HC 1 is primarily another French Aerospatiale design, the aircraft for the Royal Air Force were assembled by Westland who were also involved in much of the development of the type. (The French design designation for the Puma HC 1 is SA 330E.) The first examples were delivered to the Royal Air Force commencing in

A Puma HC 1 loading troops during a NATO exercise in Norway.

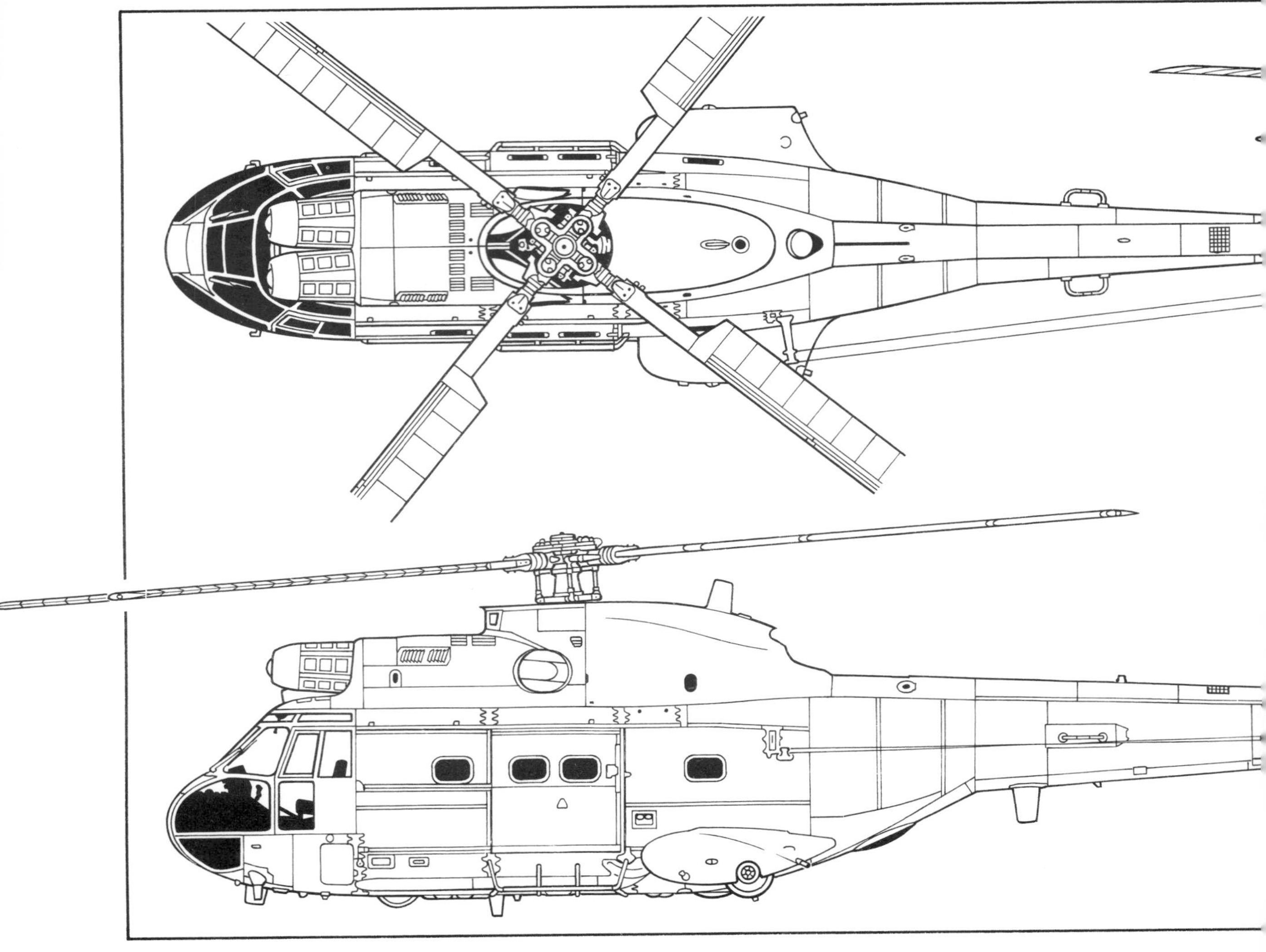

1971, since when the type has supplemented the Wessex in the general support role. The initial RAF order for the Puma was 40 but some attrition has taken place and a further seven were delivered, starting during 1980.

The Puma HC 1 is a sound, reliable helicopter with a capacious main cabin. It can carry up to 16 fully-equipped troops or 20 unencumbered passengers. In the aeromedical role it can carry up to six stretchers and six seated casualties. Supplies can be carried in the cabin but bulky loads are usually slung under the fuselage. These loads can weigh up to 2,500 kg and can include such items as a 105 mm Light Gun.

Over the years few changes have been made to the airframe or the engines but recently some Pumas have been fitted with what are known as 'polyvalent' air intake extensions for the engines to provide some engine protection when operating in icy conditions. This is important for the two Puma HC 1 squadrons are very likely to find themselves operating in extremely cold climates. No 230 operates from RAF Gutersloh as part of RAF Germany and in direct support of 1(BR) Corps. The United Kingdom-based squadron is No 33, which is based at RAF Odiham but pledged for the support of the Army's contribution to the NATO AMF(L), and as such is likely to find itself operating in Northern Norway on the NATO flank. The squadron frequently exercises in the region. The

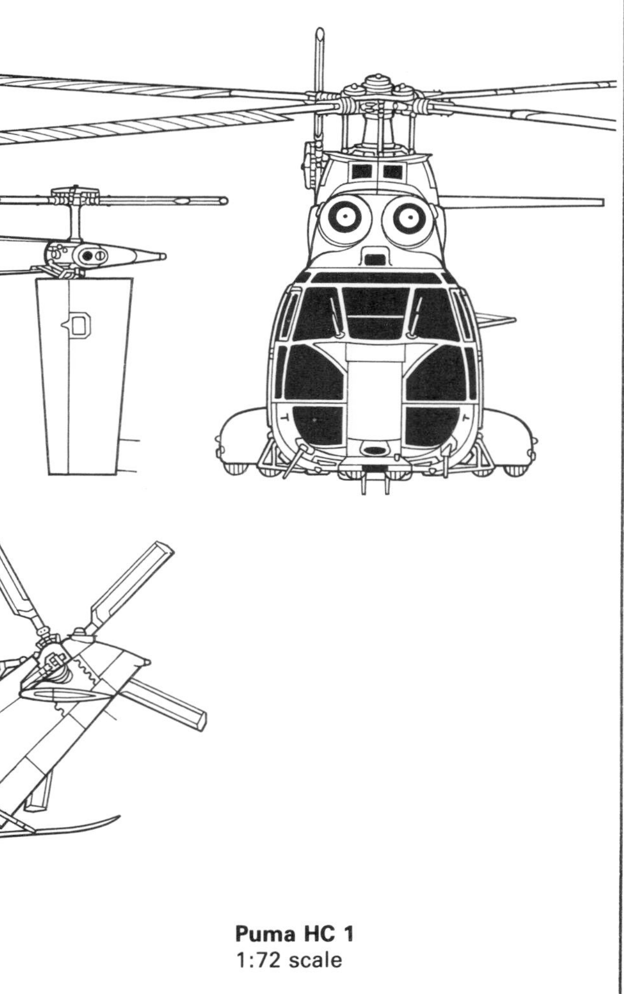

A Puma HC 1 carrying a 105 mm Light Gun.

Puma OCU is No 240, shared with the Chinook HC 1, at RAF Odiham.

As with so much other Royal Air Force equipment, the Puma seems set for a long spell of service to come. Changes already in the pipeline are for the fleet to be equipped progressively with composite rotor blades to increase performance, and reduce the maintenance load (the 1980 batch already has these blades). The long-term replacement for the Puma is something of a mystery at the time of writing. In the long term it is expected that a tactical transport form of the Anglo-Italian EH 101 helicopter will be selected but the EH 101 is some way off in the future. In the meantime, and to boost the numbers of helicopters available to carry the Army around the 1 (BR) Corps area, a number of American Sikorsky UH-60 Black Hawk helicopters might be obtained.

However, funds are short and at present there is a degree of argument between the Army and Royal Air Force as to exactly who should be in operational control of battlefield helicopter operations. At present the Army uses them but the RAF flies them so at times there are difficulties as to who has the more important say in operational matters, especially when some RAF helicopter squadrons are also NATO resources as well as British resources (as is the case with the RAF Germany Chinook squadron). The Army is thus making a bid for full operational control of the available helicopter squadrons which could then pass from being RAF units to becoming Army Air Corps units. Needless to say this has aroused a great deal of inter-service discussion, not all of it polite, and the outcome may not be known for years yet.

Above *Sea King HAR 3 at RAF Coltishall.*

Sea King HAR Mark 3

Crew 4 + 19; **Rotor diameter** 18.9 m; **Length (fuselage)** 17.01 m; **Height** 5.13 m; **Normal take-off weight** 9,525 kg; **Max speed (cruising, approx)** 208 km/h; **Armament** nil; **Engines** 2 × Rolls-Royce Bristol Gnome 1400 turboshafts.

By any standards the Sikorsky S-61 helicopter has been one of the most successful of all helicopter designs and has been built in numerous forms and for many roles. Westland Helicopters of Yeovil, Somerset, have long had a happy association with Sikorsky, and the S-61 was a natural choice for license production which commenced during 1967, at first in an anti-submarine form for the Fleet Air Arm. When the Royal Air Force required a replacement for the ageing Whirlwind search and rescue helicopter then in service, the Westland S-61 derivative, known as the Sea King, was an equally obvious choice and the first Sea King HAR 3 flew in 1977. The last of a batch of 15 was delivered in 1979.

In almost every way the Sea King HAR 3 is a definite improvement over the old Whirlwind, in terms of speed, range, equipment carried and capacity. The crew consists of two pilots, an air electronics/winch operator and an air loadmaster/winchman. There is seating capacity for up to 19 persons but when stretchers are carried (up to six) this seating is reduced accordingly. The range is considerable and even unrefuelled the radius of action is about 480 kilometres. There are two pilots to spread the cockpit workload and the electronics carried are mainly devoted to navigation.

The Sea King HAR 3s are operated by one unit only, No 202 Squadron, which has its administrative and engineering base at RAF Finningley. However, none of the Sea Kings operate from there as they are currently based at four locations in four Flights of two or three helicopters at each. 'A' Flight is at RAF Boulmer, 'B' Flight at RAF Brawdy and 'D' Flight at RAF Lossiemouth. 'C' Flight would normally operate from RAF Coltishall but at the time of writing is way to the south in the Falklands, and is now part of No 78 Squadron at RAF Mount Pleasant. Cover for RAF Coltishall has been provided by two Wessex HAR 2s from RAF Manston and RAF Leconfield, and stand-by long range cover is provided (as would normally be the case, even with Sea Kings) by the 67th Aerospace Rescue and Recovery Squadron, US Air Force, which is based at RAF Woodbridge in Suffolk and uses HH-53C helicopters and special rescue HC-130H Hercules.

The prime task of No 202 Squadron is the rescue and recovery of Royal Air Force aircrew who are forced to land in the sea. Having said that, their normal peacetime role is that of rescuing anyone who finds themselves in any sort of difficulty at sea, from children on inflatable rafts to large-scale rescues of mariners from wrecked ships. As with all other search and rescue helicopters operated by the Royal Navy and the Royal Air Force, they operate under the control of the two Rescue Co-

Above *Sea King HAR 3 of 'D' Flight, 202 Squadron, flying near Lossiemouth.*

Below *Sea King HAR 3 carrying out rescue training near RAF Valley.*

ordination Centres (RCC), the northern one at Pitreavie, Edinburgh, and the southern one at Plymouth. These are manned round the clock and all year round, and the Coastguard frequently has to call on the Sea Kings to assist in civilian rescues. Sometimes the Sea Kings (and the Wessex HAR 2s) are called upon to assist in searches or other operations carried out by the Royal Air Force Mountain Rescue Service. These teams again have a primary military task but are often called out to assist civilians in distress. Each team is from 30 to 36 men strong and is made up of volunteers grouped around a small permament cadre. Teams are based around the United Kingdom at RAF Leeming, RAF Kinloss, RAF St Athan, RAF Stafford and RAF Valley. They are unusual in that they operate under the control of the Home Office.

To return to the Sea King HAR 3s, aircrew are trained on the type at the Sea King Training Unit (SKTU) at RAF Culdrose. Once on the squadron they are kept very busy throughout the year and on duty are kept on 15-minute standby for operations throughout the day and maintain a 45-minute standby at night.

The Sea King HAR 3 will remain in service for some years to come while the eventual replacement could well be a version of the EH Industries EH-101, a joint Westland-Italian venture, but the first production examples of that are not expected before 1988. In the meantime, improvements to the Sea King navigational aids can be expected, among them an American-developed satellite-aided tracking system for accurate position fixing.

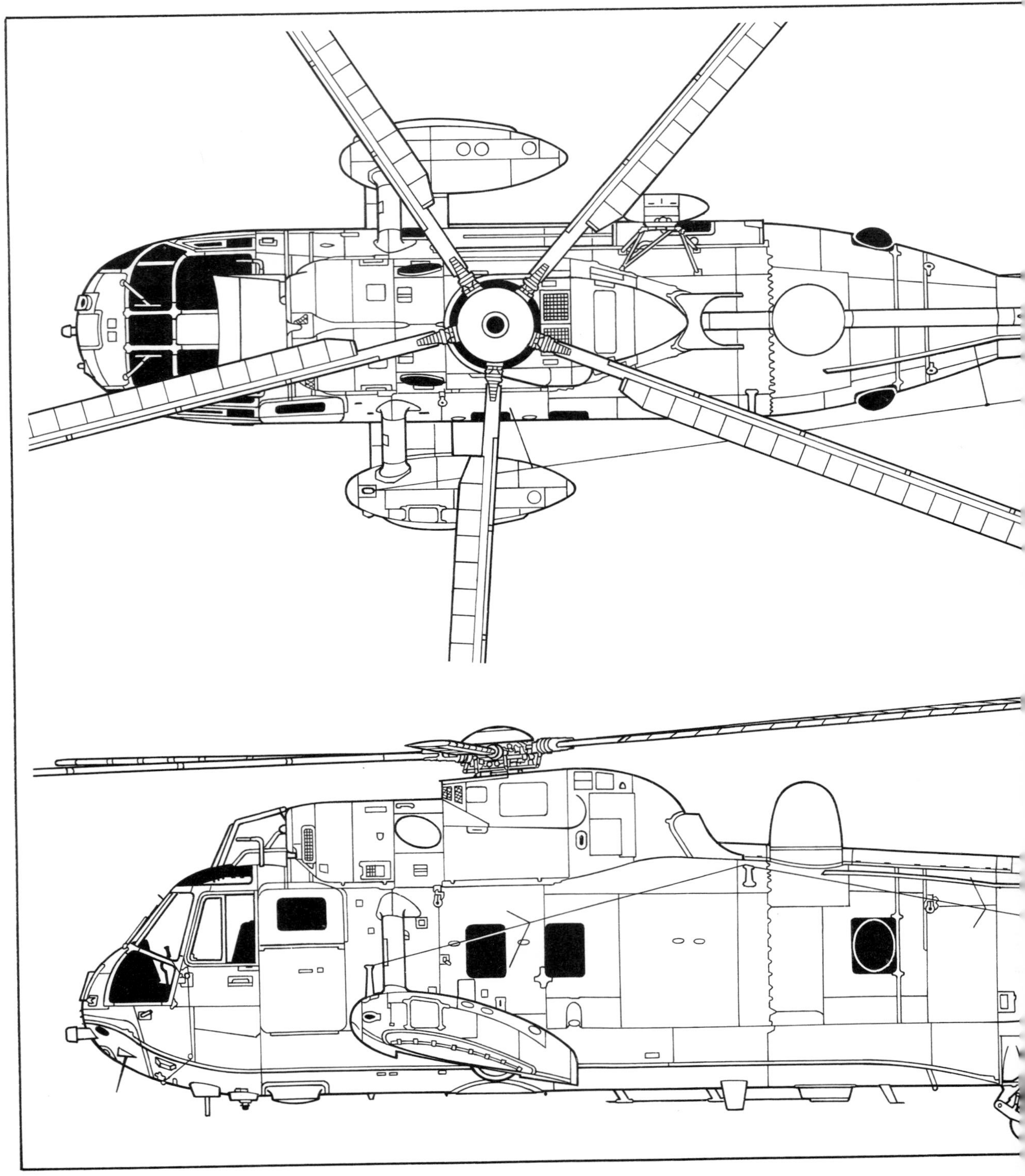

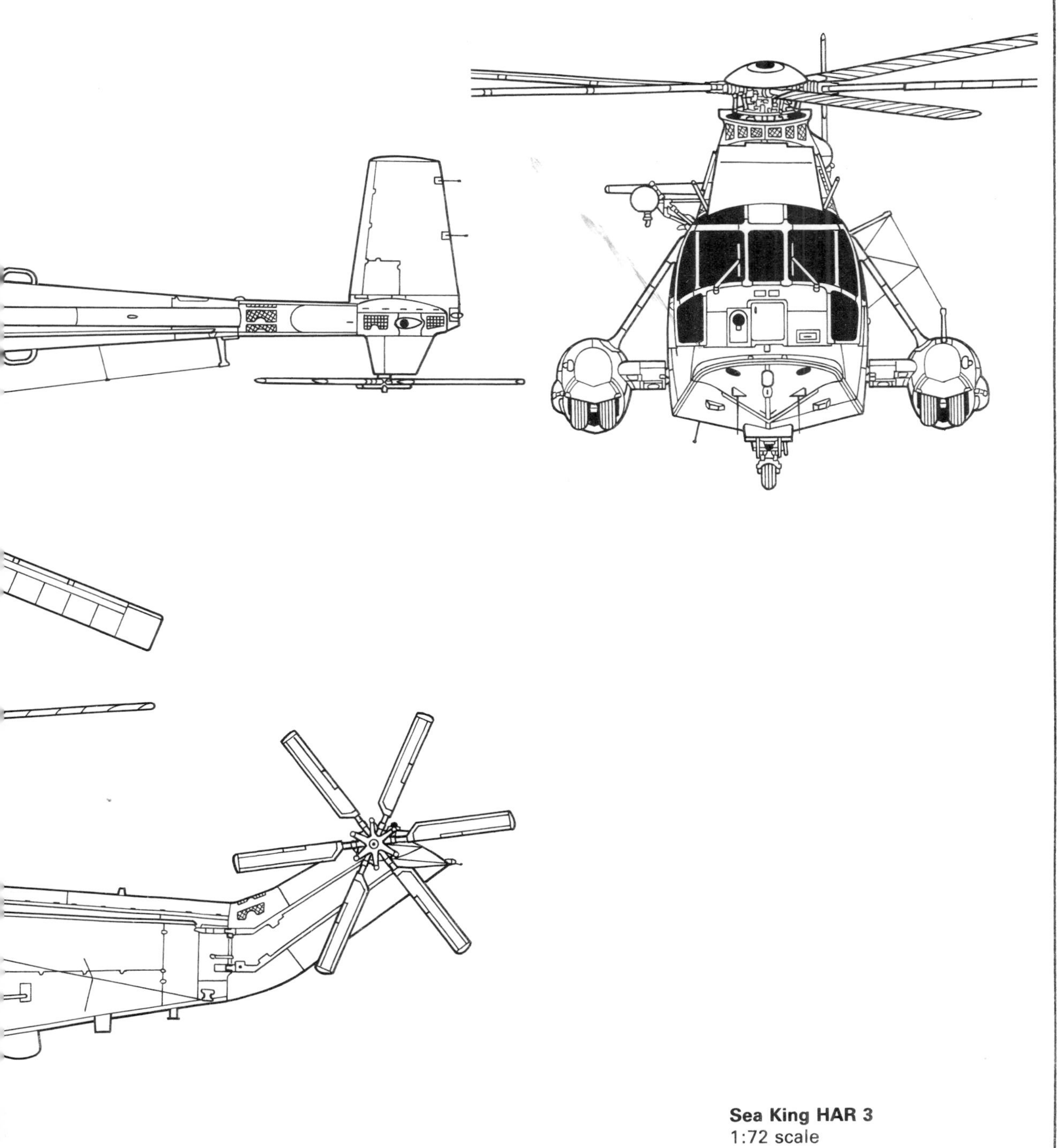

Sea King HAR 3
1:72 scale

Wessex HC 2.

Wessex HC Mark 2, HAR Mark 2 and HCC Mark 4

Crew 2 + 16; **Rotor diameter** 17.07 m; **Length (fuselage)** 14.74 m; **Height** 4.93 m; **Max take-off weight** 6,120 kg; **Max speed** 212 km/h; **Armament** nil; **Engines** 2 × Rolls-Royce Bristol Gnome 110/111 turboshafts.

The Wessex HC 2 is the Royal Air Force's version of the Westland licence-built version of the Sikorsky S-58. Fitted with twin turboshafts in place of the original American single radial piston engine, the Wessex largely replaced the old Whirlwind in Royal Air Force service back in 1963 and has been around ever since. It is still in squadron service and does sterling work with the search and rescue flights around the United Kingdom.

The basic aircrew for the Wessex is two pilots but there is usually another man in the main compartment to operate the winch and act as loadmaster. In many instances the second pilot is replaced by a navigator. The main compartment can carry up to 16 troops or seven stretchers. Oversize cargo weighing up to 1,630 kg can be carried slung under the fuselage.

The Wessex can be used in either the troop-carrying role, as in Northern Ireland, or as a search and rescue helicopter. Strictly speaking, the designation Wessex HAR 2 for the search and rescue role is 'unofficial' but is frequently encountered; the correct designation is Wessex HC 2. This designation is certainly used by the Wessexes of No 72 Support Helicopter Squadron who operate out of RAF Aldergrove in Northern Ireland in support of the Army units based in the province. These aircraft frequently operate away from their main base and act in a wide variety of ways from carrying in supplies to some of the more isolated Army and Royal Ulster Constabulary posts along the Border to carrying squads of armed troops for search missions and road blocks. The squadron has a secondary search and rescue role, but the main United Kingdom Wessex unit devoted to that role is No 22 Squadron headquartered at RAF Finningley. As with the other UK-based search and rescue squadron (No 202, Sea King HAR 3), RAF Finningley acts only as an administrative centre for the squadron has five flights scattered around the United Kingdom. 'A' Flight is at RAF Chivenor, 'B' Flight at RAF Leuchars, 'C' Flight at RAF Valley, 'D' Flight at RAF Leconfield and 'E' Flight at RAF Manston. To confuse matters further, the squadron also has a detachment ('F' Flight) at RAF Coltishall formed from one aircraft from 'D' Flight and one from 'E' Flight. These provide some SAR cover for the missing No 202 Squadron Sea King HAR 3s in the Falklands. The engineering base for these Wessexes is the Wessex Aircraft Servicing Flight at RAF Benson. To continue this saga of Wessex-orientated units, 'C' Flight at RAF Valley pools its helicopters with the Search and Rescue Training Unit, operating from the same base, and the Wessex HC 2 is also operated by 2 FTS at RAF

Shawbury for helicopter pilot training.

Away from the United Kingdom, going east, No 84 Squadron operates from RAF Akrotiri in Cyprus. This unit divides its attentions between operating a search and rescue flight for units training locally (there are no permanent flying squadrons based in Cyprus other than No 84 Squadron) and providing a flight for the support of UNIFCYP (United Nations Forces in Cyprus). A lot further east, in Hong Kong, is No 28 Squadron which has a very busy time covering just about everything from supporting the locally based Gurkha regiments and providing a search and rescue service to patrolling the border with China to watch for illegal immigrants.

Back in the United Kingdom, mention must be made of the superbly maintained Wessex HCC 4s of the Queen's Flight. There are two of these based at RAF Benson, each with specially-fitted interiors. One odd point regarding these two Wessexes is that despite their VIP function the Queen herself rarely uses them—normally she is not allowed to fly by helicopter for reasons of State.

The Wessex seems set for a long period of service to come as there is no apparent replacement for the type, other than perhaps the Puma. The Wessex is still much favoured as a general hack and research helicopter by several of the various aircraft and research establishments, but many of their Wessexes are ex-Royal Navy aircraft.

Left *A 28 Squadron HC 2 about to lift a 4,000 lb/1,814 kg container.*

Below left *Gurkhas loading a Wessex HC 2 of No 28 Squadron in Hong Kong.*

Below *One of the Wessex HCC Mark 4s of the Queen's Flight.*

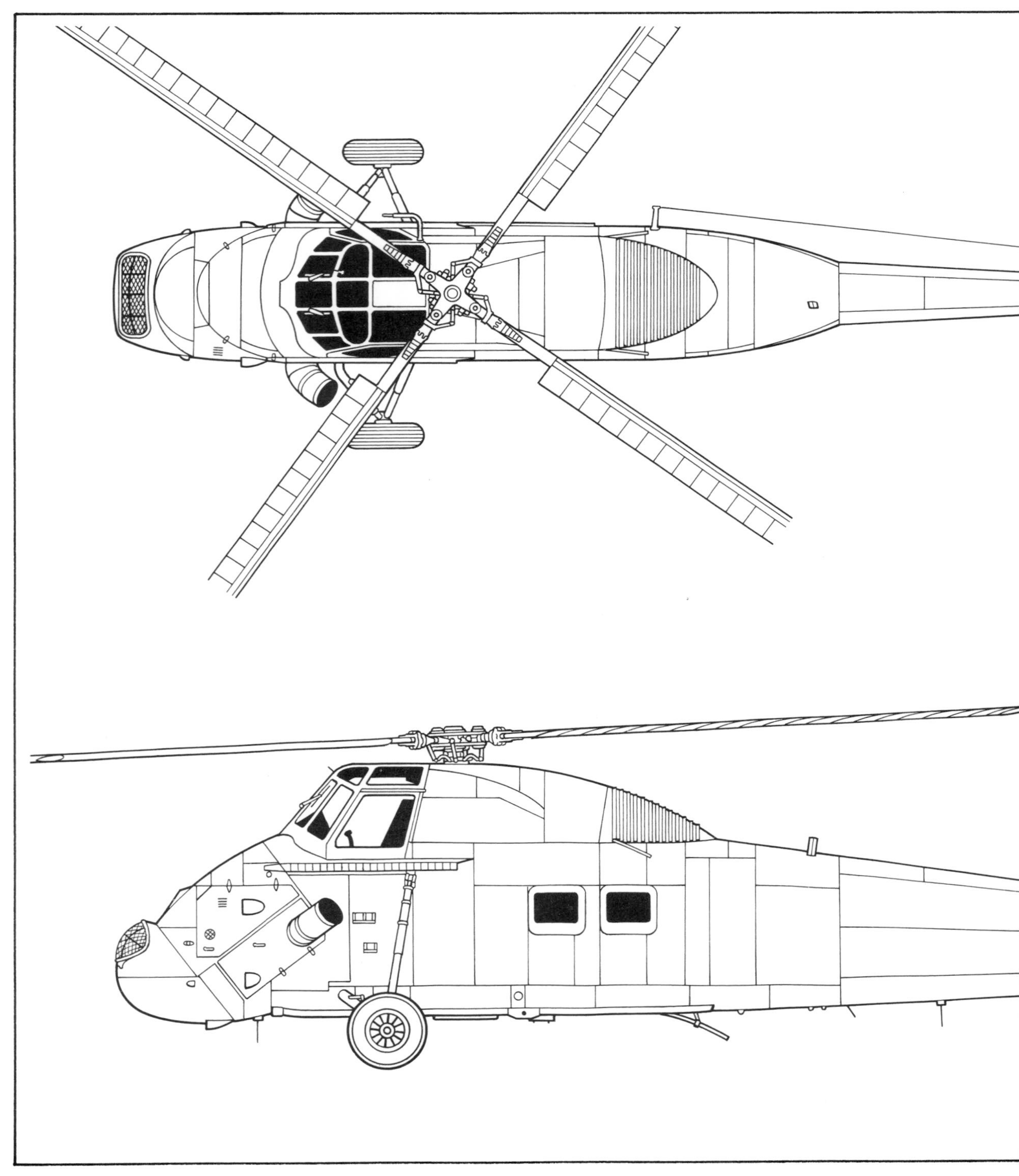

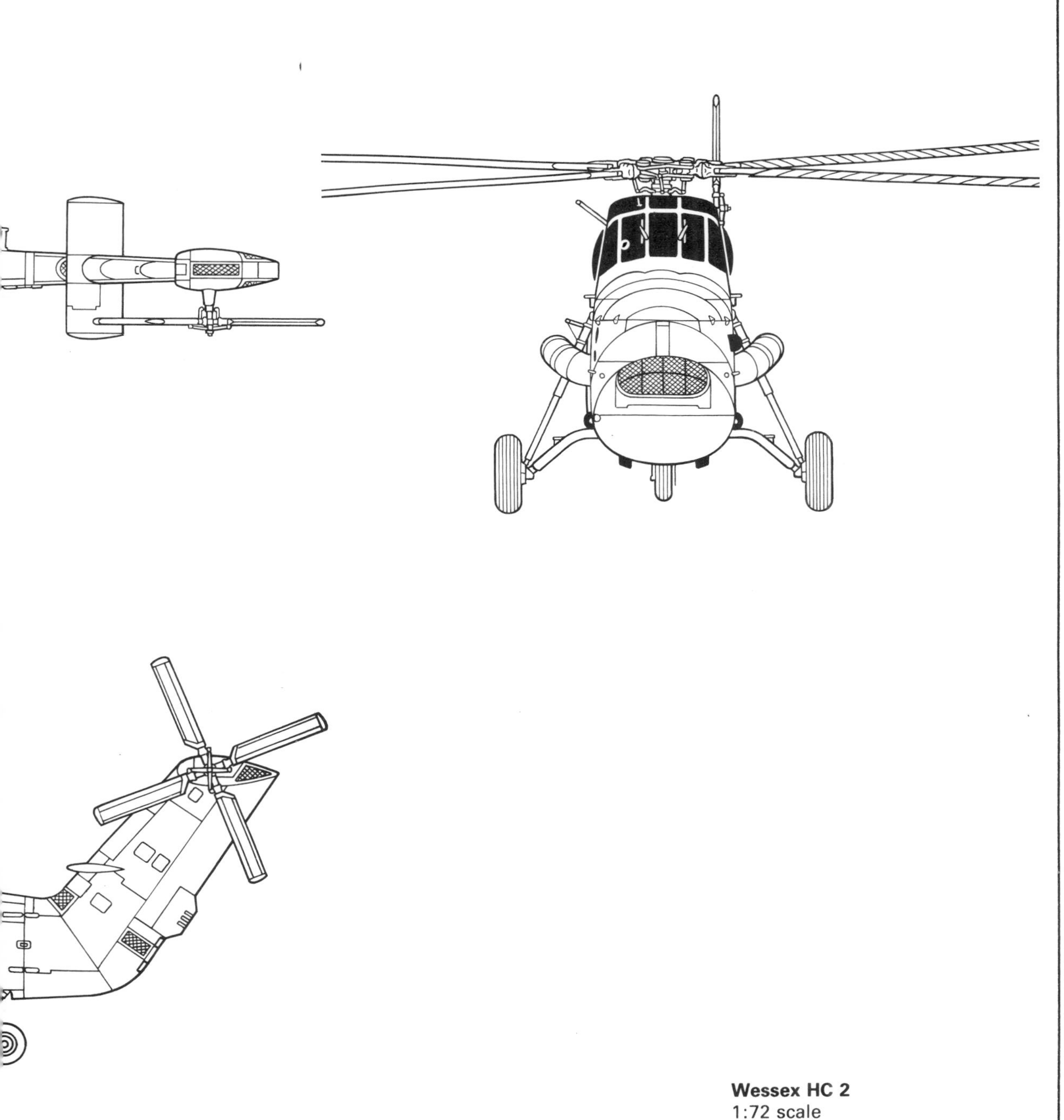

Wessex HC 2
1:72 scale

Gazelle HT Mark 3 and HCC Mark 4

Crew 2 + 3; **Rotor diameter** 10.5 m; **Length (fuselage)** 9.53 m; **Height** 3.15 m; **Max take-off weight** 1,800 kg; **Max speed** 310 km/h; **Armament** nil (with RAF); **Engine** 1 × Turbomeca Astazou 3N turboshaft.

The Gazelle is an example of a happy international co-operation programme for it was originally a French design and the SA 341D Gazelles for the Royal Air Force were developed in France by Aerospatiale. The first Royal Air Force example flew in 1972 and ever since then the type has been a popular little helicopter with a remarkable turn of speed. It is easily recognisable through its unique 'fenestron' shrouded tail rotor.

Within the Royal Air Force, the Gazelle is mainly used for helicopter flying training as the Gazelle HT 3. In this form it is equipped with side-by-side dual controls and the seating at the rear is rarely used apart from the odd 'over-the-shoulder' flying training. The main 'home' for the Gazelle is RAF Shawbury where it is used by 2 FTS for helicopter training, but the machine is also in use by No 32 Squadron at RAF Northolt as a light communications helicopter. No 32 Squadron also uses the only example of the Gazelle HCC 4 which has a

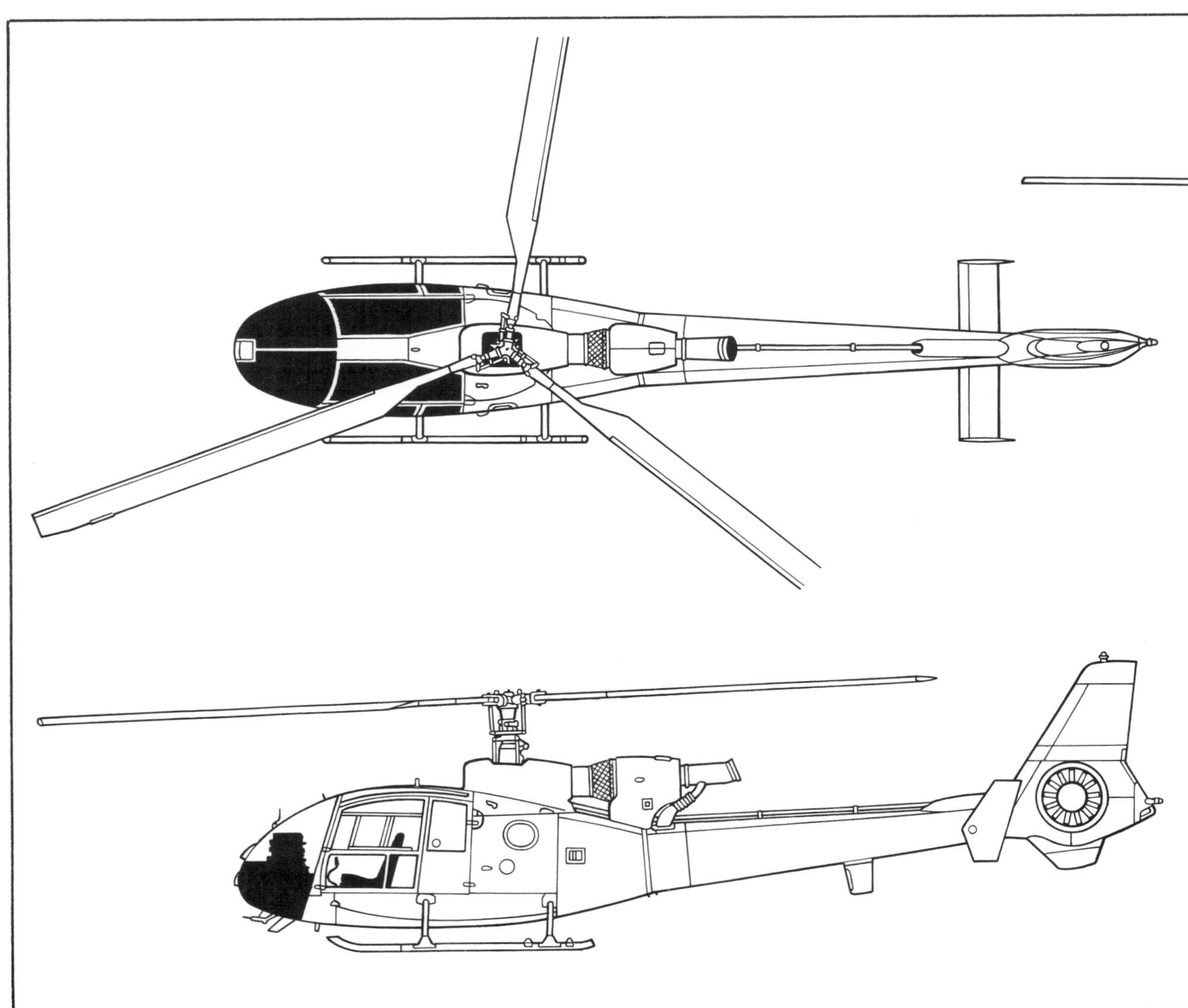

The sole Gazelle HCC Mark 4 operated by No 32 Squadron from RAF Northolt.

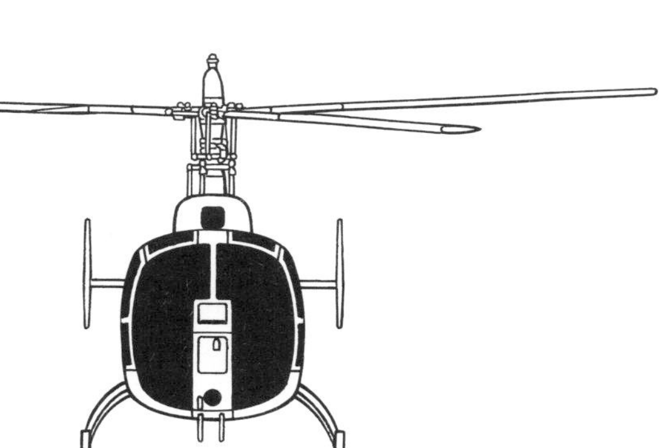

Gazelle HT 3
1:72 scale

VIP interior and is not capable of use for the training role.

The Shawbury Gazelles do have one operational task in time of war and that is as an airfield battle damage assessment helicopter for the four RAF Germany bases. In time of war eight Gazelles would fly to RAF Germany where they would be distributed in pairs to each RAF Germany airfield. Following an attack they would be sent aloft to survey the damage caused to enable commanders to work out repair priorities and areas that could still be used.

There are 24 Gazelle HT 3s in service plus the one Gazelle HCC 4. Not surprisingly, the main Gazelle servicing base is also RAF Shawbury.

The instrument panel of a Gazelle

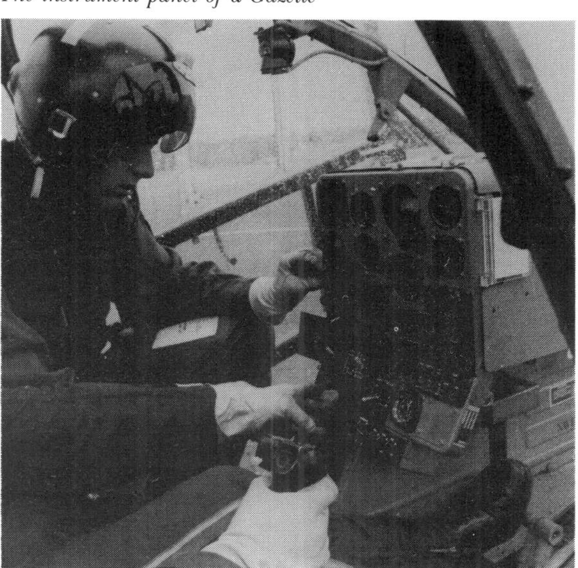

Guided missiles

Bloodhound Mark 2

Span 2.83 m; **Max body diameter** 0.546 m; **Length** 8.46 m; **Range** approx 80 km.

The Bloodhound Mark 2 started life back in the early 1950s under the code designation of Red Duster and entered Royal Air Force service in mid-1958. In the same year the development of a new Mark 2 version commenced and this started to be used during 1964. The Mark 2 has now entirely replaced the Bloodhound Mark 1 and the missiles are all based in the United Kingdom under the control of No 11 Group. The missiles are widely dispersed at sites close to the East Coast or just inland and are operated by two squadrons, Nos 25 and 85, both having their administrative and engineering base at RAF West Raynham.

To engage a target, a long-range surveillance radar picks it up and passes information to the Bloodhound missile section. Each of these sections has four Bloodhounds ready on their launchers, a target illuminating radar (TIR) and a launch control post (LCP). The TIR (known as Firelight) is directed towards the target by the surveillance radar and the reflected radar energy can then be used by the Bloodhound's guidance system to direct the missile to the target. The missile is launched under the control of the LCP at the correct instant, using data from a high capacity computer. This computer not only acts as a fire control computer but is also used to monitor missile readiness and other in-house tasks.

Above *Bloodhound Mark 2 on its launching post and ready to fire.*

Left *An RAF Police dog handler and his charge patrolling the Bloodhound Mark 2 installations at RAF West Raynham.*

On firing, the missile uses four rocket boosters using solid propellants; once sufficient velocity has been reached propulsion is assumed by two Rolls-Royce Bristol Thor ramjets. Flight guidance for the Bloodhound is of the twist-and-steer variety using stub wings and once close to the target the high explosive warhead is detonated using a proximity fuze. The maximum range of the Bloodhound Mark 2 is about 80 kilometres and targets flying as low as 300 metres have been engaged in tests.

Although the Bloodhounds have been in service for some years they will remain for some time to come. As recently as early 1987 the Ministry of Defence announced that a programme to extend the useful operational life of the Bloodhounds was under way.

Harpoon

Span 0.91 m; **Length** 3.84 m; **Body diameter** 0.34 m; **Weight** 522 kg; **Weight of warhead** 225 kg; **Max range** 110 km;

The Harpoon is a powerful and long-range anti-shipping missile that is one of the most important in the American inventory. It entered Royal Air Force use during the Falklands campaign when the missile was fitted to the Nimrod MR 2. Designated the AGM-84A, the Harpoon can be air-launched from the Nimrod's bomb bay and before launch is 'informed' of its target's position and track. After launch the missile is powered by a small turbojet and, as it flies towards its target, an internal computer uses three-axis sensors and a radar altimeter to make in-flight corrections. At a pre-programmed point the missile commences a wave-hugging flight path and the final attack phase is carried out under the control of an active radar seeker. The warhead is of the blast type and is powerful enough to sink or seriously damage any vessel.

Above *Harpoon missile being carried here by a US Navy P-3 Orion. In RAF use they are carried by Nimrod MR 2s.*

Left *The AJ 168 version of the Martel showing the video camera panel in the nose.*

Martel

Span (approx) 1.2 m; **Length** (AS 37) 4.2 m, (AJ 168) 3.9 m; **Body diameter** 0.4 m; **Weight** Not released; **Weight of warhead** 150 kg(?); **Max range** 60 km(?).

Martel is a missile about which few details have been released officially. It is an Anglo-French missile produced in two versions, one radar-seeking and the other using video guidance. Both are intended for air-to-ground use, primarily against shipping although land targets can also be engaged. The warhead used on Martel is large and is reported to weigh as much as 150 kg, while the range is estimated to be about 60 km, although this will depend on such factors as launch height.

The radar-guided version of Martel, the AS 37, is primarily a French responsibility. The radar-seeking head can find its own target while still mounted on the launch aircraft and present its findings to the crew. While this version has the advantage that it is a passive system, once the target realises it is under attack it can upset the Martel guidance system by simply switching off its radar(s). This is avoided in the video-guided Martel, the AJ 168, which is the British development responsibility. The AJ 168 has a small television camera in the nose and can transmit video information and other data along a link with the launch aircraft. Using this data link, one of the launch aircraft crew can make guidance corrections and even steer the missile along its final flight path at the target. Both types of missile have the same basic autopilot that can automatically guide the missile along a choice of possible flight paths until the guidance system assumes final command.

Within the Royal Air Force, Martel is used on the Buccaneer S 2B. In time it will be supplemented and eventually replaced by Sea Eagle. This replacement will not be overdue for, although Martel is still a powerful weapon, its development commenced as long ago as 1964 and technology has made considerable advances since then.

The AS.37, the radar-guided version of Martel, seen here under a Buccaneer wing.

Sea Eagle

(Data provisional.) **Span** 1.2 m; **Length** 4.1 m; **Body diameter** 0.4 m; **Range** up to 100 km.

Sea Eagle was originally code-designated the P3T when its development was started in 1979. Flight tests began in 1981 but there was a short period when it appeared that the Sea Eagle was due to become yet another 'project cancelled'; fortunately, that did not happen and full production was given the go-ahead in February 1982.

Sea Eagle will be a big and powerful anti-shipping missile with an anticipated range of about 100 km. It will be propelled by an air-breathing turbine engine which will provide the missile with a high subsonic speed performance. A new form of multi-role radar homing head will be employed, and this will be controlled by an internal digital computer. The computer will be used as a data processor for pre-launch information, management of the transmit and receive functions and target acquisition, detection and tracking. The computer will also have an ECCM role.

Once launched, the Sea Eagle can assume a sea-skimming flight path to elude detection, and in this phase will be under the control of a radar altimeter feeding the flight computer. Various flight paths can be pre-programmed in the computer and the system is capable of detecting one particular ship target in a group, if required. One source has stated that the 150 kg warhead of the Martel will be retained.

Initially, Sea Eagle will be used on the Buccaneers of No 18 Group but eventually they may be fitted to Tornados operating in the anti-shipping role. British Aerospace Dynamics Group are acting as prime contractors.

Development models of the Sea Eagle anti-shipping missile being carried by a Fleet Air Arm Sea Harrier FRS 1

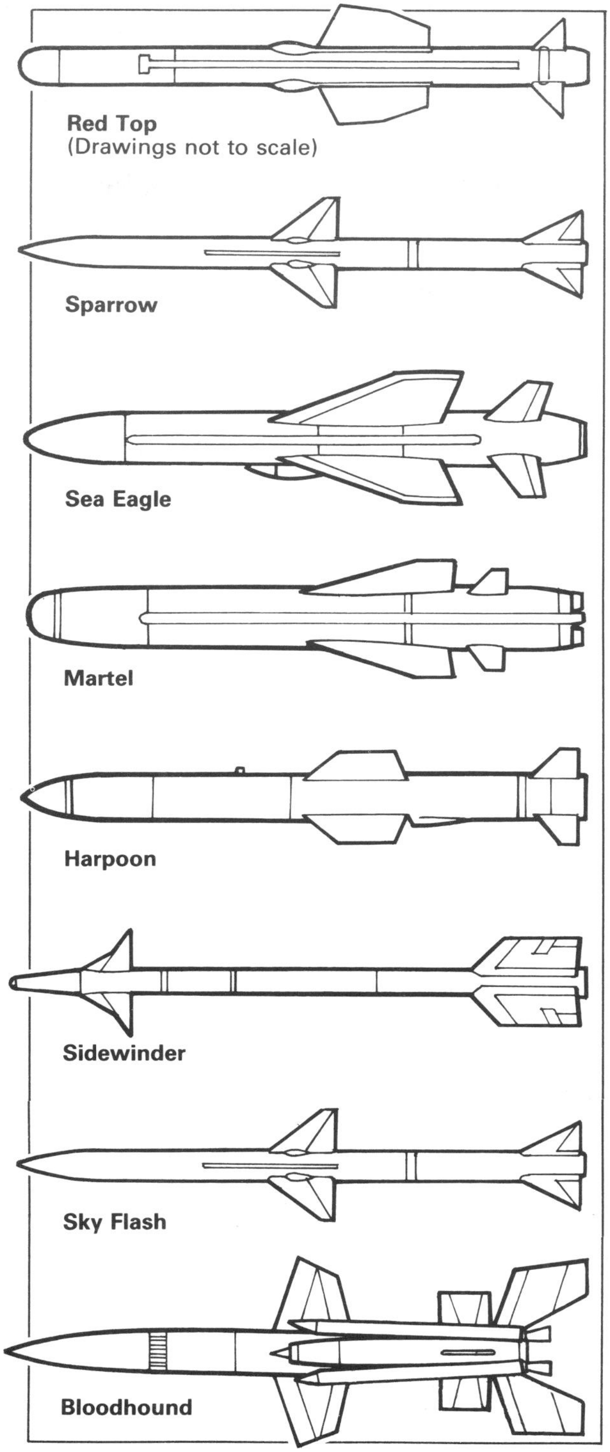

Red Top
(Drawings not to scale)

Sparrow

Sea Eagle

Martel

Harpoon

Sidewinder

Sky Flash

Bloodhound

Sky Flash

Span 1.02 m; **Length** 3.7 m; **Body diameter** 0.203 m; **Weight** 192 kg; **Weight of warhead** 30 kg; **Range** 40 km; **Propulsion** solid Aerojet Mk 52 Mod 2.

Sky Flash was initially known as Project XJ521 and was based on the American Raytheon Sparrow missile but with an entirely new electronics system. Initial development work was completed in 1973 and full production commenced during 1975. Today, the Sky Flash is in service mounted on the Phantom FGR 2 and will be the main armament of the Tornado F 2 when it enters service.

Sky Flash uses a new advanced guidance system developed by Marconi Space and Development Systems (MSDS). The prime contractor is the British Aerospace Dynamics Group; EMI Electronics Limited make the radar proximity fuze. Using a monopulse radar seeker, the missile can cope easily with targets at all altitudes from very low down to the other altitude extreme and, if necessary, the Sky Flash can be launched at altitudes as low as 100 metres. The technology involved in Sky Flash is very advanced and has already been updated to include such refinements as solid state electronics and thermal batteries.

Armourers loading a Sparrow missile under fuselage of a Phantom FGR 2.

Sparrow

Span 1.02 m; **Length** 3.66 m; **Body diameter** 0.2 m; **Weight** 227 kg; **Weight of warhead** 40 kg; **Range** 40 km plus.

The Sparrow is an American missile with the US designation of AIM-7. In the Royal Air Force it is used only by the Phantom FGR 2, but has now been largely replaced by Sky Flash (itself a British version of the Sparrow). There are several versions of the Sparrow but that used by the Phantoms is radar-guided and known as the AIM-7E. This missile has a maximum speed of Mach 3.5 and a range of over 40 km, but it still has a good 'dogfight' capability. A contact or a proximity fuze can be fitted.

Above *Sidewinder missiles about to be loaded on to a No 29 Squadron Phantom FGR 2 at RAF Coningsby.*

Left *An armourer checking a Sparrow missile fitted to a No 19 Squadron Phantom FGR 2 at RAF Wildenrath.*

ASRAAM

ASRAAM is the acronym for Advanced Short-Range Air-to-Air Missile and it is an international programme that is intended to provide the replacement missile for the long-lived Sidewinder family. The companies involved are British Aerospace, the German Bodenseewerk Geratechnik and the Hughes Aircraft Company. France is also involved. Feasibility studies for a missile that could be fired at a target from any direction from a range of approximately 1,000 metres were completed in 1983. Current forecasts are that ASRAAM will have a velocity of over Mach 3 and will weigh approximately 120 kg, 5 kg of which will be the warhead. The main Royal Air Force users will be the Tornado F 3 squadrons along with any Phantoms that are still in use when ASRAAM is ready.

Sidewinder

Tail fin span 0.56 m; **Length** 2.83 m; **Body diameter** 0.13 m; **Weight** 72 kg; **Weight of warhead** 2.83 kg; **Range** 3.5 km approx.

The Sidewinder has been one of the most successful short range air-to-air guided missiles ever developed, for the basic design dates back to the early 1950s. Ever since then the Sidewinder, or AIM-9, has been produced and used in a long string of models and sub-types that has now reached the AIM-9P. The type used by the Royal Air Force is the AIM-9L and, while some missiles have been obtained direct from the United States, future procurement will be from a European consortium that has been established to produce the missile. This consortium includes West Germany, Italy, Norway and the United Kingdom.

The Sidewinder is an infra-red seeking missile used for close-in 'dogfighting'. A heat-seeking head in the nose of the missile is used for basic guidance and in-flight corrections are made by small delta-shaped fins just behind the missile head.

The importance of the Sidewinder to the Royal Air Force is such that it is used by more aircraft types than any other missile. It is carried by the Phantom FGR 2, the Buccaneer S 2, the Jaguar GR 1, the Harrier GR 3 and even the mighty Nimrod MR2. In time of war the Sidewinder would also be used by Hawk T 1 (A) units operating in the interceptor role. Tornado GR 1s can also carry the Sidewinder for self-defence.

Red Top

Span 0.908 m; **Length** 3.27 m; **Body diameter** 0.222 m; **Weight** Not released; **Weight of warhead** 31 kg; **Range** approx 12 km.

Red Top was originally known as Firestreak Mark 4 and has now replaced the Firestreak, although the latter may still be used for training or practice. Red Top is now used only by the Lightning squadrons and is due to be phased out of service when the Lightnings are replaced. Red Top is an infra-red-seeking guided missile with a good performance, ie, it can be used against head-on targets and is not just a tail-chaser. It has a large seeker head with the warhead situated just behind it. Maximum speed attainable is reported to be around Mach 3 but the range is limited to about 12 km and the design is now considered to be at best obsolescent.

ALARM

ALARM stands for Air-Launched Anti-Radar Missile which effectively sums up its purpose as it is intended to seek out and destroy enemy radars. Still under development it will normally be carried by such aircraft as the Tornado GR 1 and Buccaneer S 2. The missile uses a broadband passive radar seeker to find and home onto its target. Powered by a two-stage solid fuelled motor ALARM has a range of up to 10 kilometres. For certain types of mission it can be launched from high altitude and then hangs on a rotating parachute to find a radar target. When a target is detected the motor fires for the target approach and the kill. On other types of mission specific types of radar signature for attack can be fed into the missile's memory software.

It is expected that ALARM will enter service sometime after 1987. Weight at launch is understood to be 180 kg.

Shrike

Span 0.914 m: **Length** 3.048 m; **Body diameter** 0.2 m; **Weight** 177 kg; **Weight of warhead** 66 kg; **Range (estimate)** 12–16 km.

The Shrike anti-radiation missile entered the Royal Air Force inventory during the Falkland Islands campaign when it was carried on the 'Black Buck' missions by the Vulcan B 2s of No 44 Squadron. That squadron has now been disbanded but there is no reason to suspect that the Shrike has been dispensed with, for it has an important operational role in knocking out energy-emitting

Lightning F 6 of RAF Binbrook armed with Red Top missiles.

Shrike anti-radiation missile being carried here by a US Marine Corps A-4M Skyhawk. These missiles were carried by RAF Vulcan B 2s during the 'Black Buck' missions of the Falkland Islands campaign.

radar systems. Even if the Shrikes are not launched the enemy might expect their use and switch off their radars, thus making them 'blind' for what could be important periods of time.

The initial use of radar by an enemy would normally be detected by sensors in the launch aircraft. Once detected, the radar-seeker head of the Shrike would be switched on to gain a 'fix' on the radiation source; this having been achieved, the missile is launched and is guided to its target by the seeker head alone. The problem with the Shrike is that radars cover a wide band of frequencies and subsequently special seeker heads for various frequency bands and/or types of radar have to be provided. To date no less than 13 different seeker heads are known to be in American service and there may well be more. Exactly what type the Royal Air Force uses is not known.

The American service designation for the Shrike is AGM-45A. It uses a high fragmentation warhead.

Other weapons

JP233 Low Altitude Airfield Attack System

The JP233 Low Altitude Airfield Attack System is a new weapon for the Royal Air Force, production of which commenced during 1983. It is intended for use by the Tornado GR 1 although other aircraft types can carry the system. Development of the JP233 started during 1977 and was initially a joint UK-USA programme. However, the United States withdrew in 1980 leaving the United Kingdom to carry on with the project. As a result, the prime contractor for the system is now Hunting Engineering Limited, although a large number of other companies and government establishments are also involved.

The JP233 weapon system comprises two separate types of submunition, each carried in its own dispenser under the fuselage of a Tornado GR 1. The two types of submunition are dispensed simultaneously as the Tornado flies fast and low over its

A Tornado GR 1 dispensing bomblets from its JP233 low altitude airfield attack system—the two sizes of sub-munition can be clearly detected.

target. One is a cratering submunition, the SG357 which can cause severe damage to concrete surfaces and structures; the other is the HB876 area denial dual-purpose mine that stays on the surface to cause damage to vehicles and provide an obstacle to clearance and repair. Both types of mine are dispensed at high speed under the control of an electronic distributor system. The cratering SG357 submunitions dig themselves in for detonation once released but the HB876 area denial submunitions float to earth suspended from small parachutes. Once on the ground spring steel legs place the mine in the upright position ready for use.

Although JP233 is primarily intended for use against enemy airfields, it obviously has many other targets including road and rail junctions and bridges, and area targets in the open such as armoured concentrations. It thus makes an ideal weapon for striking at the rear echelons of any Warsaw Pact aggressor and by the time it enters Royal Air Force operational use some time in the mid-1980s it will be a considerable headache for any potential enemy.

BL755 Cluster Bomb

Weight 277 kg; **Length** 2.451 m; **Diameter** 0.419 m; **Payload** 147 bomblets.

The BL755 is a weapon system designed for use against area targets and, in particular, armoured formations or groups of vehicles in the open. It is dropped at relatively high speeds but usually at low altitudes.

In appearance the BL755 container resembles a bulky but conventional aircraft bomb. It may be carried in the internal bomb bay of the Buccaneer S 2 but is more usually carried slung from a weapon pylon. When released, the 'windmill' on the bomb nose turns to arm the primary striker. After a timed interval, the striker operates and the primary cartridge is fired. This cartridge builds up a gas pressure internally to push off the two-part bomb body skins. Once these are clear, the main cartridge fires to eject the bomblets.

There are 147 bomblets on the BL755, carried in seven bays with 21 bomblets in each. The design detail is such that the bomblets are ejected at varying velocities to ensure a good spread and resultant ground pattern. Each bomblet is armed after a short period of flight. They are stabilised in flight by a sprung steel tail and their warhead is a small shaped charge with a simple stand-off detonator device in front. As the bomblet strikes a target the shaped charge produces an armour-piercing fire jet that can penetrate up to 250 mm of armour; the bomblet casing also explodes into over 2,000

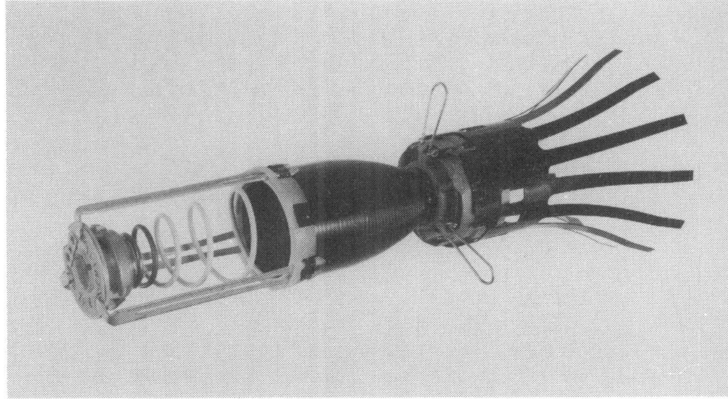

Close-up of a BL755 bomblet.

fragments for use against personnel and soft targets such as trucks.

There are four marks of BL755. The Mark 2 differs from the basic Mark 1 in having a shorter in-flight arming delay for low altitude use. The Mark 3 uses a twin-lug suspension in place of the single-point lug of the Mark 1 and 2, while the Mark 4 is a version with twin-lug suspension and the short delay.

The BL755 is primarily produced by Hunting Engineering. It is carried by the Harrier, Jaguar, Phantom and Buccaneer and was used during the Falkland Islands campaign.

Unloading BL755s in the field.

Bomb Retarding Tails

One of the problems of delivering explosive ordnance from low and fast-flying aircraft is that conventional 'iron' bombs with fixed tails can often bounce or ricochet off hard surfaces and explode while the aircraft is still in the vicinity. This can be avoided by fitting the bombs with retarding tails. The Royal Air Force uses such a system produced by Hunting Engineering Limited.

The tail has conventional fins at the rear for the short period after the bomb leaves the aircraft but, as the bomb descends further, a short lanyard initiates a timer mechanism. The timer then releases some powerful springs that force outwards the tail panels to act as retarders, the effect being amplified by fabric ribbons connected between the panels. The retard effect is such that the bomb then falls to the ground at a much reduced velocity and also at a better attack angle, enabling the attacking aircraft to leave the area safely.

The Royal Air Force uses two main types of retarder tail. One is the Type 117 which is 1.035 metres long and with a span of 0.584 metres. It is used on 1,000 lb bombs and comes in two marks: the Mark 3 has the span already mentioned and is suitable for use on external weapon pylons; the Mark 4 is for use from internal bomb bays and has a reduced tail fin diameter of 0.419 metres. The Mark 4 can also be used from external pylons if required.

The other type of retarder tail is the Type 118 for use on the 540 lb bomb. It is 0.97 metres long and 0.463 metres in diameter.

Above *An armourer on a training exercise held at RAF Akrotiri prepares a 1,000 lb/454 kg bomb with a retarding tail prior to loading on a Buccaneer.*

Below *An 'iron' bomb with a retarding tail being prepared for loading on to a No 6 Squadron Jaguar GR 1 at RAF Coltishall.*

Above *Hawk T 1 with 68 mm SNEB rocket pod under its starboard wing, a 30 mm Aden Gun pod under the fuselage and a practice bomb carrier under the port wing.*

68 mm SNEB rockets

The 68 mm SNEB unguided rocket is a standard NATO weapon and is widely produced and used. Originally the rocket was manufactured (and still is) by the French company of Thomson-Brandt, but it is based on German research carried out before 1945. The launcher employed with these rockets is also of French origin and is produced by Matra.

A wide range of rockets is produced in 68 mm calibre, some of which are listed below – not all may be in use with the Royal Air Force. Within the Royal Air Force, the main users of the SNEB rockets are the Harrier squadrons but they may also be used by the Buccaneer S 2 and even the Hawk T 1. Each of the rockets has eight folding fins that extend as the rocket leaves the launcher. Once extended they impart a spin rate of about 30 spins per second for stabilisation, and the maximum velocity of the rocket is augmented by the aircraft velocity, ie, the velocities shown in the table are those of the rocket fired from a static launcher.

Below *SNEB rocket launcher pod (top) with (below) practice bomb pannier with an unfuzed bomb in place.*

Type	Length	Weight	Warhead	Warhead type	Velocity
250	911 mm	5.05 kg	1.8 kg	smoke/practice	600 m/s
251P	847 mm	4.3 kg	1.05 kg	blast	800 m/s
252	924 mm	5.06 kg	0.8 kg	inert/practice	-
253	924 mm	5.06 kg	1.8 kg	anti-armour	600 m/s
256P	924 mm	6.26 kg	3 kg	fragmentation	450 m/s

Airborne ordnance

M61A1 20 mm Vulcan gun system

Calibre 20 mm; **Length** 1.675 m; **Weight** 120 kg; **Muzzle velocity** 1,036 m/s; **Rate of fire** max 6,600 rpm; **Round weight** 0.25 kg; **Projectile weight** 0.1 kg.

The M61A1 is an American aircraft gun designed on the same principles as those used in the original Gatling Gun of the last century. It has six barrels that rotate about a central axis. As they rotate, they are progressively loaded, fired and the spent case is ejected ready for the cycle to start again. This cycle is carried out at a very high rate for the maximum rpm of 6,600 means 110 rounds every second. It takes time to build up this rate of fire which is not reached until 0.3 second has passed; the time to run down after firing is 0.5 second.

The exact model of the M61A1 used by the RAF is known as the GAU-4A, carried in a SUU-23A pod. In this pod the gun is run up to its operating speed by an electric starter motor after which the firing gases are used to power the gun mechanism and also drive a shaft which in turn powers a helix for the ammunition feed. This system effectively synchronizes the feed mechanism and the ammunition feed. Firing is electrical. The rounds fired come in a wide variety of types and include straightforward high explosive or armour piercing.

The high rate of fire system has several advantages in air-to-air combat. The obvious one is that a large number of projectiles can be fired into a target in a very short period of time (and in air warfare a target will only be presented for fleeting seconds). The other less obvious advantage is in gun life for, despite the high rate of fire, the rotary Gatling principle gives plenty of time between shots for each barrel to cool; fouling is also thereby reduced.

The maximum ammunition load is about 1,200 rounds and, while this may not seem much, it is usually more than sufficient to last most air combats. The M61A1 is fitted to only one aircraft type with the Royal Air Force and that is the Phantom. Both the Phantom FG 1 and the FGR 2 have one M61A1.

27 mm Mauser cannon

Calibre 27 mm; **Length overall** 2.3 m; **Length of barrel** 1.7 m; **Weight (approx)** 100 kg.

The 27 mm Mauser cannon has been under active development by Mauser-Werke Oberndorf GmbH since 1976 when the Panavia concern decided to include a twin-gun fixed armament in their MRCA, now the Tornado. Mauser were given a challenging brief to produce a weapon that would have a high muzzle velocity, a high degree of accuracy and reliability, identical external ballistics for all types of ammunition to be used, and projectile fuzes that would operate at even extreme angles of impact. To Mauser's credit they appear to have produced the goods but to date few details of the cannon have been released and the above data is only a rough outline.

Armourer connecting the ammunition feed of an M61A1 Vulcan 20 mm gun under a 19 Squadron Phantom FGR 2 at RAF Wildenrath.

The 27 mm × 145 ammunition is fed into the cannon in a metal linked belt. Once in the cannon the rounds are pushed from the links into a rotary chamber not unlike that of a revolver and the gas-operated mechanism rotates the round until it is in line with the barrel when it is electrically fired. The five-position rotary chamber is then turned to eject the spent cartridge case and the cycle continues.

The ammunition used with this cannon falls into three categories. One of these is the air-to-air combat ammunition which is of two types, high explosive (HE) and high explosive self destruct (which will detonate after a fixed time). The second category is air-to-ground combat ammunition which is all armour piercing; there are three rounds available; one is straightforward armour piercing (AP), the second armour piercing high explosive (APHE) and the third armour piercing high explosive with a self destruct element. The third category is the training ammunition with one type being straightforward target practice (TP), another being target practice with a frangible warhead that breaks up into small fragments after a certain distance has been travelled, while the third type is an inert drill round. The last type is used for training armourers and for checking the gun mechanism on the ground.

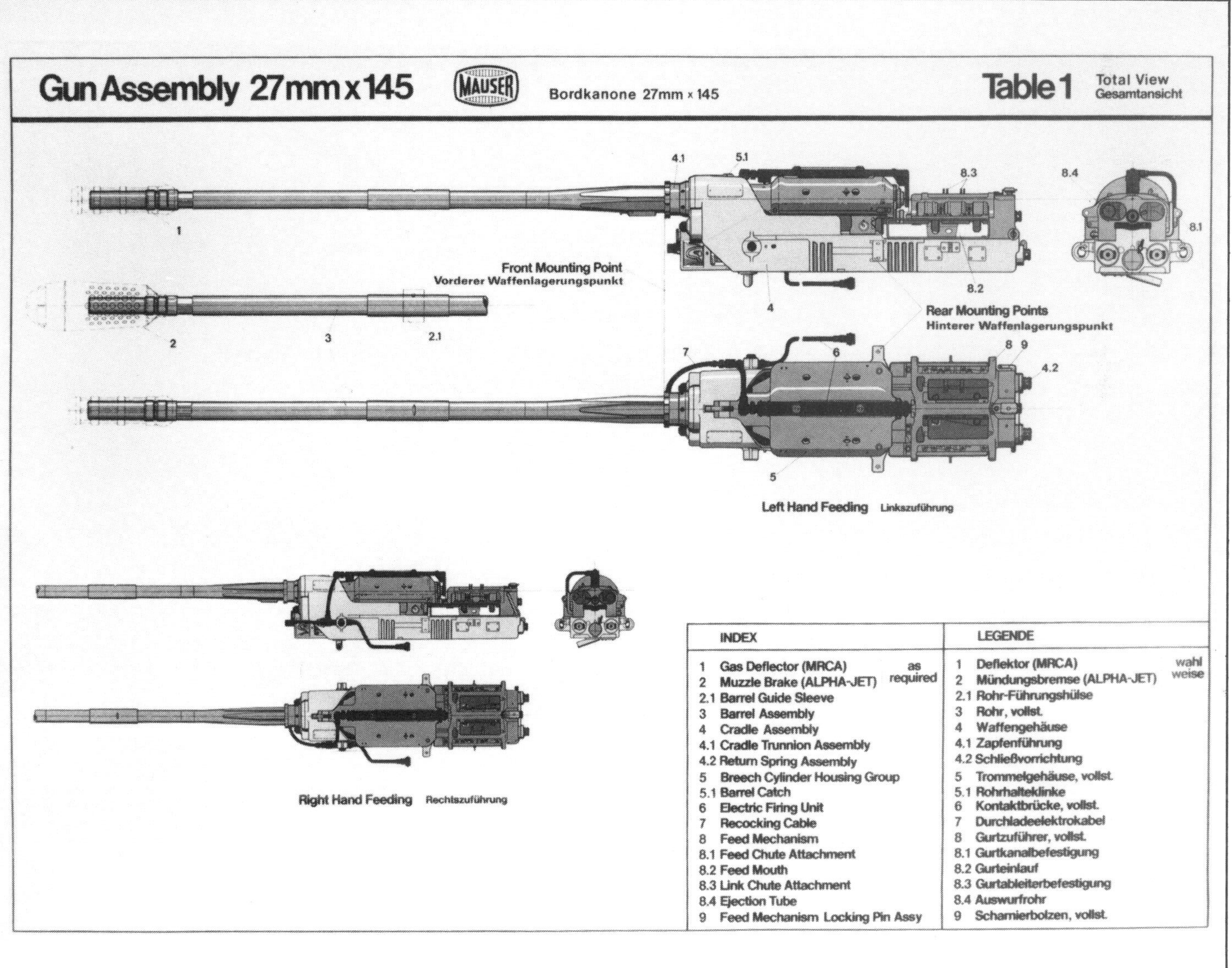

General arrangement of 27 mm Mauser cannon.

Armourer working on an Aden Gun in a station armoury workshop.

The Tornado GR 1 has two of these 27 mm cannon, one in each side of the forward lower fuselage. The Tornado F 3 has only one on the starboard side. It will almost certainly be part of the armament of the next generation of Royal Air Force combat aircraft.

30 mm Aden gun (Mark 5)

Calibre 30 mm; **Length overall** 1.59 m; **Length of barrel** 1.08 m; **Length of body** 0.742 m; **Height** 0.246 m; **Width** 0.24 m; **Weight complete** 87 kg; **Weight of barrel** 12.25 kg; **Number of rifling grooves** 16, RH twist; **Muzzle velocity** 790 m/s; **Rate of fire** 1,200–1,400 rpm.

The term Aden stands for 'Armament Development Enfield' which places its origins in the Royal Small Arms Factory at Enfield Lock in Middlesex. Actually, the gun's origins can be traced to the late war years in Germany, for Enfield Lock used as one of their starting points the overall concept of the German 30 mm MK 213 aircraft gun with its superb rotary feed system, a feature carried over to the Aden. The first batch of Aden guns was produced in 1949 but it was some years before the fully developed model was ready for service. The first aircraft type to use the gun operationally was the Hunter, which originally carried four guns in a single pack. Newspapers of the time made great headlines out of the fact that a burst from all four guns on a Hunter was equivalent in firepower to a broadside from a wartime destroyer, whatever that might mean in air combat terms.

The Aden is a 30 mm gas-operated gun with a revolver feed system and can be used in both the air combat or the ground attack role. In both instances its firepower can destroy almost any aircraft or ground target. The gun operates by means

Hand-winching a 30 mm Aden Gun into a Jaguar.

of a revolving drum having five chambers into which rounds are fed in two stages. The drum is indexed by the movement of a gas-operated slide. The gun will fire only when the round is in line with the barrel and the drum and barrel are in line and locked. On firing, gas pressure passes through a barrel gas port and acts via a piston against a slide mechanism. This travels rearward within the gun cradle unit to revolve the breech cylinder and the ammunition feed drum. When this is complete the slide mechanism is then pushed forward by return springs to complete the rotation of the drum and feed the next round, ejecting the spent case as it does so.

The ammunition used by the Aden is fed into the gun in belts made up from individual pressed steel links. The disposal of these links during firing was at one time a source of problems on the early Hunters, for the clips had an alarming habit of finding their way into the engine intakes after disposal. This led to the development of the special clip hoppers nicknamed 'Sabrinas' after the principal attributes of a female entertainer of the time, and these Sabrinas have been retained on Hunters ever since. That apart, the Aden fires three main types of ammunition, high explosive (HE), armour piercing (AP) and practice (Prac). The HE projectile has a boat-tailed configuration and contains 48 grams of explosive. It has a delay nose fuze which is effective against aircraft structures and lightly armoured ground targets such as trucks. Weight of the HE round is 496 grams. The AP round weighs 495 grams and has a tungsten carbide core which is effective against nearly all battlefield targets apart from the really heavy main battle tanks. The practice round is inert and is fired for training and gun testing.

The Aden is in service on the Jaguar, Hawk and the Harrier. The Lightning can carry two Adens in a belly pack. Installations such as those on the

Harrier have the guns mounted in a pack under the aircraft complete with the ammunition as one unit. In these pack systems cocking is pneumatic and firing is electrical.

Aden 25

Calibre 25 mm; **Length overall** 2.285 m; **Length of barrel** 1.7 m; **Length of body** 0.789 m; **Height** 0.246 m; **Width (max)** 0.25 m; **Weight (twin pod installation)** 430 kg; **Weight of barrel** 18 kg; **Muzzle velocity** 1050 m/s; **Rate of fire** 1,650–1,850 rpm.

Throughout its life the 30 mm Aden cannon has been the subject of a great deal of experimental work to increase its rate of fire, effective range and so forth but the limitations of the 30 mm round have always limited any potential improvements. With the advent of the NATO standard 25 mm round great improvements proved to be possible. With the new Aden 25 cannon it is now possible to deliver three times the previous kinetic energy for only a slight increase in weight. Much of this is made possible by the increased rate of fire but the 25 mm cartridge also has a much higher muzzle velocity than the old 30 mm round.

The Aden 25 retains much of the basic operating mechanism and feed of the 30 mm cannon. It will be used initially on the Harrier GR 5 where it will be carried in a twin-cannon pack under the fuselage along with 200 rounds of ammunition. Ammunition is fed into the cannon using a disintegrating link system and a percussion firing system is employed.

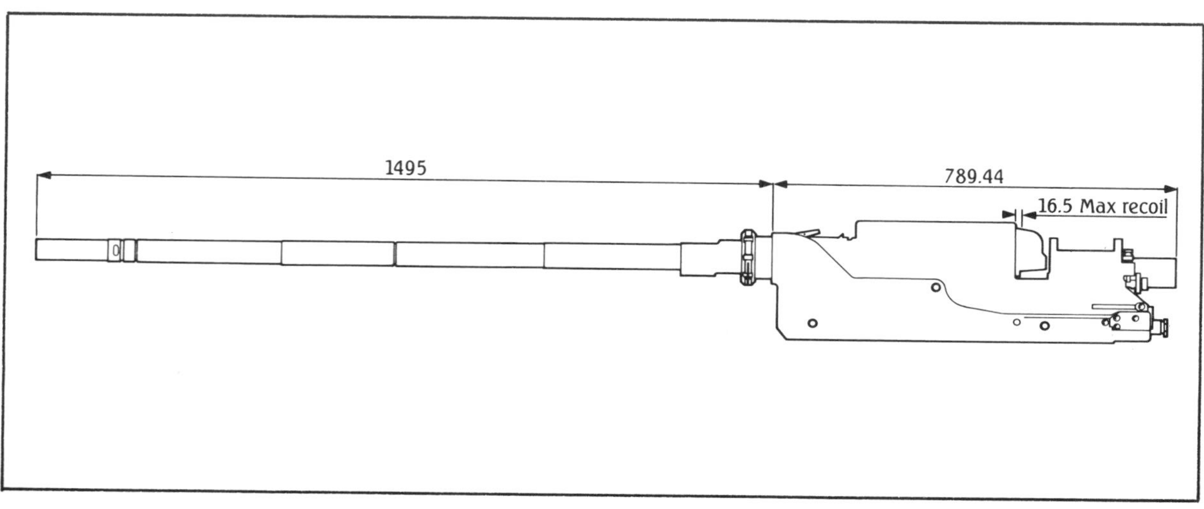

RAF 'B' vehicles

In common with all modern armed forces, the Royal Air Force has to use a huge fleet of 'B' vehicles. These 'B' vehicles are used for just about every purpose it is possible to conceive from routine domestic chores to fire fighting and otherwise operating in dangerous combat areas. Add to these the numbers of trailers employed and the list gets even longer; even that will still not leave room for the various 'one off' oddities that have to be used from time to time, or for the assorted local modifications that have to be made to meet local requirements.

The listing that follows can mention only the main types in use. It has been compiled from a number of sources and the illustrations show some vehicles and types of vehicle that are not in the official lists. The list cannot be comprehensive and does not pretend to be so for, even as these words are written, new vehicles and types are being taken on the strength and others are being removed from service. But it does include the main types and some of the photographs have captions that explain their function more fully than the designation.

For ease of reference a dimensions code has been employed. All dimensions are in mm and the symbols are as follows: **L** length; **W** width; **H** height; **WB** wheelbase; **BC** bogie centres; **GC** ground clearance. Wheelbases of six-wheelers are usually front axle to bogie centre with the rear bogie suspension added. If this separation is not given then the wheelbase (**WB**) is probably still measured from front axle to bogie centre even when the **BC** dimension is not provided.

Where provided, the drawings, by Ken Musgrave, are 1:76 scale.

Ambulance, 2-stretcher, 4 × 2, Bedford CAL
L 4,410, **W** 1,940, **H** 2,220, **WB** 2,640, **GC** 150, internal headroom 1,520.
Bedford Dormobile.

Ambulance, 4-stretcher, LHD Rover
L 4,390, **W** 2,130, **H** 2,690 (with beacon fitted), **WB** 2,560, **GC** 250.
Forward control 1-tonne Land Rover (101-in WB).

Ambulance, 2/4 stretcher, 4 × 4, Rover 9
L 4,740, **W** 1,880, **H** 1,990, **WB** 2,770, **GC** 250.
Used for airfield crash/rescue duties.

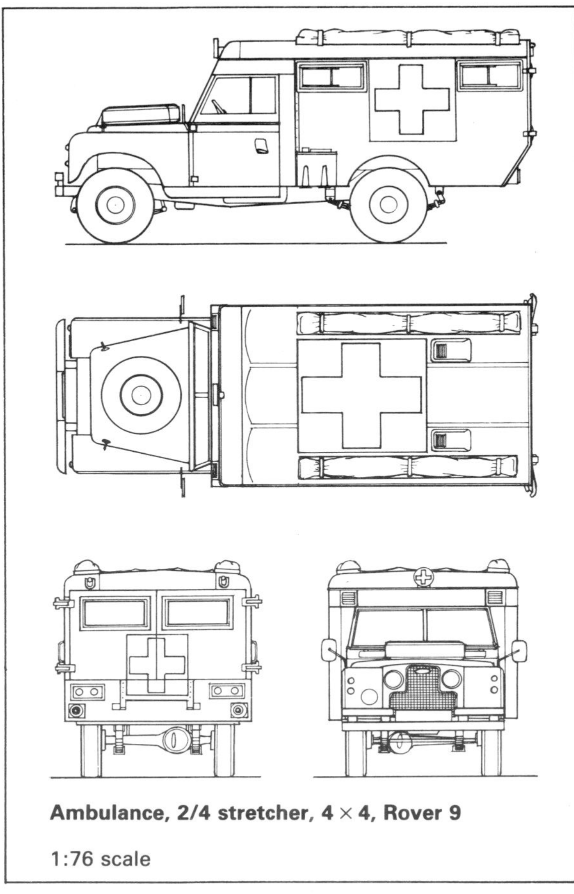

Ambulance, 2/4 stretcher, 4 × 4, Rover 9

1:76 scale

Left *Ambulance, 2/4-stretcher, 4 × 4, Rover 9.*
Above *Ambulance, Domestic, 2-stretcher, 4 × 2, Bedford CF.*

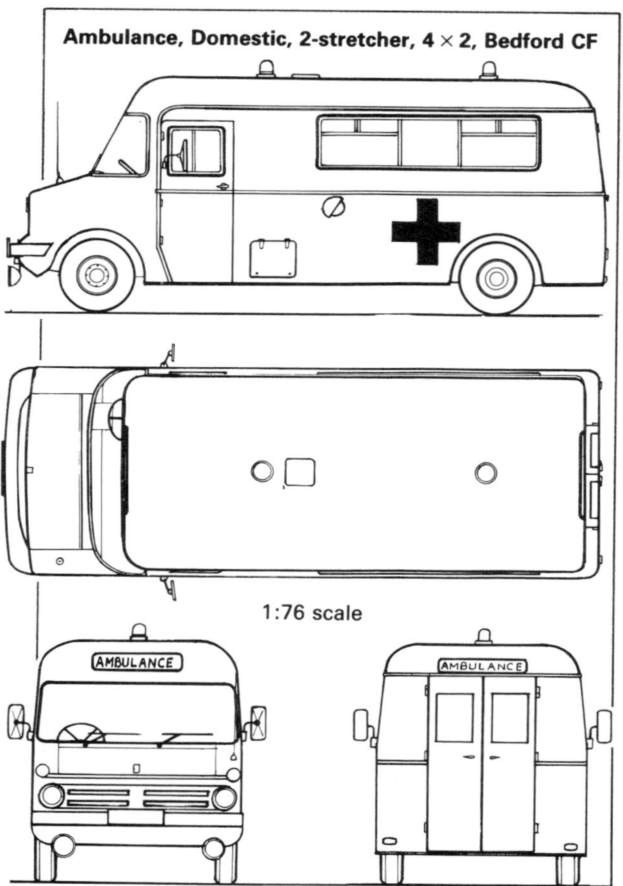

Ambulance, Clinic, 12-seater, 4 × 2, Bedford PJK 1 BZO
WB 4,170, **GC** 190.
Adapted bus.

Ambulance, Domestic, 2-stretcher, 4 × 2, Bedford CF
L 6,140, **W** 2,130, **H** 2,510

Car, Limousine, Grade 1, 4 × 2, Daimler 4.2-litre
L 5,740, **W** 1,970, **H** 1,530, **WB** 3,580, **GC** 180.
Staff car.

Car, Saloon, Grade 4, 4 × 2, Hillman Hunter GL
L 4,360, **W** 1,620, **H** 1,420, **WB** 2,500, GC 140.
Interim vehicle brought in between BMC 1800 and Ford Cortina Mark IV.

Car, Saloon, Grade 4, 4 × 2, Austin 1800 Mark 2
L 4,220, **W** 1,680, **H** 1,430, **WB** 2,690, **GC** 150.
Obsolete but still in use.

Car, Saloon, Grade 4, 4 × 2, Ford Cortina Mark IV
L 4,590, **W** 1,800, **H** 1,570.
In widespread use but now being supplemented by Vauxhall Cavalier.

Car, Saloon, Grade 5, 4 × 2, Morris Mini.

Car, Utility, Small, 4 × 2, Ford Escort Estate, now being phased out in favour of the Vauxhall Chevette. This example has RAF Police extras.

Car, Saloon, Grade 4, 4 × 2, Vauxhall Cavalier
L 4,366, **W** 1,668, **H** 1,395, **WB** 2,574.
Car, Saloon, Grade 5, 4 × 2, Morris Mini
L 3,050, **W** 1,390, **H** 1,310, **WB** 2,040, **GC** 150.
In widespread use but due to be supplemented by Metro.
Car, Saloon, Grade 2, 4 × 2, Rover, 3½-litre
L 4,750, **W** 1,790, **H** 1,550, **WB** 2,810, **GC** 180.
Car, Utility, 4 × 2, Vauxhall Chevette E
L 4,190, **W** 1,570, **H** 1,320, **WB** 2,390, **GC** 170.
Vauxhall Chevette Estate.
Car, Utility, Small, 4 × 2, Ford Escort Estate
L 4,060, **W** 1,560, **H** 1,340, **WB** 2,410, **GC** 130.
In widespread use as general utility vehicle, now being replaced by Chevette.
Car, Utility, Large, 4 × 2, 6-seater, Bedford CF 97170
L 4,300, **W** 1,940, **H** 1,850, **WB** 2,690, **GC** 120.
Now in service in small numbers only as replaced by Leyland Sherpa.

Car, Utility, Large, 4 × 2 (Leyland Sherpa).

Car, Utility, Large, 4 × 2 (Leyland Sherpa)
L 4,623, **W** 2,102 (including mirrors), **H** 2,022, **WB** 2,896.
Carrier, Full Tracked, Articulated, LHD, Volvo Bv 202E, Mark 2
L 6,175, **W** 1,780, **H** 2,220.
In use in small numbers only, probably for reserve RAF Regiment use.
Motor Coach, Small, 4 × 2, 14-seater, Bedford CDJ 1BZO
L 5,660, **W** 2,030, **H** 2,640, **WB** 3,020, **GC** 200.
The Bedford J1Z2 is similar but has a **WB** 3,050.
Motor Coach, Small, 4 × 2, 14-seater, Ford Transit
L 5,180, **W** 2,060, **H** 2,110, **WB** 3,000, **GC** 180.
Motor Coach, Large, RAF Band, 4 × 2, 40-seater, Leyland Leopard PSU5 D5R; Motor Coach, Large, with Ambulance role, 4 × 2, 54-seater, Leyland Leopard PSU5 D5R
L 11,870, **W** 3,180, **H** 2,540, **WB** 6,100, **GC** 220.
Motor Coach, Large, 4 × 2, 39-seater, LHD, Bedford SB3 (also RHD); Motor Coach, Large, 4 × 2, with Ambulance role, LHD, Bedford SB3
L 9,270, **W** 2,920, **H** 2,440, **WB** 5,490, **GC** 250.
Most have two forward seats removed to become

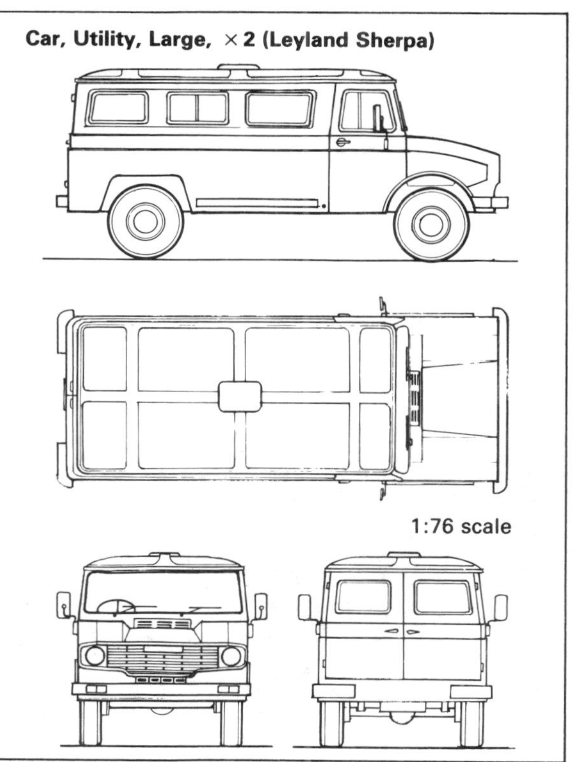

Left *Bedford 39-seater Motor Coach.*

Above *Crane, Truck Mounted, 10/25- ton, F/Slewing, Smith, T25R Vickers, 6 × 4.*

Below left *Crane, Truck Mounted, 5-ton, F/Slewing, Coles/Steel, GP 6 × 6, with jib extended.*

Below *Crane, Wheel Mounted, Fast Mobile, 4-ton, F/Slewing, Btl and C, Iron Fairy, 4FM.*

37 seater. Carries 16 stretchers in ambulance role. Now in process of replacement.

Crane, Truck Mounted, 5-ton, F/Slewing, Coles/Steel, GP, 6 × 6

L (inc jib overhang) 8,990, **L** (chassis) 7,470, **W** 2,330, **H** 4,040, **WB** 3,960.

Crane, Truck Mounted, 10-ton, F/Slewing, Coles/Steel, L96404-4 (DSL), Dual Control, 6 × 6

L (inc jib overhang) 11,880, **L** (chassis) 7,160, **W** 2,480, **H** 4,180, **WB** 4,490, **BC** 1,370, **GC** 210.

Old type Coles crane on AEC chassis.

Crane, Truck Mounted, 12½-ton, F/Slewing, Jones, 10-10 (GP and Aircraft)

L 12,490, jib length 9,140, **W** 2,510, **H** 4,270.

Crane, Truck Mounted, 10/25-ton, F/Slewing, Smith, T25R Vickers, 6 × 4

L (jib over cab) 12,040, **W** 2,670, **H** 4,520, **WB** 4,880, **GC** 250.

Crane, Wheel Mounted, Fast Mobile, 4-ton, F/Slewing, Btl and C, Iron Fairy, 4FM

L 5,230 (inc 1,440 jib overhang at front), **W** 2,360, **H** 2,560, **WB** 2,130, Track (front and rear) 1,980, **GC** 250.

Truck, Fork Lift, Self-Side Loading, Diesel Engine Driven, 6-ton, Mark 1 and 1A, Lancer Boss

	Mark 1	**Mark 1A**
L	4,720	5,280
W	2,480	2,480
H (mast lowered, travelling)	2,940	2,840
H (mast raised)	4,570	4,570
H (platform)	1,160	1,160
W (platform)	1,750	1,750
WB	2,740	2,740
GC	200	200

Used by Bloodhound missile units.

Above *Crane, Truck Mounted, 5/10-ton, F/Slewing, 4 × 4, Smith's Crane Traveller.*

Below *Truck, Fuel Servicing, Aircraft, 4-ton, 4 × 4, 1,000-gallon, Air Transportable Mark 5.*

Crane, Truck Mounted, 5/10-ton, Fully Slewing, 4 × 4, Smith's Crane Traveller
L (inc jib) 8,735, **W** 2,500, **H** 3,375.
Trailer, Tanker Fuel, 21-ton, 4TW, 4,500-gallon, Gloster Saro
L 9,560, **W** 2,490, **H** 2,670, **WB** 5,000, **GC** 380.
Trailer, Tanker, Oil, 5-ton, 4-wheel, 450-gallon, Eagle
L (less drawbar) 4,800, **L** (with drawbar) 6,580, **W** 2,260, **H** 2,060, **WB** 2,640, **GC** 230.

Truck, Fuel Servicing, Aircraft, 4-ton, 4 × 4, 1,000-gallon, Air Transportable Mark 5
L 6,910, **W** 2,440, **H** 2,670, **WB** 3,960, **GC** 340.
Truck, Fuel Servicing, Aircraft, 3-ton, 4 × 4, 1,000-gallon, Air Transportable, Bedford RL
L 7,120, **W** 2,280, **H** (cab roof) 2,480, **H** (cab roof removed) 1,880, **WB** 3,960.
Truck, Fuel Servicing, Aircraft, 7-ton, 4 × 2, 1,000-gallon, Dual Purpose Delivery, Bedford KFL (Mark 2)
L 6,700, **W** 2,210, **H** 2,560, **WB** 4,250, **GC** 260.
Truck, Fuel Servicing, Aircraft, 10-ton, 4 × 2, 200-gallon, Air Transportable, AEC Mercury Mark 2 (Avtur/Avtag, Pressure/Open Line Mark 4)
L 9,150, **W** 2,430, **H** (normal) 2,480, **H** (air transportable) 1,870, **WB** 5,250, **GC** 250.
Truck, Fuel Servicing, Aircraft, 10-ton, 6 × 4, 3,500-gallon, Air Transportable, AEC 0859 coupled to **Trailer, Tanker, Fuel, Tecalemit Zwicky, 21-ton, 4 twin wheels, 4,500-gallon, Cranes**

	Prime Mover	**Trailer**
L	8,880	7,440
W	2,430	2,430
H	3,200	3,200
WB	4,870	3,710
H (drawbar)	-	760
GC	280	-
Track (front)	2,000	2,130
Track (rear)	1,920	2,130
BC	1,370	-

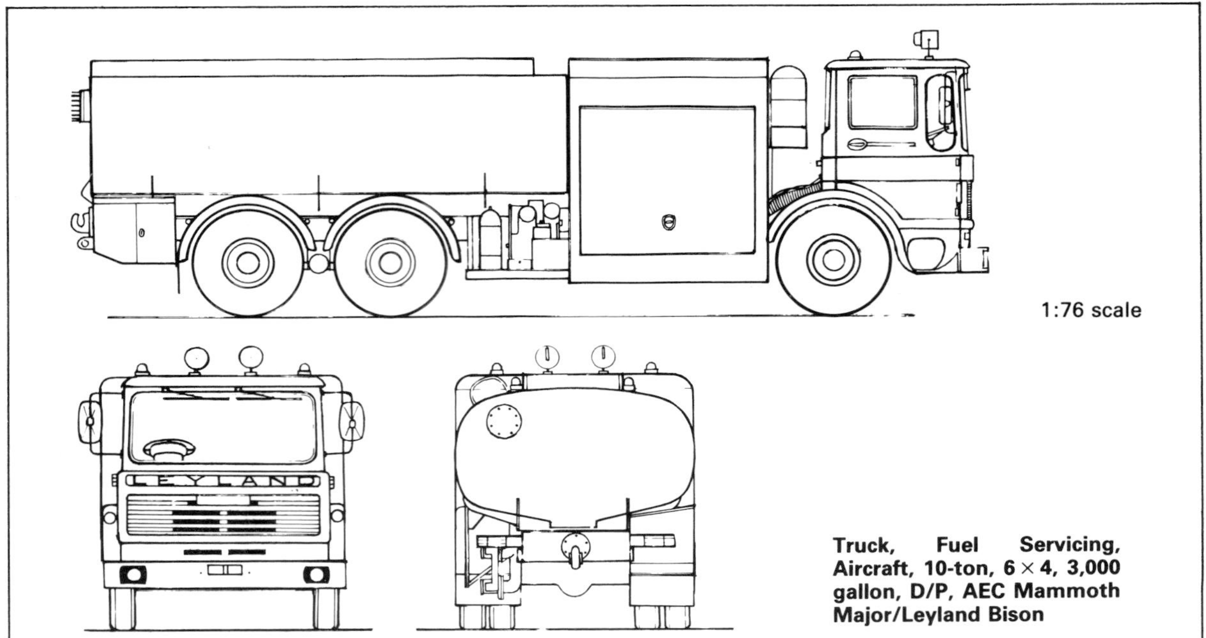

Truck, Fuel Servicing, Aircraft, 10-ton, 6 × 4, 3,000 gallon, D/P, AEC Mammoth Major/Leyland Bison

Right *Truck, Fuel Servicing, Aircraft, 10-ton, 6 × 4, 3,000-gallon, D/P, AEC Mammoth Major TG6RB with snow plough fitted.*

Below *Truck, Tanker, Fuel, 10-ton, 6 × 4, 4,000-gallon, AEC Mammoth Major TG6RB.*

Truck, Fuel Servicing, Aircraft, 10-ton, 6 × 4, 2,500-gallon, 300 gpm, Leyland 19H/1E (Avtur/Avtag, Pressure/Open Line Mark 1)
L 8,530, **W** 2,380, **H** 3,580, **WB** 4,730, **BC** 1,360, **GC** 330.

Truck, Fuel Servicing, Aircraft, 10-ton, 6 × 4, 3,000-gallon, D/P, AEC Mammoth Major TG6RB
L 9,910, **W** 2,460, **H** 2,670, **WB** 5,230, **BC** 1,460, **GC** 260.

May be fitted with attachments for snow plough or Machine, Runway De-icing (MRD)

Truck, Tanker, Water, 7-ton, 4 × 2, Aircraft Replenishment, 600-gallon, Bedford EJQ 1 BCO (KFSC5)
L 6,560, **W** 2,260, **H** 2,310, **WB** 3,840, **GC** 260.

Truck, Tanker Water Methanol, 7-ton, 4 × 2, 950-gallon, Bedford EJQ 3 BCO (KFLC5)
L 7,010, **W** 2,210, **H** 2,530, **WB** 4,250, **GC** 260.

Truck, Tanker, Fuel, 10-ton, 6 × 4, 4,000-gallon, AEC Mammoth Major TG6RB
L 9,910, **W** 2,460, **H** 2,140, **WB** 5,230, **BC** 1,460, **GC** 260.

Fuel Dispensing Unit, Aircraft, Truck Mounted, 3-ton, 4 × 2, Karrier Bantam FBV 398
L 5,110, **W** 2,030, **H** 2,290, **WB** 2,490, **GC** 170.

Tractor, Wheeled, Aircraft Towing, Heavy with Winch, Douglas Tug Mentor, Mark 3
L 7,160, **W** 2,640, **H** 3,270, **WB** 3,660.

Tractor, Wheeled, Aircraft Towing Power Servicing, Heavy, 20,000 lb, Sentinel, Mark 1, with or without winch
L 6,500, **W** 2,430, **H** 2,180, **WB** 2,790, **GC** 250.

Tractor, Wheeled, Fork Lift, Rough Terrain, Explosive Handling, Ferguson 2203
L 5,330, **W** 1,870, **H** 1,390, **WB** 1,900, **GC** 320.

Used in bomb dumps and known as Rough Terrain Fork Lift (RTFL) or 'Forky'.

Tractor, Wheeled, Fork Lift, 4,000 lb, Rough Terrain, Light, Eager Beaver Mark 2
L (inc forks at ground level) 5,460, **W** 1,860, **H** (with cab) 2,590, **H** (air portable) 1,750, **WB** 2,540.

Tractor, Wheeled, Industrial, Aircraft Towing, Light, Douglas Taskmaster, Diesel
L 3,450, **W** 1,750, **H** (with cab) 2,290, **H** (without cab) 1,520, **WB** 1,830, **GC** 240.

May be used with or without cab.

Tractor, Wheeled, Industrial, Aircraft Support, Multipurpose, Unimog 406-120

Below right *Tractor, Wheeled, Industrial, Aircraft Towing, Light, Douglas Taskmaster, Diesel, without cab.*

Bottom right *Tractors, Wheeled, Industrial, Aircraft Support, Multipurpose, Unimog 406-120 on Semi-Trailer, Cargo, CL, 20-ton, 4 twin wheels, Dropside, Tasker.*

Below *Tractor, Wheeled Fork Lift, 4,000 lb, Rough Terrain, Light, Eager Beaver Mark 2, carrying BL 755 bomb in forward area.*

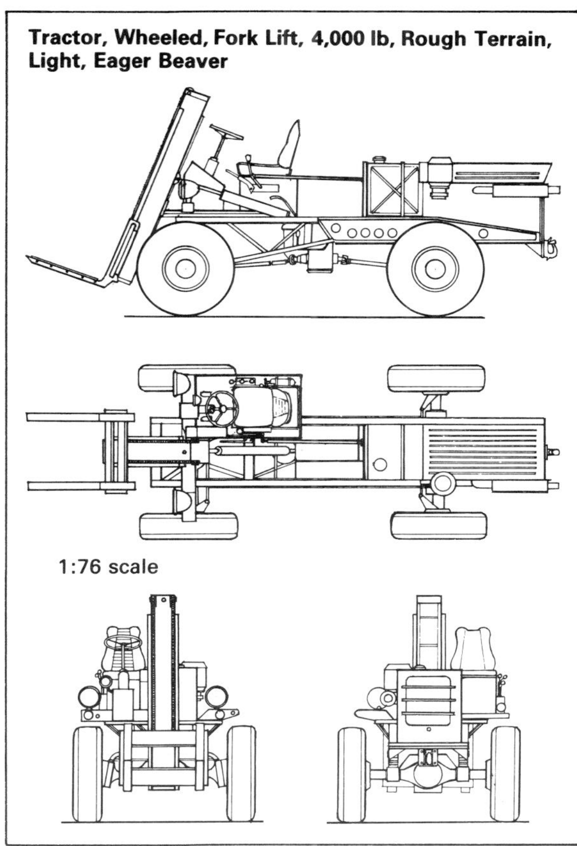

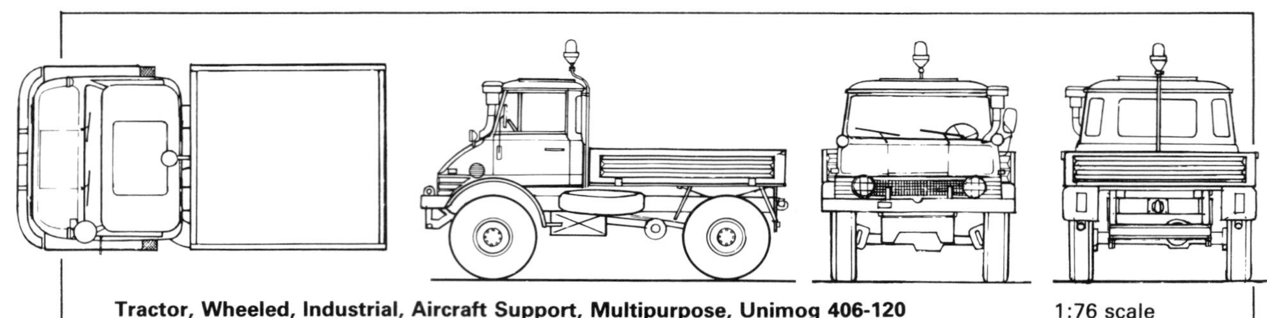

Tractor, Wheeled, Industrial, Aircraft Support, Multipurpose, Unimog 406-120 1:76 scale

L 4,100, **W** 2,000, **H** 2,680, **WB** 2,380, **GC** 440, **H** (trailer coupling) 880.

Used by Harrier squadrons. May be fitted with fork lift attachment on front.

Tractor, Wheeled, Industrial, Aircraft Towing, Medium, David Brown

L 3,350, **W** 2,230, **H** (with searchlight) 1,440, **H** (without searchlight) 1,340, **WB** 2,210, **GC** 200.

Tractor, Wheeled, Industrial, Aircraft Towing, Medium, Douglas Taskmaster, Diesel

L 3,580, **W** 1,760, **H** 1,520, **WB** 2,050, **GC** 240.

May be used with or without cab.

Tractor, Wheeled, Industrial, Aircraft Towing, Medium, w/winch, Douglas Taskmaster

L 3,610, **W** 1,750, **H** (with cab) 2,290, **WB** 2,060, **GC** 240.

Tractor, Wheeled, Semi Trailer, 20-ton, 4 × 2, LHD, Seddon Atkinson

L 5,160, **W** 2,480, **H** 3,050, **WB** 2,900, **GC** 300.

Tractor, Wheeled, Semi Trailer, 6-ton, 4 × 2, Automatic Coupling, Bedford TK, Diesel

L 4,390, **W** 2,220, **H** 2,230, **WB** 2,440, **GC** 170.

Tractor, Wheeled, Semi Trailer, 10-ton, 4 × 2, coupling to BSAU 1 and 3, (1963), AEC Mercury, TGM4R

L 5,000, **W** 2,440, **H** 2,560, **WB** 2,890, **GC** 240.

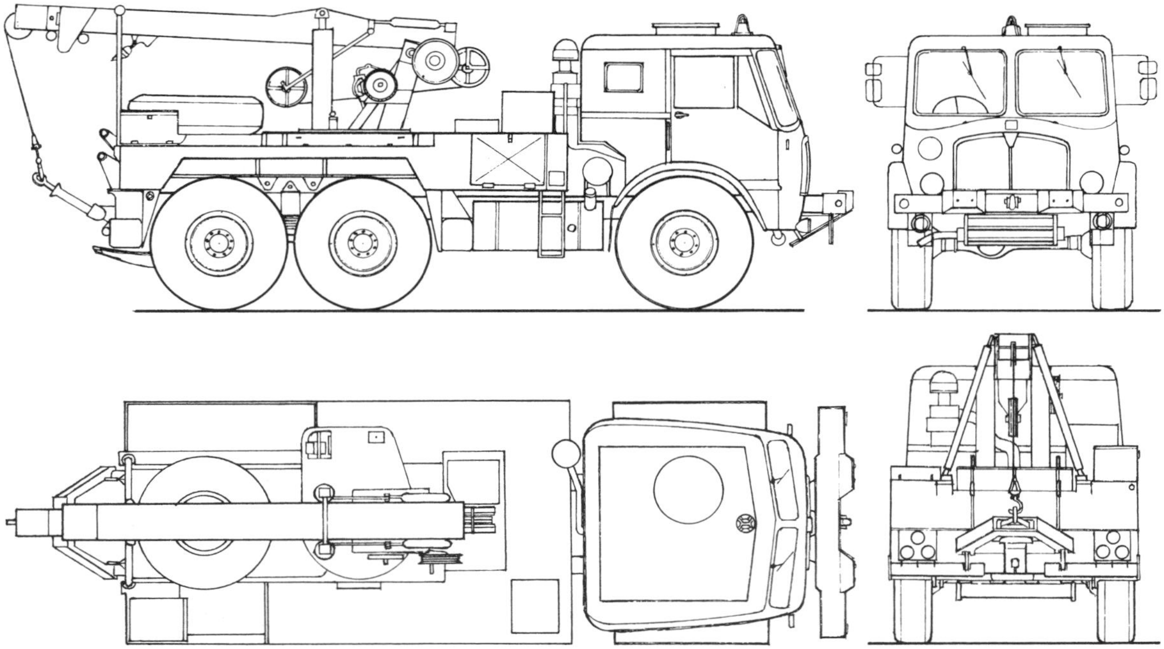

Recovery Vehicle, Wheeled, Medium, AEC Mark 3 1:76 scale

Recovery Vehicle, Wheeled, Medium, AEC Mark 3
L 8,310, **W** 2,490, **H** 3,150, **WB** (front axle to **BC**) 4,000, **GC** 350.

Same as Army FV11044 AEC Militant Mark 3.

Recovery Vehicle, Wheeled, Medium, 6 × 6, Scammell
L 6,240, **W** 2,640, **H** 3,200, **WB** 3,500, **BC** 1,290, **GC** 330.

Above *Recovery Vehicle, Wheeled, CL, 35-ton, 6 × 4, Scammell/EKA.*

Below *Trolley, Weapon Loading, Type W, used for weapon loading on Tornado.*

Snow Removal Unit, Self-Propelled, 5-ton, 6 × 4, Rotary, All Wheel Drive
L 9,440, **W** (complete) 2,630, **W** (chassis only) 2,380, **WB** 3,650, **GC** 220.

Known as T54.

Recovery Vehicle, Wheeled, CL, 35-ton, 6 × 4, Scammell/EKA
L 8,300, **W** 2,500, **H** 3,250, **WB** 5,270, **GC** 250.

One only in RAF Germany. Same as Army equivalent.

Truck, Aircraft Baggage Loader, LHD, 6-ton 4 × 2, Dodge
L (elevator lowered) 8,630, **W** 2,510, **H** 3,300.

Sweeper, Rotary, Self-Propelled, 6-ton, 4 × 2, Bedford SL3
L 6,720, **W** 2,510, **H** 3,350, **WB** 3,960, **GC** 170.

Truck, Aircraft Baggage Loader, 4-ton, 4 × 2, Karrier Gamecock, Diesel
L (elevator lowered) 7,670, **W** 2,430, **H** 3,220.

Truck, Aircraft, Cargo Loading-Unloading, 36,000 lb, 6 × 2, LHD, Condec Model 2161
L 8,170, **W** 3,870, **H** (platform raised, rails removed) 3,990, **H** (cab stowed, catwalks off) 2,790, **H** (platform lowered, rails removed) 950, **WB** 6,270, **GC** (normal) 200, **GC** (raised) 360, **GC** (lowered) 120.

Truck, Bomb Loading, 3/5-ton, 4 × 2, with power-operated platform, Bedford SLC3, 4W/2L
L (platform stowed) 8,430, **W** 2,230, **W** (side stabilisers extended) 3,400, **H** (platform stowed) 5,020, **WB** 3,960, **GC** 270.

Truck, Cargo, w/2-ton crane, 3-ton, 4 × 2, Bedford EJQ 1DCO (KFSC5)
L 7,210, **W** 2,280, **H** 2,880, **WB** 3,830, **GC** 260, **L** (body) 4,410, **W** (body) 2,130, **H** (tailboard) 1,310, **H** (sides and tailboard) 450.

HIAB crane behind cab—vehicle known as HIAB.

Truck, Cargo, Elevating Body, 6-ton, 4 × 2, Aircraft Loading, 100-ft lift, Bedford EJQ 1BCO
L 6,450, **W** 2,310, **H** (body raised) 5,480, **H** (body lowered) 3,100, **WB** 3,830, **GC** 260;
L (body internal) 4,260, **W** (body internal) 2,130, **H** (body internal) 1,820, **H** (platform raised) 3,650, **H** (platform lowered) 1,260.

Truck, Cargo, Elevating Body, 7-ton, 4 × 2, Aircraft Loading, 10-ft lift, Bedford SLC3
L 6,240, **W** 2,280, **H** (body lowered) 2,920, **H** (body raised) 4,670, **WB** 3,960, **GC** 250;
L (body internal) 4,280, **W** (body internal) 2,180, **H** (sideboards) 660.

Truck, Cargo, Elevating Body, 6-ton, 4 × 2, Bedford EPR1CCO
L 6,470, **W** 2,340, **H** (body lowered) 3,090, **H** (body raised) 5,490, **WB** 3,840, **GC** 250;
L (body internal) 4,260, **W** (body internal) 2,130, **H** (under canopy) 1,820, **H** (platform lowered) 1,220, **H** (platform raised) 3,580.

Truck, In-Flight Catering, High Lift, 5-ton, 4 × 2, Karrier Gamecock, WCFS 541
L 6,930, **W** 2,280, **H** 3,670, **WB** 3,580, **GC** 120; **L** (body) 4,260, **W** (body) 2,280, **H** (body) 2,210.

Truck, Parachute Transporter, 7-ton, 4 × 2, Bedford EFQ3BCO (KFLC3 or KFLC5)
L 7,770, **W** 2,280, **H** 3,120, **WB** 4,230, **GC** 250; **L** (body internal) 5,420, **W** (body internal) 2,180, **H** (body internal) 2,330.

Truck, Refuse Collection, 3-ton, 4 × 2, Karrier Bantam, FAH 398
L 4,990, **W** 2,150, **H** (body level) 2,190, **WB** 2,480.

Truck, Cargo, 5-tonne, 4 × 2, with tail lift, Bedford (EJN3BCO)
L 7,170, **W** 2,800, **H** 3,430, **WB** 3,840, **GC** 250.

Truck, Van, 3-ton, 4 × 2, Forward Supply, Karrier Bantam, FAH 398
L 5,200, **W** 2,010, **H** 3,070, **WB** 2,480; **L** (body) 3,250, **W** (body) 1,820, **H** (body) 2,030.

Obsolete.

Truck, Van, 3-ton, 4 × 2, Ground Equipment, Servicing, Karrier Bantam (FAH 398)
L 5,230, **W** 2,040, **H** 2,990, **WB** 2,480, **GC** 120; **L** (body internal) 3,250, **W** (body internal) 1,820, **H** (body internal) 1,900.

Truck, Van, 3-ton, 4 × 4, Helicopter Support, Queen's Flight, Bedford RL
L 7,110, **W** 2,430, **H** 2,740, **WB** 3,960, **GC** 320.

Truck, Van, Pantechnicon, 6-ton, 4 × 2, Bedford CFN3B (J5LC3)
L 7,390, **W** 2,360, **H** 3,400, **WB** 4,240, **GC** 230; **L** (body internal) 4,670, **W** (body internal) 2,110, **H** (centre body) 2,430, **H** (tailboard) 1,160, **H** (loading) 610.

Aircraft De-icing Equipment, Truck Mounted, 7-ton, 4 × 2, Bedford EJQ3BCO (KFLC5)
L 7,080, **W** 2,210, **H** 2,430, **WB** 4,250, **GC** 260.

Airfield Control, Truck Mounted, 2-ton, 4 × 2, Karrier Bantam Mark 5
L 4,900, **W** 2,130, **H** 3,050, **WB** 2,490, **GC** 120.

Airfield Control, Truck Mounted, 2-ton, 4 × 2, Karrier Bantam, FA 398
L 4,900, **W** 2,150, **H** 3,170, **WB** 2,540, **GC** 170.

Runway Control, Truck Mounted, 3-ton, 4 × 2, Bedford Mark 2
L 5,840, **W** 2,310, **H** 3,960, **WB** 2,920, **GC** 190.

Truck, Compressed Gas Cylinders, 10-ton, AEC, 2TG 6RB
L 9,720, **W** 2,430, **H** 2,580, **WB** 5,230, **BC** 1,460, **GC** 290.

Uses AEC 6 × 4 chassis.

Servicing Platform, Truck Mounted, 7-ton, 4 × 2, Bedford EPR3CCO (KGLC 60)
L (platform stowed) 10,970, **W** 2,280, **W** (stabilisers extended) 4,110, **H** 3,500, **WB** 5,480, **GC** 260.

Spreader, Loose Material, Truck Mounted, 3-ton, 4 × 4, Bedford RL

	Vehicle	With snow plough frame fitted	With snow blade fitted
L	5,610	6,910	8,050
W	2,430	2,430	2,690
H	3,090	3,090	3,090
WB	3,350	3,350	3,350
GC	320	120	nil

Spreader, Loose Material, Truck Mounted, 10-ton, 6 × 4, Leyland 19H/7
L 9,010, **W** 2,430, **H** 2,970, **WB** 4,720, **BC** 1,360, **GC** 340.

Van, Photographic Handling, 1¾-ton, 4 × 2, Bedford CDDOB20 (JIZ2)
L 5,540, **W** 2,050, **H** 2,590, **WB** 3,020, **GC** 200; **L** (body internal) 3,170, **W** (body internal) 1,850, **H** (body internal) 1,770.

Sweeper, Rotary, Self-propelled, 6-ton, 4 × 2, Lacre
L 7,150, **W** 2,500, **H** 3,200, **WB** 4,240, **GC** 130.

Late model has Bedford TK type cab.

Sweeper, Rotary, Self-Propelled, 6-ton, Bedford (Lacre)
L 5,460, **W** 2,310, **H** 2,810, **WB** 3,040, **GC** 250.

Aircraft, De-icing Equipment, Truck Mounted, with high access platform, 10-ton, 6 × 4, AEC 2 TG6RB

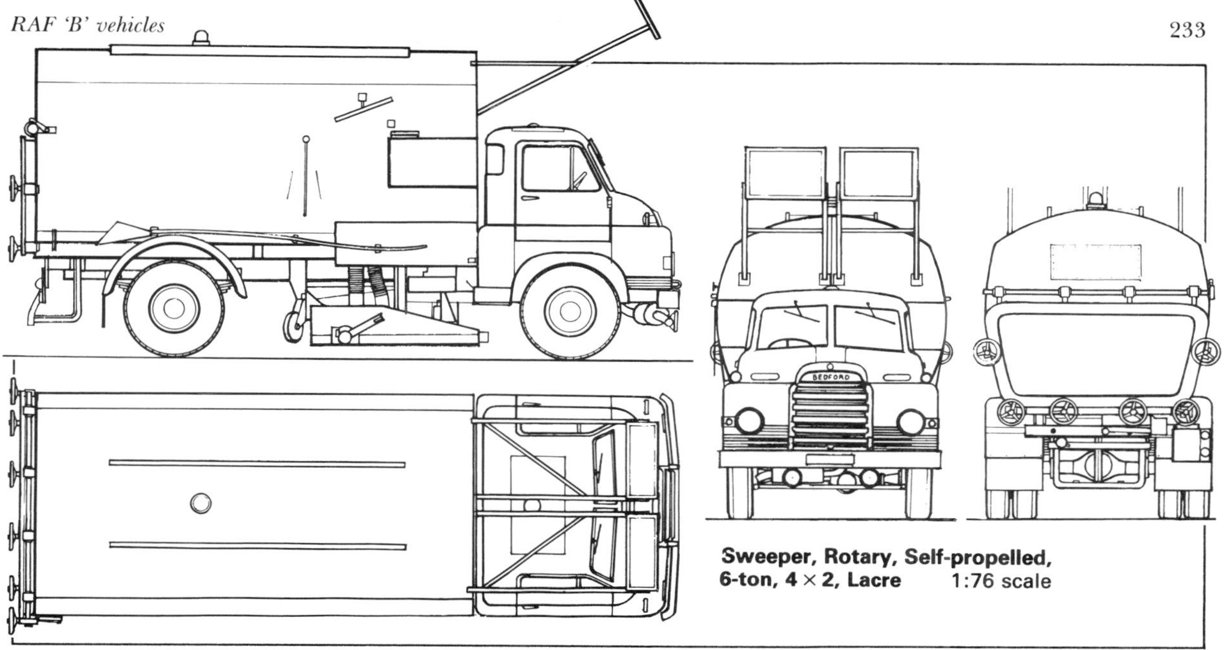

Sweeper, Rotary, Self-propelled, 6-ton, 4 × 2, Lacre 1:76 scale

L (platform stowed) 12,980, **W** 2,440, **W** (stabilisers extended) 4,120, **H** (platform stowed) 3,960, **WB** 5,230, **BC** 1,460, GC 260.

Truck, Cargo, 1½-ton, 4 × 2, Hard Top, Bedford JIC2
L 5,240, **W** 2,080, **H** 2,230, **WB** 3,050, **GC** 200; **L** (body internal) 2,480, **W** (body internal) 1,970, **H** (body internal) 1,570.

Truck, Cargo, 13-ton, 4 × 2, Dropside, Bedford EDLOBCO
L 7,720, **W** 2,430, **H** 2,840, **WB** 3,420, **GC** 120; **L** (body internal) 4,260, **W** (body internal) 2,360, **H** (body internal) 1,700; **H** (loading) 1,060.

Truck, Cargo, CL, 3-ton 4 × 2, Bedford AHGDBCO
L 5,700, **W** 2,200, **H** 2,250, **WB** 2,900, **GC** 200; **L** (load platform) 3,500, **W** (load platform) 2,100, **H** (load platform) 400.

Truck, Cargo, 4-ton, 4 × 4, with trailer braking, Bedford RL

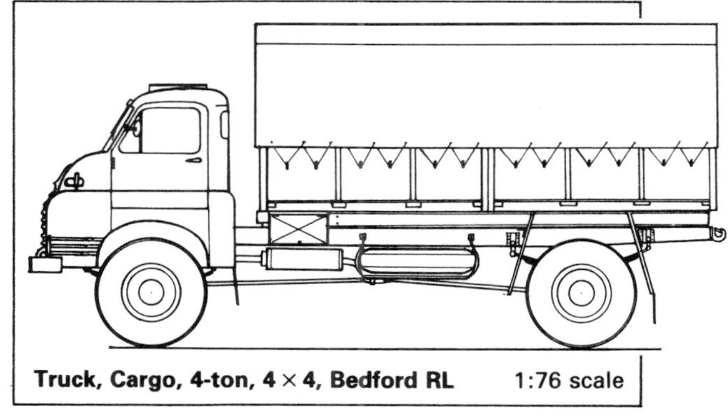

Truck, Cargo, 4-ton, 4 × 4, Bedford RL 1:76 scale

Below left *Sweeper, Rotary, Self-propelled, 6-ton, Bedford (Lacre).*

Below *Sweeper, Rotary, Self-propelled, 6-ton, 4 × 2, Lacre.*

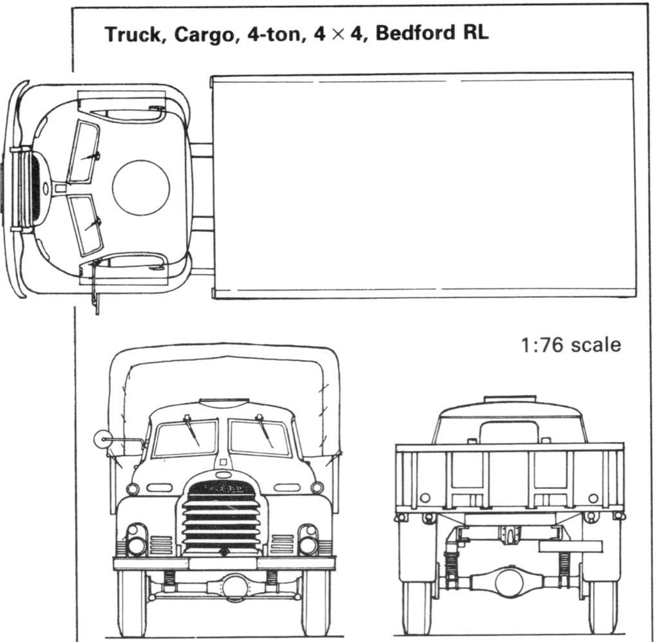

L 6,340, **W** 2,380, **H** (tilt) 3,060, **H** (less tilt) 2,590, **WB** 3,960, **GC** 300; **L** (body) 4,280, **W** (body) 2,230, **H** (body) 1,740.

Truck, Cargo, 4-ton, 4 × 4, Bedford MKP2BMO; Truck, Cargo, 4-ton, 4 × 4, with winch, Bedford MKP2WMO

L 6,630, **W** 2,480, **HH** 3,400, **H** (loading) 1,370, **WB** 3,960, **GC** 330; **L** (body) 4,280, **W** 2,290, **H** 1,840 or 1,520.

Truck, Cargo, Armoured Half Cab, 3-ton, 4 × 4, Bedford RL

L 6,340, **W** 2,430, **H** 3,040, **H** (loading) 1,290, **WB** 3,960, **GC** 310; **L** (body) 4,260, **W** (body) 2,180, **H** (body) 1,670.

Very few left in service.

Truck, Cargo, CL, 5-ton, 4 × 2, Dropside, 2-speed axle, Bedford EJQ3ECO (KFLC5)

L 7,210, **W** 2,280, **H** 2,870, **H** (loading) 1,320, **WB** 4,260, **GC** 250.

Truck, Cargo, CL, 8-ton, 4 × 2, Dropside, Bedford, ERL3CCO

L 7,670, **W** 2,460, **H** 2,340, **WB** 4,240, **GC** 250.

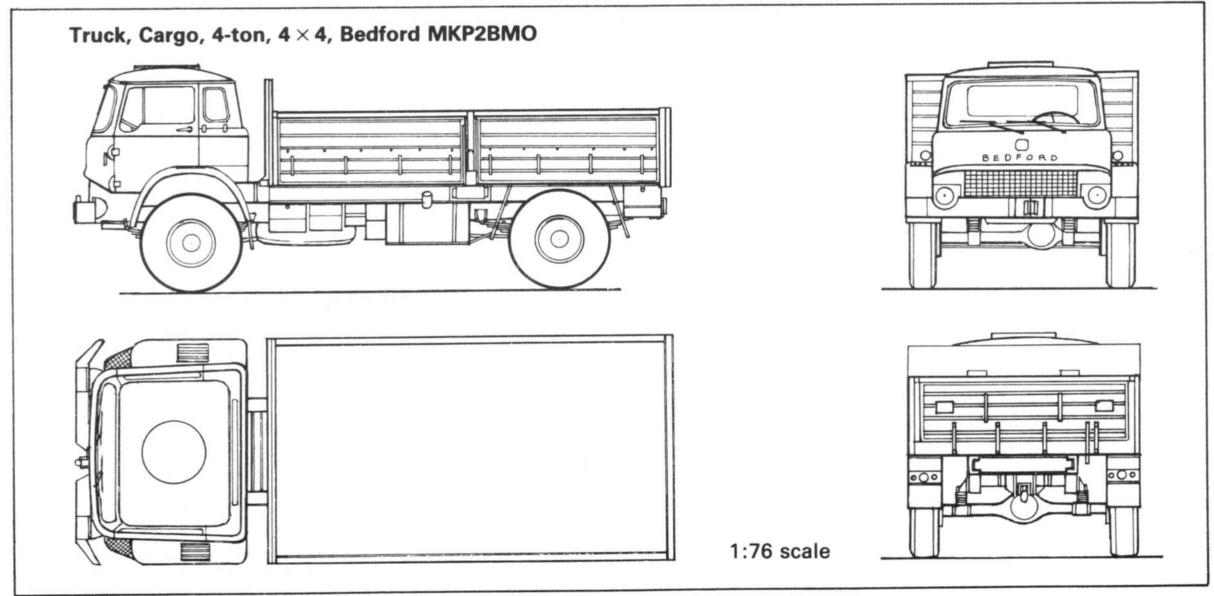

Truck, Cargo, 8-ton, 4 × 4, MMLC, Bedford
L 6,670, **W** 2,460, **H** 3,290, **WB** 4,370, **GC** 355; **L** (body) 4,470, **W** (body) 2,320, **H** (body) 1,820.
Five versions in use.

Truck, Cargo, CL, 10-ton 6 × 4, Dropside, AEC TG6 RB
L 9,750, **W** 2,460, **H** 2,530, **WB** 5,230, **BC** 1,460, **GC** 260; **L** (body) 7,310, **W** (body) 2,330, **H** (loading) 1,440.

Truck, Tipper, 6-ton, 4 × 2, Bedford J5 SC3
L 5,300, **W** 2,180, **H** (over cab shield) 2,380, **H** (side and bulkhead) 530, **H** (tailboard) 630, **WB** 3,040, **GC** 240; **L** (body) 2,280, **W** (body) 1,970.

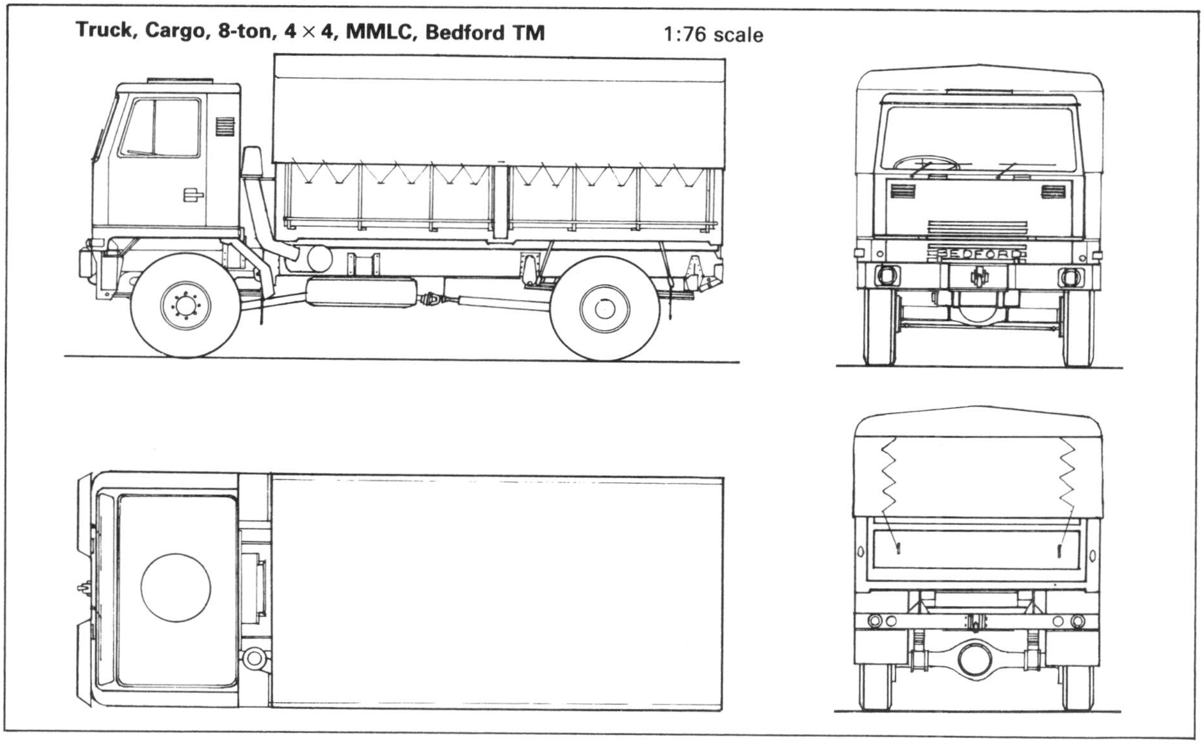

Truck, Cargo, 8-ton, 4 × 4, MMLC, Bedford TM 1:76 scale

Facing page *Truck, cargo, 4-ton, 4 × 4, Bedford MKP2BMO with sides and tailboard removed.*

Left *Truck, Cargo, 8-ton, 4 × 4, MMLC, Bedford, seen here still with Army registration but in use with an RAF Regiment Light Armoured Squadron.*

Truck, Utility, ¼-ton, 4 × 4, Rover 88 inch, Series 11ACP (also Rover 6)
L 3,750, **W** 1,620, **H** 1,960, **WB** 2,230, **GC** 200; **L** (body) 1,140, **W** (body) 1,420, **W** (between wheel boxes) 910, **H** 1,210.

Truck, Utility, ½-ton, 4 × 4, Rover 1
L 3,730, **W** 1,620, **H** 1,960, **WB** 2,230, **GC** 200; **L** (body) 1,140, **W** (body) 1,420, **W** (between wheel boxes) 910, **H** 1,210.

Truck, Utility, ½-ton, Rover Series 3 with hard top.

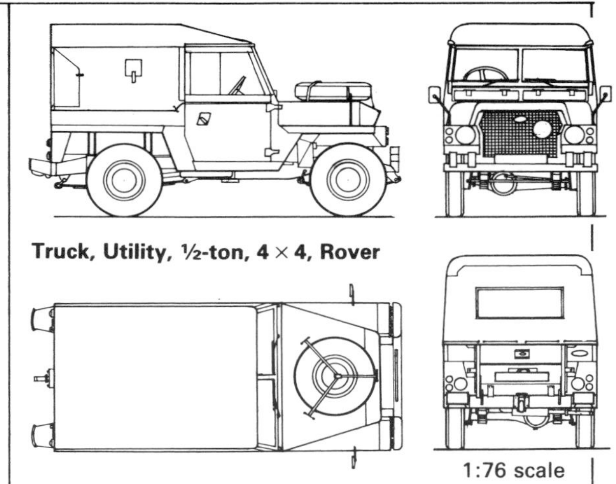

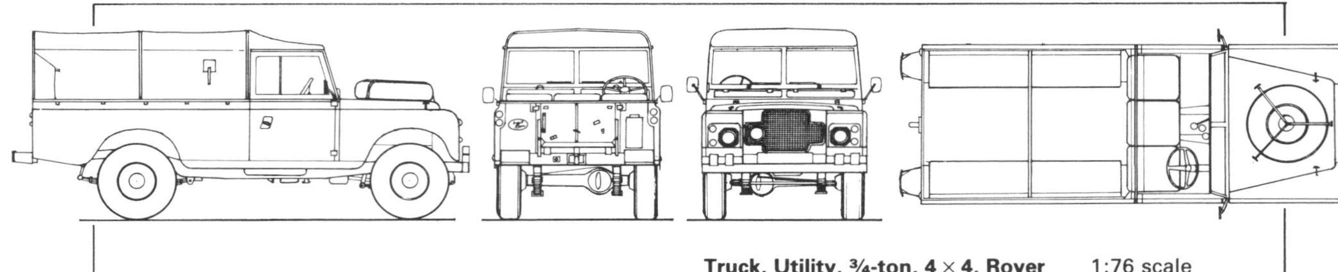

Truck, Utility, ½-ton, 4 × 4, Rover Series 3
L 3,670, **W** 1,520, **H** 1,950, **WB** 2,230, **GC** 220.
Truck, Utility, ½-ton, 4 × 4, Anti-spark, Rover Series 3, Diesel
L 3,670, **W** 1,520, **H** 1,950, **WB** 2,230, **GC** 200. Used in bomb dumps.
Truck, Utility, ¾-ton, 4 × 4, Rover 109-inch, Series 11A
L 4,750, **W** 1,630, **H** 2,060, **WB** 2,770, **GC** 250. Used with both soft or hard tops.
Truck, Utility, FFR, ¾-ton, 4 × 4, 24 V, Rover, Series 3
L 4,560, **W** 1,680, **H** 2,030, **WB** 2,770, **GC** 230.
Truck, Utility, FFR, ¾-ton, 4 × 4, Rover 11L
L 4,620, **W** 1,680, **H** 2,030, **WB** 2,760, **GC** 220.
Van, ¼-ton, 4 × 2, Morris Mini
L 3,030, **W** 1,420, **H** 1,340, **WB** 2,030, **GC** 150.
Van, Firefighting and Rescue, 1¾-ton, 4 × 2, Bedford CF 97790; Van, 1¾-ton, Forward Supply, 4 × 2, Bedford CF 97790; Van, Medium, 4 × 2, 370 cu ft, Bedford CF 9770
L 4,920, **W** 2,080, **H** 2,610, **WB** 3,200, **GC** 130; **L** (body) 2,890, **W** (body) 1,950, **H** (body) 1,820, **H** (loading) 760.

Truck, GS, 1-tonne, 12V, W/Winch, Rover 101 of 37 Squadron, RAF Regiment.

Van, Medium, 4 × 2, 350 cu ft, BLMC 350EA, Diesel
L 4,180, **W** 1,990, **H** 2,500, **WB** 2,580, **GC** 140;

Left *Truck, Firefighting, Airfield Crash Rescue, 1-ton, 4 × 4, Rover.*
Below left *Truck, Firefighting, Foam, Mark 8, 3-ton, 4 × 4, Bedford RLHZ3.*

L (body) 2,480, **W** (body) 1,750, **H** (body) 1,720, **H** (loading) 680.

Truck, GS, 1-tonne, 12 V, with winch, Rover 101
L 4,300 **W** 1,800, **H** 2,300, **WB** 2,800, **GC** 250.
Used by Rapier squadrons of RAF Regiment.

Truck, Firefighting, ¾-ton, 4 × 4, Airfield Crash Rescue, Rover 9
L 4,420, **W** 1,700, **H** 2,510, **WB** 2,770, **GC** 200.

Truck, Firefighting, Crash (tactical), ¾-ton, 4 × 4, Rover 11 towing Trailer, Tanker, Driven Axle, Water, ¾-ton, 2-wheel, 200 gallon, Scottorn
L (inc trailer) 7,540, **W** 1,650, **H** 2,150, **WB** (Rover) 2,770, **WB** (rear axle to trailer axle) 3,070, **GC** 250.

Truck, Firefighting, Airfield Crash Rescue, 1-ton, 4 × 4, Rover
L 4,420, **W** 1,920, **H** 2,590, **WB** 2,770, **GC** 250.

Truck, Firefighting, 1¼-ton, 4 × 4, 110-in, Rover
L (inc ladder) 6,400, **W** 1,770, **H** (over ladder) 2,760, **WB** 2,790.

Truck, Firefighting, 2-ton, 4 × 2, Domestic, Water, 100-gallon, Bedford EDGOBZO
L 5,710, **W** 2,210, **H** 2,820, **WB** 2,920, **GC** 180.

Truck, Firefighting, 4-ton, 4 × 2, Domestic, Water, 450-gallon, Bedford EFN3BZO
L 6,640, **W** 2,210, **H** 2,520, **WB** 3,830, **GC** 200.

Truck, Firefighting, Foam, Mark 8, 3-ton, 4 × 4, Bedford RLHZ3
L 6,450, **W** 2,740, **H** 3,250, **WB** 3,960, **GC** 300.

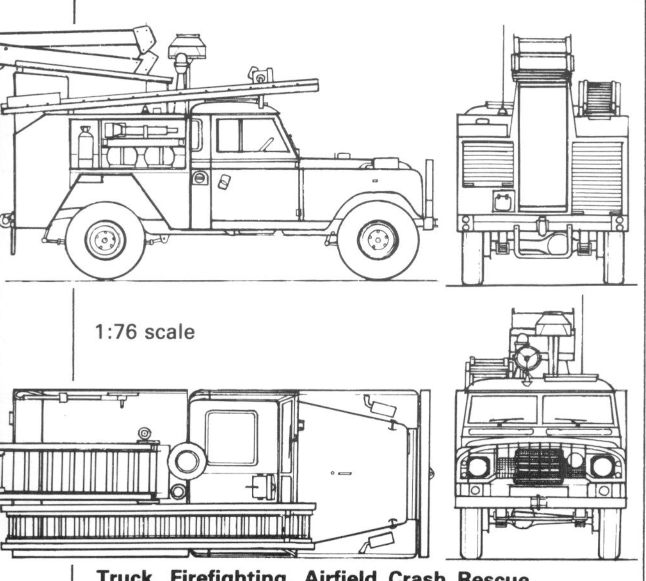
1:76 scale

Truck, Firefighting, Airfield Crash Rescue, 1-ton, 4 × 4, Rover

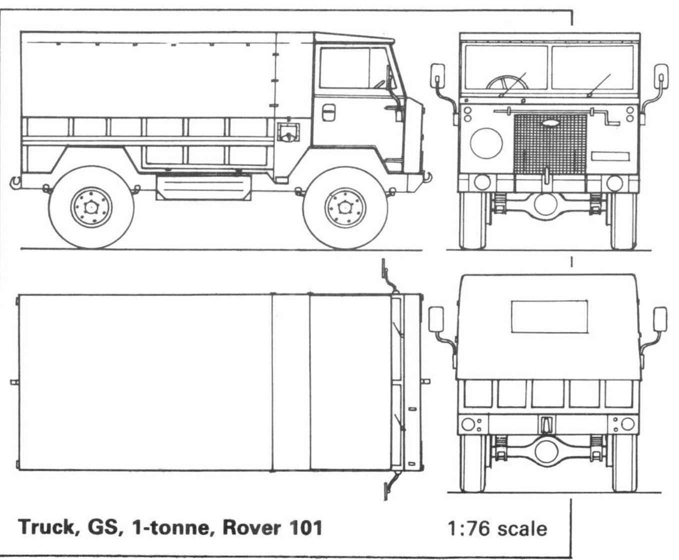
Truck, GS, 1-tonne, Rover 101 1:76 scale

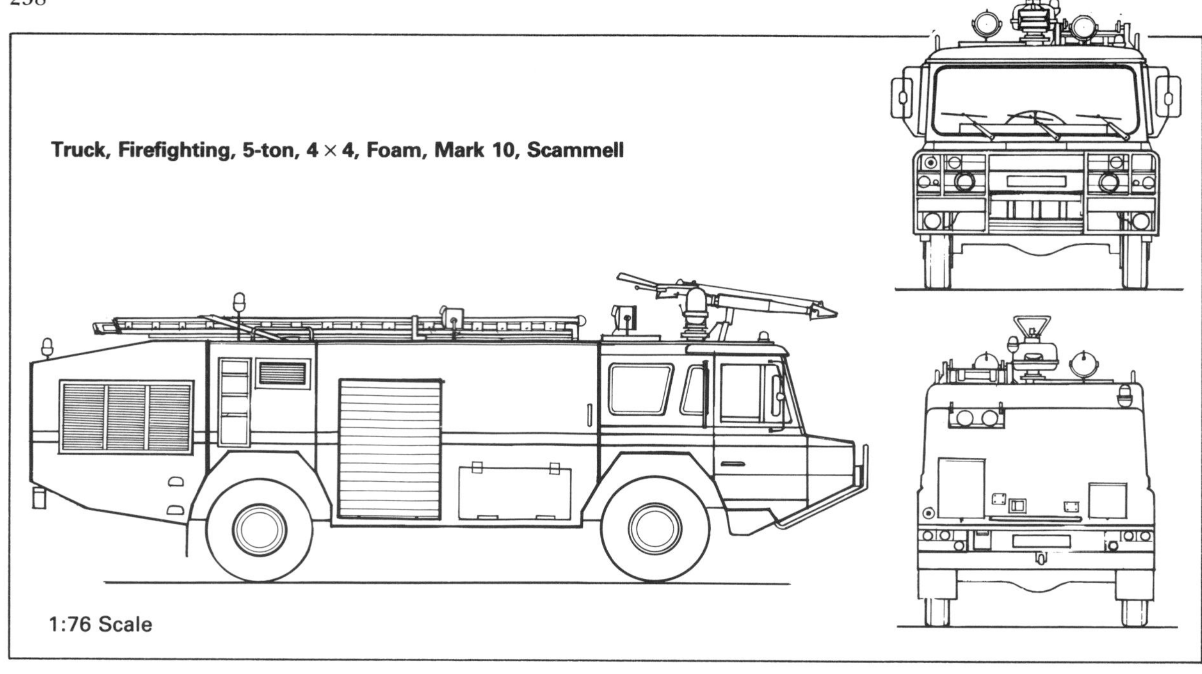

Truck, Firefighting, 5-ton, 4 × 4, Foam, Mark 10, Scammell
L 8,480, **W** 2,490, **H** 3,200, **WB** 4,000.
Truck, Firefighting, Airfield, Foam, 5-ton, 6 × 6, Mark 7, Thornycroft, TFA/B81
L 7,260, **W** 2,430, **H** 3,140, **WB** (front axle to BC) 3,050.

Mark 7A similar but with automatic gearbox.

Truck, Firefighting, 5-ton, 6 × 6, Water, Foam, DP, Mark 2, with monitor, Thornycroft TFA/B81
L 6,840, **W** 2,300, **H** 3,170, **WB** 3,730, **GC** 330.

Above left *Truck, Firefighting, 5-ton, Foam, Mark 10, Scammell.*

Left *Truck, Firefighting, Water, Foam, DP, Mark 3, 5-ton, 6 × 6, Thornycroft TFA/B81.*

Truck, Firefighting, Water, Foam, DP, Mark 3, 5-ton, 6 × 6, Thornycroft TFA/B81
L 6,590, **W** 2,330, **H** (with lamp extended) 3,730, **WB** 3,730, **GC** 400.
Truck, Firefighting, 5-ton, 4 × 4, Crash, Mark 5, Thornycroft, TF/B80
L 6,700, **W** 2,310, **H** 3,220, **WB** 3,650, **GC** 330.
Truck, Firefighting, 5-ton, 4 × 4, Foam, Mark 5A, Thornycroft, TF/B80
L 6,400, **W** 2,300, **H** 3,050, **WB** 3,650, **GC** 300.
Truck, Firefighting, 10-ton, 6 × 6, Foam, Mark 9, Thornycroft Nubian Major

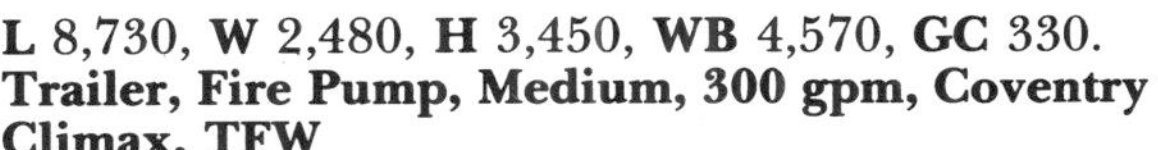

L 8,730, **W** 2,480, **H** 3,450, **WB** 4,570, **GC** 330.
Trailer, Fire Pump, Medium, 300 gpm, Coventry Climax, TFW
L 2610, **W** 160, **H** 134 (all with pump and hose on trailer).
Semi-Trailer, Cargo, 6-ton, 2 twin wheels, Dropside, Tasker
L 5,720, **W** 2,500, **H** 1,730, coupling to axle 3,810, **GC** 290.
Semi-Trailer, Cargo, CL, 20-ton, 4 twin wheels, Dropside, Tasker
L 12,421, **W** 2,500, **H** (platform, unladen) 1,400, **GC** (unladen) 360, **L** (platform) 12,192.
Semi-Trailer, Low Platform, CL, with winch, 15-ton, 2 twin wheels, Crane Fruehauf
L 10,830, **W** 2,440, **H** (with winch) 226, **H** (deck) 590, **H** (upper deck less winch) 1,590, **H** (coupling) 1,120, **GC** 280.
Semi-Trailer, Low Platform, 10-ton, 2 wheeled, LWB, 9 ft 6 in wide; SWB, 8 ft 6 in wide; SWB, 9 ft 6 in wide, Tasker
L (SWB & LWB) 12,980, **W** (SWB & LWB) 2,890, **W** (SWB) 2,590, **H** 1,520, **GC** 230; **L** (internal, SWB & LWB) 10,430, **W** (internal, (SWB) 1,820.

Known as 'Queen Elizabeth' as it replaced the old 'Queen Mary'.

Above *Truck, Firefighting, 10-ton, 6 × 6, Foam, Mark 9, Thornycroft Nubian Major.*

Right *One of the more unusual RAF vehicles is the Canadian Bombardier Muskeg, used by EOD teams for removing explosive ordnance from sandy areas.*

Below *To be seen on every airfield somewhere is a selection of crash recovery equipment.* **L-R** *Trolley, Salvage, Tracjac; Trolley, Salvage, Main, Type C; Trolley, Salvage, Nose, 15-ton.*

Above *One unusual and little-seen RAF vehicle is this Austin London taxi used on some stations as a light ambulance for taking personnel and their families to nearby hospitals for treatment at a far lower cost than using the usual Service ambulances.*

Semi-Trailer, Low Platform, CL, with winch, 15-ton, 2 twin wheels, Tasker
L 10,580, **W** 2,440, **W** (with load restraining shackles) 2,540, **H** (deck) 610, **H** (coupling) 1,290, **L** (lower deck) 6,710, **GC** (unladen) 200.
Trailer, Cargo, ½-ton, 2-wheeled, Mark 1 and Mark 2, Brockhouse
L 2,890, **W** 1,390, **H** 1,060, **H** (loading) 1,060, **GC** 210.
Trailer, Cargo, ¾-ton, 2 wheeled, Sankey
L 2,930, **W** 1,420, **H** 1,080, **H** (loading) 610, **GC** 200.
Trailer, Cargo, 5-ton, 4 wheeled, Dropside, Tasker
L 6,880, **W** 2,430, **H** 1,670, **H** (loading) 1,220, **WB** 3,200, **GC** 300, Track 200.
Trailer, Cargo, CL, 5-tonne, 4 wheels, Dropside, Oldbury
L 6,800, **L** (less towbar) 5,100, **W** 2,460, **H** 1,700, **WB** 3,450, **GC** 43.
Trailer, Cargo, 5-ton, 4 wheeled, Dropside, Mark 3, Tasker
L 6,740, **W** 2,500, **H** 1,740, **WB** 3,150, **GC** 350; **L** (body) 4,870, **W** (body) 2,390, **H** (body) 1,280.
Trailer, Cargo, 10-ton, 4 twin wheels, Dropside, Primrose Third Axle
L (with towbar) 9,040, **L** (less towbar) 7,620, **W** 2,500, **H** 1,470, **WB** 5,900, **GC** 280; **L** (body) 6,930, **W** (body) 2,280, **H** (loading) 1,010.

Trailer, Cargo, 1¾-tonne, GS, 2 wheeled, Arrow
L 3,800, **W** 2,460, **H** 1,240, **H** (loading) 1,240, **GC** 240.
Trailer, Flat Platform, Air Portable, 5-ton, 4-wheeled, MEXE
L (with tow beam) 5,530, **L** (less tow beam) 3,960, **W** 2,490, **H** 960, **WB** 2,950.
Trailer, Bomb Trolley, 10-ton, 4 twin wheels, Type 4 (UK only), FV 3511A

Above *Trolley, Weapon Loading, Type V, used for loading weapons on to Jaguars and Buccaneers.*

L (with drawbar) 13,100, **W** 2,760, **H** 3,270, **WB** 5,380, **GC** 350.
Trailer, Caravan, GCA Crewroom, 2-ton, 4-wheeled, Tasker
L (with drawbar) 6,970, **L** (less drawbar) 5,570, **W** 2,280, **H** 2,940, **WB** 4,160, **GC** 550.
Trailer, Recovery, Fork Lift, Transporter, 5½-ton, 4 wheeled, IBBETT Eng Co (EEZION)
L 5,860, **W** 2,430, **H** 1,440, **H** (towing, 4 heights) 450, 610, 810, 960, **WB** 1,060, **GC** 330, Track 2,210; **L** (towing gear) 450, **L** (internal) 4,110, **W** (internal) 1,720, **H** (loading) 160.
Trailer, Recovery, Fork Lift, Transporter, 5¾-ton, 4-wheeled, IBBETT Eng Co (EEZION)
L 5,760, **W** 2,500, **H** (tailboard raised) 1,440, **L** (internal) 3,960, **W** (internal) 1,720.
Trailer, Snow Removal Unit, 4½-ton, 5-wheeled, Mark 1, Sicard SW112
L 10,970, **W** (broom central) 4,690, **W** (broom set 30° L or R) 5,330, **W** (less broom) 3,140, **H** 2,540, **L** (broom) 4,210, Broom diameter 910.
Mark 2 SW112 and Mark 3 SW212 similar.
Generator Set, Diesel Engine, Trailer Mounted, AC, 27½ kVA, 415/240 V, 208/120 V, 3 phase, 50/60 c/s, 2-ton, 4-wheeled, Sentinel
L (towbar vertical) 5,330, **L** (towbar horizontal) 6,500, **W** 2,130, **H** 2,430, **WB** 3,650, **GC** 250.
Launcher, Glider, Trailer Mounted, 5-ton, 4-wheeled, Eagle/Brockhouse

Above *Snow-clearing unit using two old Derwent jet engines attached to the front of an AEC Mammoth Major tanker.*

Right *Trailer, Snow Removal Unit, 4½-ton, 5-wheeled, Mark 1, Sicard SW112.*

Below *Truck, Van, Pantechnicon, 6-ton, 4 × 2, Bedford.*

L (with drawbar) 6,700, **L** (less drawbar and front platform) 4,870, **W** 2,210, **H** (with cage) 3,220, **H** (less cage) 2,360, **WB** 2,590, **GC** 350.

Light Beacon, Trailer Mounted, 1-ton, 2-wheeled, Brockhouse

L 3,680, **W** 2,080, **H** 2,940, **GC** 530.

Office, Trailer Mounted, 2-ton, 4 wheeled, Sentinel

L (less drawbar) 5,180, **W** 2,280, **H** 3,250, **WB** 3,650, **GC** 250.

Spreader, Loose Material, Trailer Mounted, ¾-ton, 2-wheeled

L 3,400, **W** 1,930, **H** 1,730, **GC** 200.

Spreader, Loose Material, Trailer Mounted, 2-ton, 2-wheeled, Type C, Atkinson

L 4,060, **W** 1,670, **H** 140, **GC** 270.

Trailer, Cargo, Maintenance, FRTV, 1-ton, 2-wheeled, (Rapier) FV 2412

L 3,632, **W** 1,752, **H** 1,346, **GC** 268, Track 149; **L** (internal) 245, **W** (internal) 121, **H** (floor) 770.

Trailer, Caravan, Boundary Layer

L (with drawbar) 8,410, **W** 2,440, **H** 3,400, **GC** 770, Track 2,130; **L** (internal) 6,830, **W** (internal) 2,300, **H** 2,240.

Truck, Van, Pantechnicon, 6-ton 4 × 2, Bedford

No dimensions available.

Tractor, Wheeled, Industrial, Aircraft Towing, Medium, Massey Ferguson

L 3,940, **W** (over mirrors) 2,440, **H** (to top of beacon and warning triangle) 2,535, **WB** 2,076, Track front 1,372, Track rear 1,655.

Motor Coach, Large, with Ambulance role, 4 × 2, 37-seater, Bedford NJM
L 9,200, **W** 2,930, **H** 2,900.

Tractor, Wheeled, Fork Lift, Telescopic, Handler, 4,000 lb, Rough Terrain
L (vehicle + forks) 4,300 + 1,100, **W** 2,200, **H** 2,450.

In use in small numbers only. Known as Giraffe.

Left *Tractor, Wheeled, Industrial, Aircraft Towing, Medium, Massey Ferguson..*

Below left *Tractor, Wheeled, Semi-Trailer, 16-ton, 4 × 2, Leyland Mastiff.*

Bottom left *Tractor, Wheeled, Fork Lift, Telescopic, Handler, 4,000 lb, Rough Terrain.*

Tractor, Wheeled, Semi-Trailer, 16-ton, 4 × 2, Leyland Mastiff
L 5,207, **W** 2,337, **H** 2,591, **WB** 2,895.

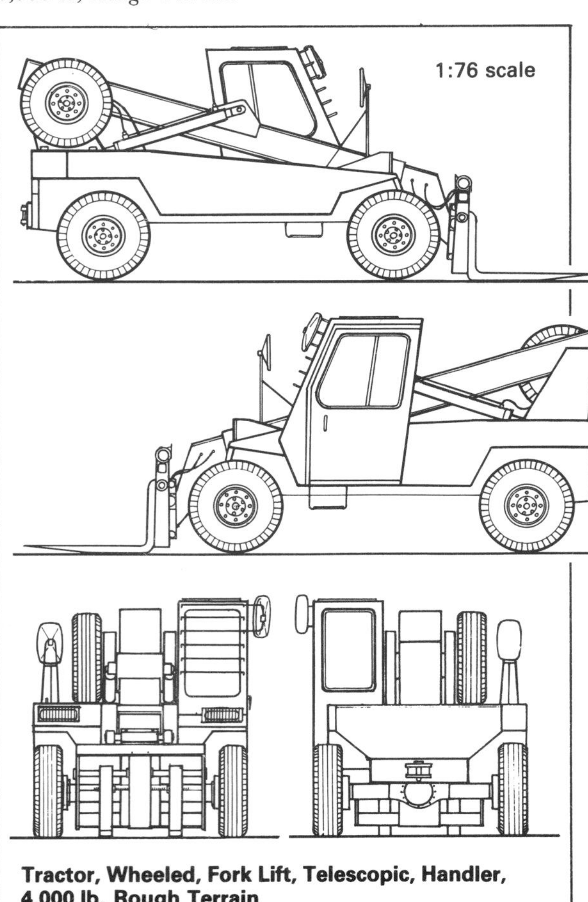

Tractor, Wheeled, Fork Lift, Telescopic, Handler, 4,000 lb, Rough Terrain

RAF uniforms and insignia

The Royal Air Force, in common with the other armed Services, lays down strict rules relating to standards of dress and the types of uniform that can be worn on all occasions. These rules are laid out in detail in a publication known as AP1358 which is a fairly lengthy tome but which does include a number of illustrations which are able to impart more information than many words. Some of these illustrations, which are Crown Copyright, are provided here to give an overall guide to the numbers of types of uniform current at the time of writing. These illustrations do not cover every possible variation in dress and they cannot cover every single form of insignia in use. What are not covered here are the types of working dress. There are many of these, several of them purely 'local' to suit some particular task or situation, and many of these can be seen in the illustrations contained elsewhere in this book.

RAF No 1 Service Dress. **1** *Officer and Warrant Officer (Warrant Officers wear officer pattern uniform and airman's No 1 SD hat with Warrant Officer badge).* **2** *NCO and airman. RAF No 2 Dress (this is an all-ranks' uniform).* **3** *Officer.* **4** *Airman.*

1

2

3

4

RAF No 2A Dress. **5** *Officer.* **6** *Airman.*

RAF No 2B Dress (the stable belt is an optional item). **7** *Officer.* **8** *Airman.*

9 *RAF No 3 (Combat) Dress.*

RAF No 4 Dress. **10** *Officer.* **11** *Airman.*

12 *RAF No 5B Dress (5A similar but with white waistcoat).*

13 *RAF No 5 Dress (Warrant Officers and Senior NCOs (optional); Senior NCO depicted.*

14 *RAF No 6A Full Ceremonial Dress (warm-weather areas); Personal Staff Officer depicted.*

RAF No 6 Service Dress (warm-weather areas). **15** *Officer and Warrant Officer.* **16** *NCO and airman.*

RAF No 6B Parade Dress (warm-weather areas). **17** *Ceremonial (anodized buttons and belt buckle).* **18** *Non-ceremonial (black buttons and belt buckle).*

RAF No 7A and 7B Working Dress (warm-weather areas). **19** *No 7A Dress—trouser mode.* **20** *No 7B Dress—shorts mode.*

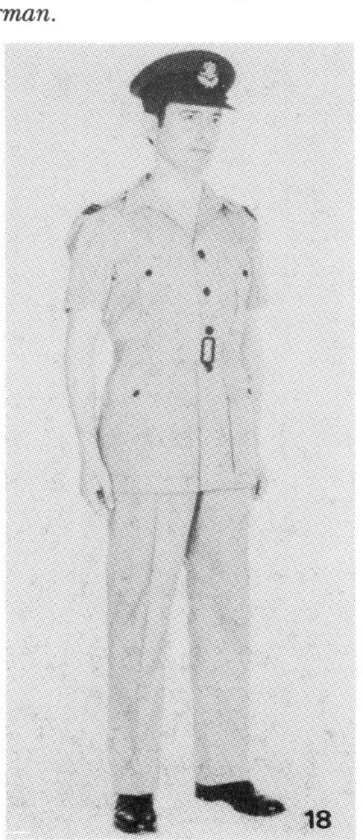

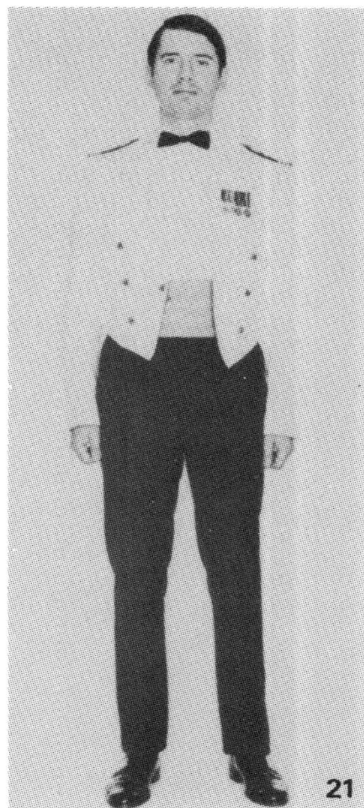

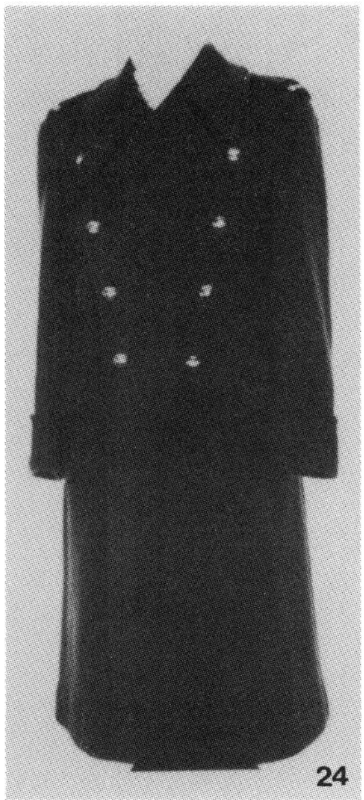

21 *RAF No 8 Mess Dress (warm-weather areas).*

RAF raincoat for all ranks (the women's raincoat is similar but with buttoning on the left). **22** *Lapel rank badges are worn by officers of the rank of Group Captain and below.* **23** *Airmen and airwomen wear arm rank badges on both sleeves.*

RAF greatcoats. **24** *Officer.* **25** *British warm (optional for officers).* **26** *Women officers and Warrant Officers (no shoulder straps on Warrant Officer version).* **27** *Male Warrant Officer.* **28** *Airman and airwoman.*

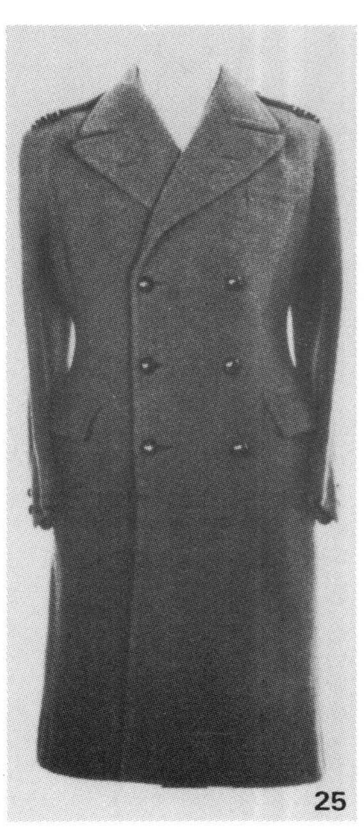

WRAF No 1 Service Dress. **29** *Officer and Warrant Officer.* **30** *Airwoman.*

WRAF No 2 Dress (this is an all-ranks' uniform). **31** *Officer.* **32** *Airwoman.*

WRAF No 2A Dress. **33** *Officer.* **34** *Airwoman.*

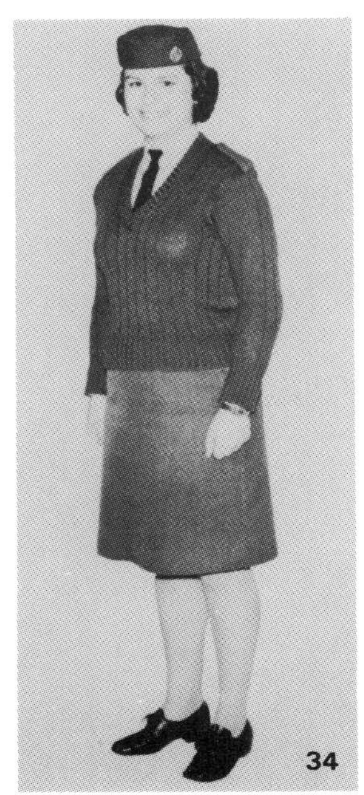

WRAF No 2B Dress (the summer shirt is optional). **35** *Officer.* **36** *Airwoman.*

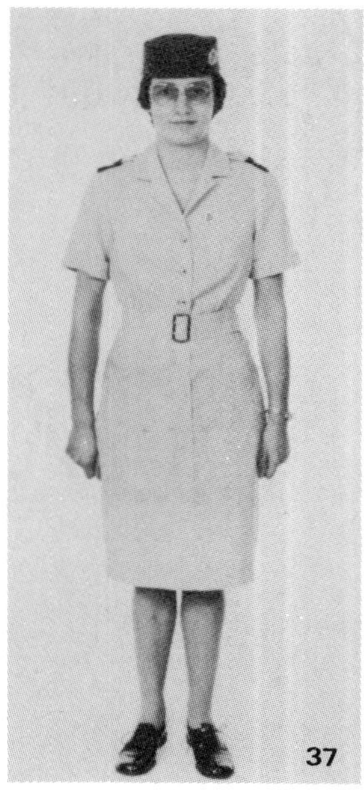

37 *WRAF No 6 Dress (airwoman); the officers' No 6 Dress is a bespoke version of the all-ranks' frock illustrated but worn with No 1 Dress hat and anodized buttons and belt buckle.*

38 *WRAF No 7 Dress (airwoman).*

39 *PMRAFNS No 2 Dress (this is an all-ranks' uniform); airwoman depicted.*

PMRAFNS No 2 Dress variants. **40** *No 2A Dress (Flight Nursing Officer).* **41** *No 2 Dress (Flight Nursing Attendant).*

42 *PMRAFNS No 3 Dress (Universal ward uniform); officer depicted. The officers' cape is discarded during warm weather and the frock worn open-necked.*

43 *PMRAFNS No 6 Dress (officer).*

44 *PMRAFNS No 7 Dress (airwoman).*

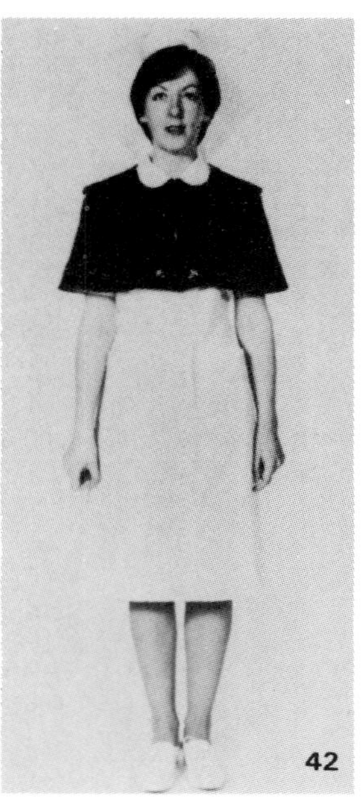

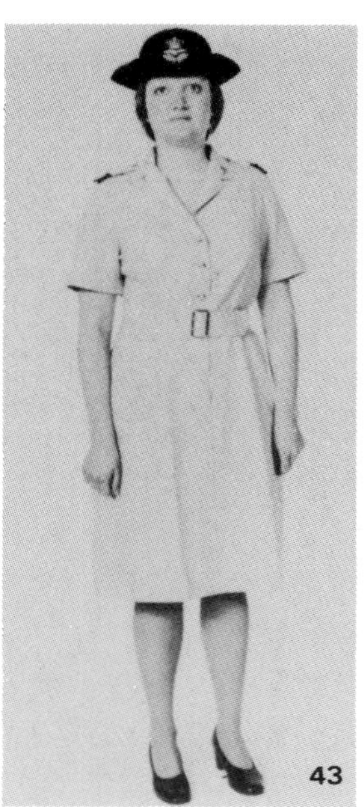

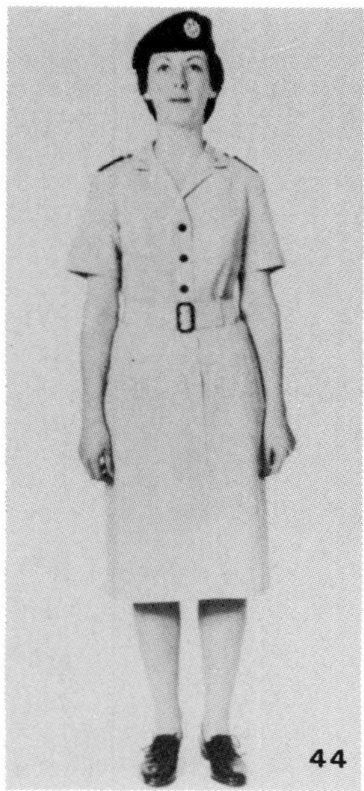

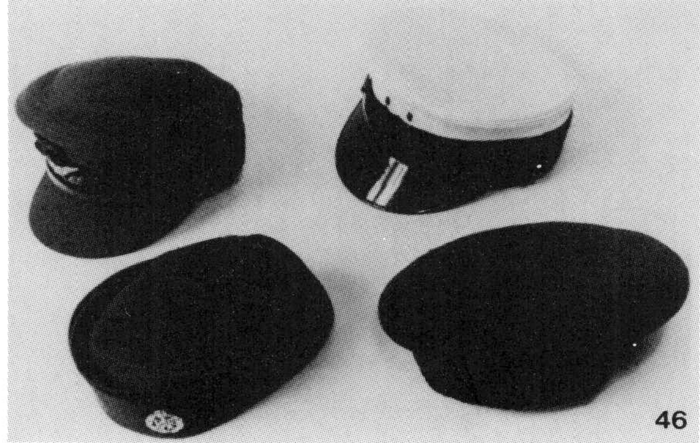

45 *RAF head-dress.* **Top row, l-r** *Air ranks (Air Commodore and above); Wing Commander and below; Group Captain.* **Second row, l-r** *Field service cap, Air ranks; other officers and Warrant Officers.* **Third row, l-r** *SB airman (WO badge depicted); Duty hat, RAF policeman; Ceremonial, musicians (the Queen's Colour Squadron wear ungilded peaks and have black side buttons).* **Bottom row, l-r** *Beret (all ranks); Field service cap (airman badge depicted); peak for ceremonial caps, Director of Music and Warrant Officer musicians.*

46 *WRAF head-dress.* **Top left** *Officer's SD, Wing Commander and below; Warrant Officers wear this hat with appropriate badge; Group Captain and above wear an embellished peak.* **Top right** *Duty hat, RAF policewoman.* **Bottom left** *SD hat for other airwomen.* **Bottom right** *Beret.*

47 *Officers' No 1 Dress sleeve rank badges (blue/black braid).*

Above, l-r *Marshal of the Royal Air Force; Air Chief Marshal; Air Marshal; Air Vice-Marshal.*

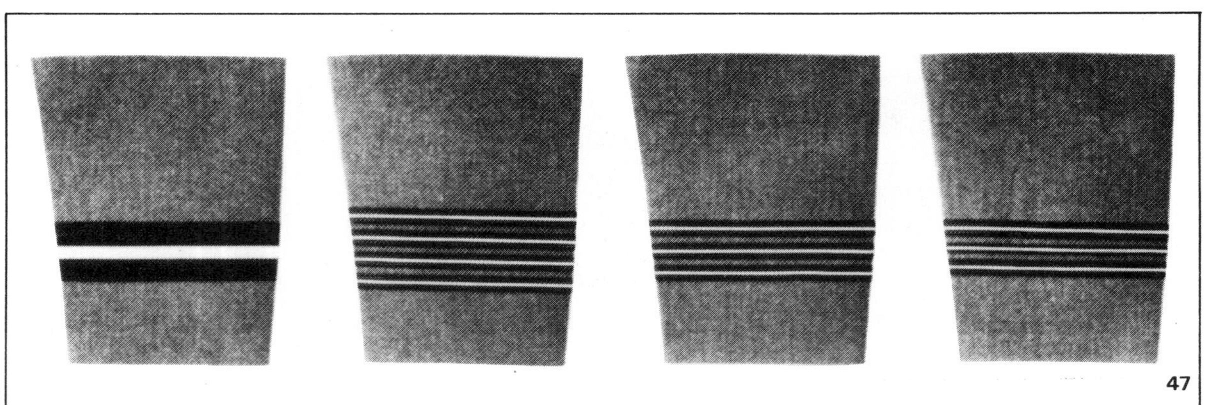

Above, l-r *Air Commodore; Group Captain; Wing Commander; Squadron Leader.*

Above, l-r *Flight Lieutenant; Flying Officer; Pilot Officer. (Note: ranking for male officers on No 5 Mess Wear jackets is in full-width gold lace, positioned as above.)*

48

49

48 *Shoulder rank badges for Warrant Officers and SNCOs. Left- and right-hand vertical rows are for aircrew, worn on right and left shoulders respectively; centre vertical row is for ground trades, worn on both shoulders.*

49 *Rank badges worn by airmen and airwomen in ground trades.* **Top** *Warrant Officer.* **Second row** *Flight Sergeant; the metal crown depicted on the left is worn with No 1 Dress only.* **Third row** *Chief Technician; Sergeant.* **Fourth row** *Corporal; Junior Technician.* **Bottom row** *Senior Aircraftman/woman; Leading Aircraftman/woman.*

50 *Flying badges.* **Left** *Preliminary (brevet) Pilot's badge.* **Centre** *Navigator's distinguishing sleeve badge; other appointments designated by the following abbreviations—AE (Air Electronics), E (Air Engineer), LM (Air Loadmaster), M (Met Air Observer). The following abbreviations may also still be seen but are obsolescent—AG (Air Gunner), B (Air Bombardier), O (Air Observer), QM (Air Quartermaster), RO (Observer Radio) and S (Air Signaller).* **Right** *Parachute Instructor.*

50

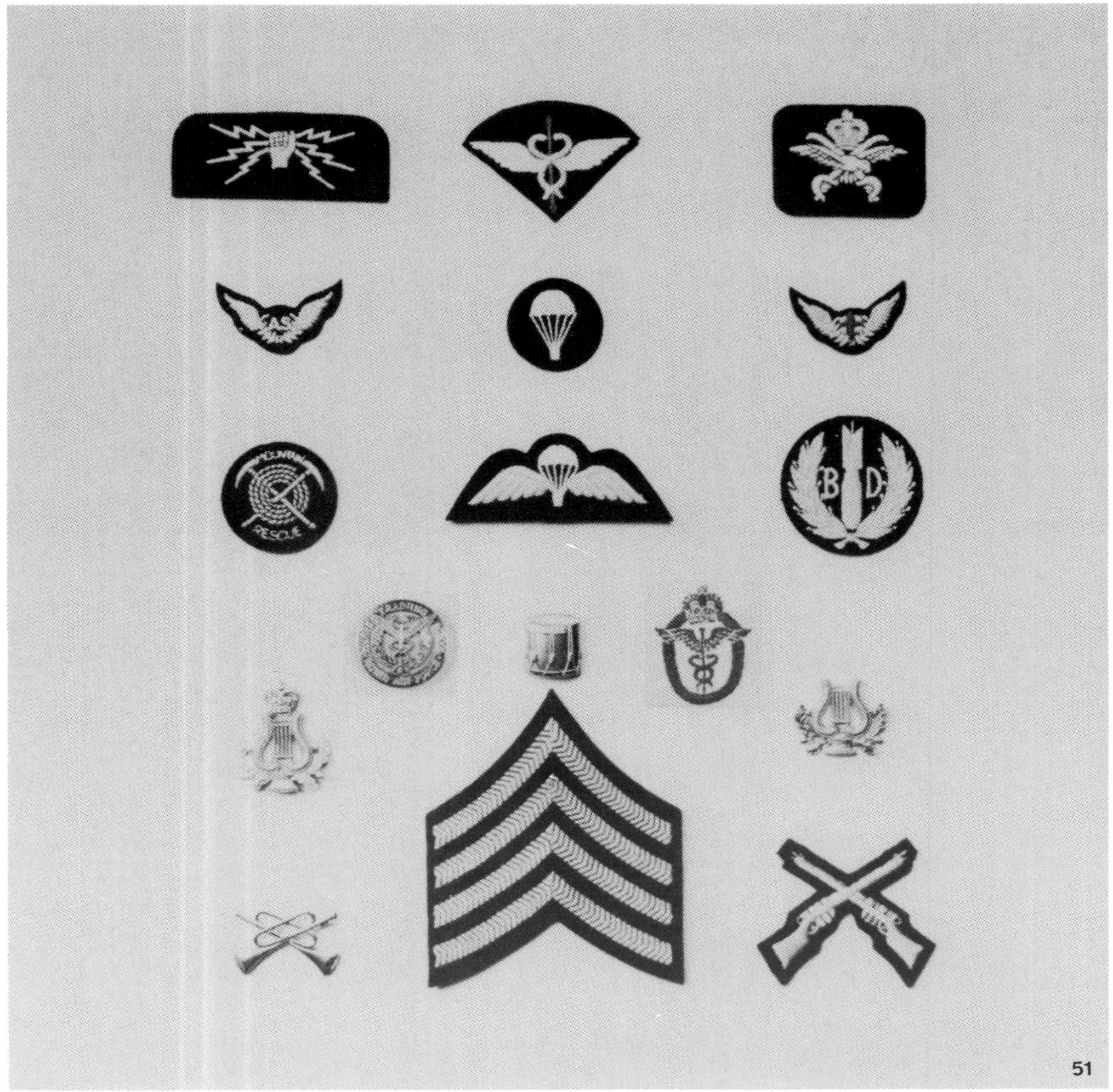

51 *Trade and qualification badges.* **Top row, l-r** *Telecommunications; Flight Medical Officer; Physical Training Instructor.* **Second row** *Air Steward; Parachutist; Flight Nursing Attendant.* **Third row** *Mountain Rescue; Parachutist badge with wings; Explosive Ordnance Disposal.* **Fourth row** *RAF Nurse Training School badge; drum, accompanying inverted chevrons below, Drum Major; Ward dress badge, PMRAFNS airwoman.* **Fifth row** *(flanking Drum Major chevrons): Musician (established bands); Voluntary Bandsman.* **Bottom Left** *Trumpeter.* **Bottom right** *Marksman.*

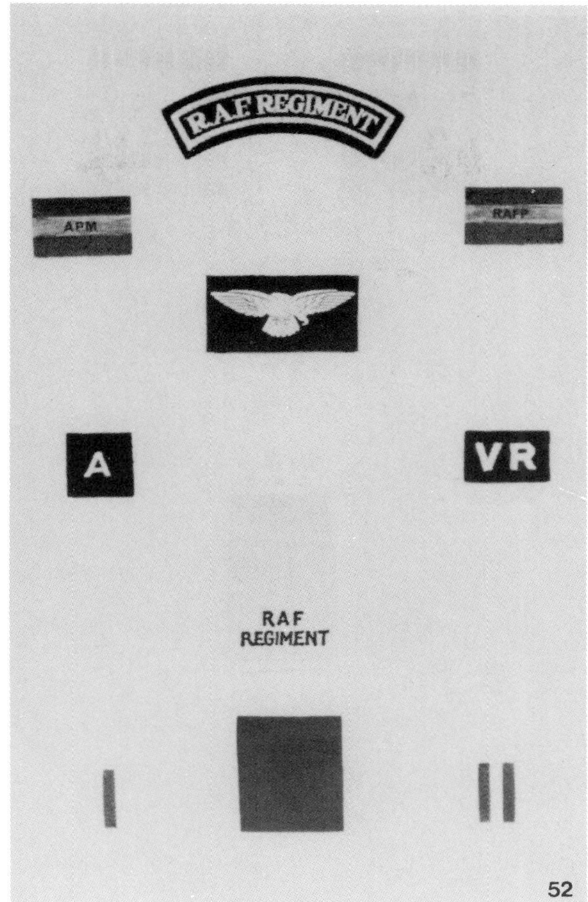

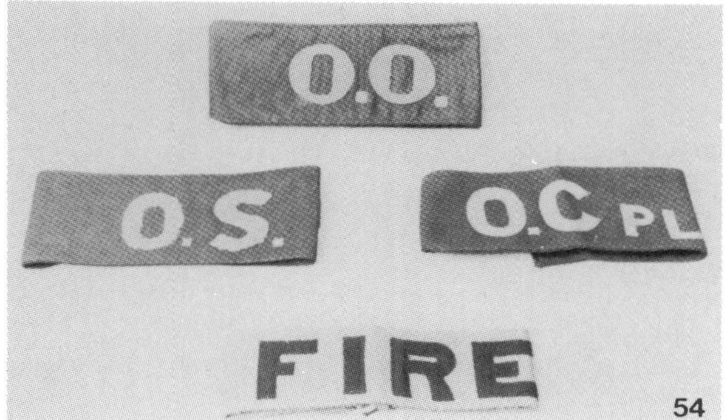

52 *Arm and shoulder distinguishing badges.* **Top** *RAF Regiment shoulder badge.* **Second row** *APM and RAFP.* **Third row (centre)** *Eagle arm badges are worn only on airman's/airwoman's greatcoat.* **Fourth row** *A and VR embroidered arm badges.* **Fifth row** *RAF Regiment shoulder slide.* **Bottom row** *left and right depict green bars on white slides denoting 1st and 2nd year pupil nurses, PMRAFNS; centre depicts qualification slide for ward dress, saxe blue for SRNs, bottle green for SENs.*

53 *Armlets—miscellaneous duties.* **Top row, l-r** *Movements control, NCO/airman; movements control, officer; officer/airman engaged in EOD duties.* **Second row, l-r** *Recruit leader; sleeve ranking for NCO on working garments not fitted with shoulder straps; deputy recruit leader.* **Third row, l-r** *Instructor; Mountain Rescue; RAF Postal Service.* **Bottom row, l-r** *Geneva Convention Red Cross; black mourning band; official.*

54 *Armlets—Station duties. Orderly Officer, Orderly Sergeant, Orderly Corporal and self-explanatory.*

Glossary and index

Sea King HAR 3 at RAF Coltishall.